THE EVOLUTION OF NORTH AMERICA

THE EVOLUTION
OF NORTH AMERICA

Revised edition

By PHILIP B. KING

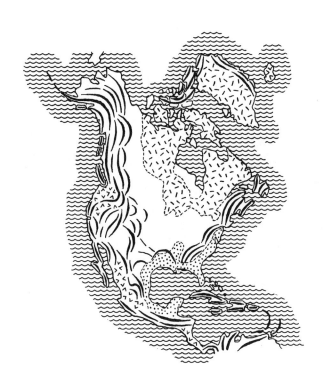

PRINCETON UNIVERSITY PRESS
PRINCETON, NEW JERSEY

Dr. Philip B. King has recently retired from his position as geologist on the staff of the U.S. Geological Survey after more than forty years of service. A great deal of his career has been devoted to geological field investigations, but most of the latter part has been spent on regional geological compilations, the most notable products of which have been the *Tectonic Map of North America* (1969) and the *Geologic Map of the United States* (1974). He has been awarded the Penrose Medal of the Geological Society of America, the Lomonosov Medal of Moscow University, and the Distinguished Service Medal of the U.S. Department of the Interior.

. . .

Printed in the United States of America
by Princeton University Press, Princeton, New Jersey

Published by Princeton University Press, Princeton, New Jersey
In the United Kingdom: Princeton University Press, Guildford, Surrey

PREFACE

Basic data for the first edition of *The Evolution of North America* were obtained by my graduate students and me in a seminar in tectonics while I was a visiting professor at the University of California, Los Angeles, during the years 1954 to 1956. The results were distilled into an undergraduate lecture course that was carried on concurrently, the texts of which were the basis of the book.

When my students and I were through, we felt that we had pretty well covered the situation in world tectonics, and the tectonics of North America in particular, but, as later events were to prove, we had merely reviewed the basic facts on which a great proliferation of new concepts were built during the 1960s. These new concepts, sometimes called "the new global tectonics" and said to have created a revolution in earth sciences, resulted primarily from knowledge of the geology of the ocean bottoms that had been obtained during the last forty years—hitherto the great unknown of geology.

Nothing that is written now on geology can fail to take account of these new concepts, which have done so much to affect our thinking on many matters, and a revised edition of *The Evolution of North America* can be no exception, even though the book remains primarily a treatise on continental geology.

Besides these new concepts in geology, many changes have occurred in the knowledge of the geology of North America itself; new facts have been obtained, especially from additional field work. Fortunately, I have been able to review these new facts as a result of my assignments for the U.S. Geological Survey, first during preparation of a tectonic map of North America, and later during preparation of a new geologic map of the United States, the latter with the able collaboration of Helen M. Beikman.

The original edition of *The Evolution of North America* met a most heartening reception from the geological public, and copies were still being sold in 1976, long after the book had passed its peak of usefulness. It is altogether appropriate now, nearly twenty years after publication of the first edition, to undertake a revision, making use of the new facts and the new concepts. Some parts of the original text have required little revision and are retained much as they were originally written. Most of the other parts have been extensively revised, or even rewritten entirely. In addition, the reference lists have been overhauled to take account of new and pertinent publications; all the text figures have been corrected, some obsolete ones have been eliminated, and many new ones have been added.

The metric system has now become the standard of measurement in scientific work, hence all measurements given here are in meters and kilometers. The only exceptions are some contour maps (Figs. 19, 20, and 65) where all the source contours were given in feet; to make a conversion would result in gross distortion of the original data.

In preparing the revised edition, I am deeply indebted to Peter J. Coney, whose encouragement and inspiration have done so much to bring the project to completion. Different parts of the text have been read and critically reviewed by various generous colleagues who are specialists in different phases of the subject. In particular, the chapter on the Interior Lowlands was reviewed by George V. Cohee, that on the Appalachians by Douglas W. Rankin, that on the Gulf of Mexico and the West Indies by James E. Case, the several chapters on the Cordillera by Gregory A. Davis, and the part on the Coast Ranges of California by Thor H. Nilsen. Their suggestions and counsel have done much to improve the manuscript, but needless to say they are not responsible for the statements made, for which I assume sole responsibility.

Los Altos, California
December 1976

Philip B. King

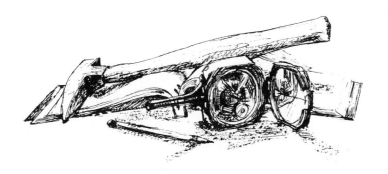

REFERENCE MATERIAL

MAPS

The story of North America rests on various kinds of maps. Some maps are included in this book to illustrate special features, but larger reference maps cannot be, even though they would aid in comprehension of the text. Large reference maps have been compiled and published under auspices of various agencies; if possible, the reader should seek them out and refer to them (see list below).

GEOGRAPHIC MAPS. North America is represented, first of all by geographic maps. The most familiar are those that show political and governmental subdivisions, but these give little idea of the fundamental nature of the continent. Better than these are maps that show physical configuration by layer tints, contour lines, or relief shading; in recent years, also, several excellent relief models of the middle part of the continent have become available. The maps used by the author during his compilations were the sheets of the American Geographical Society's "Map of the Americas" and "Map of the World" on a scale of 1:5,000,000.

But although physical maps or models give information on the height and steepness of the land, its true character and makeup are difficult to infer; a clearer idea is given by landform maps or physiographic diagrams, in which the distinctive forms of the land are shown in a semi-pictorial manner. Especially recommended are those by Erwin Raisz of the United States, Mexico, and other areas.

Geographic maps represent the appearance of North America at a moment in time—merely one "frame" of the ceaselessly changing and evolving aspect of part of the earth's surface. To understand past history of North America and how it evolved, recourse must be had to other maps.

GEOLOGIC MAPS. Geologic maps show distribution of different rocks that lie at the surface, from which the various land forms have been created. On these maps, rocks are partly differentiated as to kind—whether igneous, sedimentary, or metamorphic, and the subdivisions thereof—and partly by ages during which they were formed. Most geologic maps published in the United States follow a conventional scheme of colors. Igneous rocks are shown in vivid tints of red, purple, green, etc., without particular regard for age. Sedimentary rocks, and to a large extent the metamorphic, are shown in a sequence that follows a prismatic scale. Precambrian rocks appear in browns. Paleozoic rocks are shown in reds, purples, and blues—red for Cambrian and Ordovician, purple for Silurian and Devonian, and blue for Mississippian, Pennsylvanian, and Permian. Mesozoic rocks are shown in green—blue-green for Triassic and Jurassic, and olive-green for Cretaceous. Cenozoic rocks—the Tertiary and Quaternary—appear in shades of yellow, orange, and gray.

Geologic maps are available on various scales: the map of North America on a scale of 1:5,000,000, that of the United States on 1:2,500,000, and maps of the states on 1:500,000 (or ten times the scale of the Geologic Map of North America). Maps on still larger scales cover smaller areas in greater detail, showing not only the distribution of the rocks by color patterns but their geometry by structure symbols; such maps are the basic data from which the smaller-scaled ones have been assembled.

From geologic maps the skilled eye can infer many things about the makeup and history of an area—belted outcrops that indicate a homoclinal dip in one direction, concentric outcrops around a dome or basin, truncated outcrops that indicate an unconformity and superposition of unlike structures. Geologic maps, nevertheless, show only surface features, and much of the story is concealed. To explain the hidden parts of the story, other forms of representation have been tried.

TECTONIC MAPS. Tectonic maps are intended to show more clearly the structural makeup of the region. A small-scale example, a much generalized tectonic map of North America, is included with this book (Plate I); larger-scaled, more detailed examples are the tectonic maps of the United States, Canada, and Mexico.

On tectonic maps, folds and faults are represented by special symbols or, where rock configuration is more open, by means of structure contours. Many significant features are brought out that cannot be shown on the usual geologic maps, such as those that have been buried beneath younger deposits or broken up by later deformation. Most tectonic maps also divide the surface into colored areas, which represent tectonic units rather than the usual stratigraphic units. Basement and plutonic rocks of various ages are represented, and their cover is divided according to its origin (miogeosynclinal, eugeosynclinal, etc.) and according to its time of deformation. Because this sort of cartography is newer and less standardized than geologic maps, the schemes of coloring vary greatly from tectonic map to tectonic map.

OTHER MAPS. Various additional kinds of maps have been used to extract geologic history from the rocks. Of these perhaps the most familiar are *paleogeographic maps*, examples of which adorn most textbooks of historical geology. Paleogeographic maps of small areas may give a fairly accurate record of ancient geography, but those of the continent or its larger parts involve so much speculation and inference that they record little more than the opinions of their makers.

In more favor among professional geologists as aids to interpretation are *paleogeologic maps* that show ancient areal geology, *isopach maps* that show rock thicknesses, *lithofacies maps* showing distribution of different kinds of sedimentary deposits, and others that will be explained more fully in later pages of this book. These are less speculative than paleogeographic maps, as they can be assembled from actual data of outcrops and drill records. The most comprehensive use of these cartographic methods to date is by the Paleotectonic Map Project of the U.S. Geological Survey. Results of this project have been published for four of the geologic systems and others are in press or preparation.

The following maps are recommended:

GEOGRAPHIC MAPS:

American Geographical Society, *Map of the Americas* (1:5,000,000): "Alaska, northern Canada, and Greenland" (1948); "United States, southern Canada, and Newfoundland" (1948); "Mexico, Central America, and the West Indies" (1942). *Map of the World* (1:5,000,000): "Map of the Arctic Region" (1975).

Raisz, Erwin: *Landform map of the United States* (1:4,625,000) (1939); *Landforms of Mexico* (1:3,000,000) (1959): Institute of Geographical Exploration, Harvard University.

GEOLOGIC MAPS:

North American Geologic Map Committee (E. N. Goddard, chm.) (1965) *Geologic map of North America* (1:5,000,000): U.S. Geological Survey.

A. E. Escher, N. Henricksen, P. R. Dawes, and A. Weidick (1970) *Tectonic/geologic map of Greenland* (1:2,500,000): Geological Survey of Greenland.

H. M. Beikman (in preparation, 1976) *Geologic map of Alaska* (1:2,500,000): U.S. Geological Survey.

R.J.W. Douglas (1969) *Geologic map of Canada* (1:5,000,000): Geological Survey of Canada Map 1250 A.

P. B. King and H. M. Beikman (1974) *Geologic map of the United States, exclusive of Alaska and Hawaii* (1:2,500,000): U.S. Geological Survey. (With accompanying "Explanatory text to accompany the Geologic Map of the United States": U.S. Geol. Survey Prof. Paper 901).

S. H. Sanchez Morada and Ernesto Lopez Ramos (1968) *Carta geologica de la Republica Mexicana* (1:2,000,000): Comite de la Carta Geologica de Mexico.

Gabriel Dengo, Enrique Levy, Otto Bohnenberger, and Roberto Caballeros (1969) *Metallogenic map of Central America* (1:2,000,000): Instituto Centroamericano de Investigacion y Tecnologia Industrial.

TECTONIC MAPS:

P. B. King (1969) *Tectonic map of North America* (1:5,000,000): U.S. Geological Survey. (With accompanying "The tectonics of North America; a discussion to accompany the Tectonic Map of North America, scale 1:5,000" U.S. Geol. Survey Prof. Paper 628).

C. H. Stockwell (1969) *Tectonic map of Canada* (1:5,000,000): Geological Survey of Canada Map 1251 A).

G. V. Cohee (1962) *Tectonic map of the United States, exclusive of Alaska and Hawaii* (1:2,500,000): U.S. Geological Survey.

Zoltan de Cserna (1961) *Tectonic map of Mexico* (1:2,500,000): Geological Society of America.

PALEOTECTONIC MAPS:

E. D. McKee and others (1956) *Paleotectonic maps of the Jurassic System*: U.S. Geol. Survey Misc. Inves. Map I-175.

E. D. McKee and others (1959) *Paleotectonic maps of the Triassic System*: U.S. Geol. Survey Misc. Inves. Map I-300.

E. D. McKee and others (1967) *Paleotectonic maps of the Permian System*: U.S. Geol. Survey Misc. Inves. Map I-450.

E. D. McKee, E. J. Crosby, and others (1975) *Paleotectonic investigations of the Pennsylvanian system in the United States*: U.S. Geological Survey Prof. Paper 853.

REFERENCE LISTS

The short lists of references at the ends of the chapters are intended to serve as a guide, should the reader desire to delve further into any subject. Some references give basic factual data, others are elaborations of theories propounded in the text, and others take up alternative theories. Many of them contain extensive lists of other references. The lists are not exhaustive; nor are they intended fully to document the discussions in a particular chapter. They represent reading in which the author himself has found pleasure, instruction, and stimulation.

CONTENTS

LIST OF ILLUSTRATIONS

THE EVOLUTION OF NORTH AMERICA

CHAPTER I

THE NATURAL HISTORY OF CONTINENTS

1. LAYERS OF THE EARTH'S CRUST

RELIEF OF OCEANS AND CONTINENTS. To us land dwellers it always comes as something of a shock to realize that the normal surface of the earth is not land, but water. Seventy percent of the earth's surface is covered by water, mainly ocean; only thirty percent is dry land, mainly continents.

These differences are more than an accidental covering of parts of the surface by water, as there are certain remarkable features of the relief of this surface. The following figures have been calculated:

Thousands of meters	Depths below sea level						
	—6	5—6	4—5	3—4	2—3	1—2	0—1
Percent area:	1.0	16.5	23.3	13.9	4.7	2.9	8.5

Thousands of meters:	Heights above sea level			
	0—1	1—2	2—3	3 plus
Percent area:	12.3	4.7	2.0	1.2

From this may be derived the following principle: *The frequency curve of elevations on the earth shows two pronounced maxima, corresponding to the ocean floors and to the continental platforms.*

Referring to our table, note that 23 percent of the surface of the earth lies at a level of 4,000 to 5,000 meters below the surface of the ocean, and 21 percent lies between the surface of the ocean and 1,000 meters above it. Standing out on these dominant surfaces are the mountain ranges, some of which project nearly to 9,200 meters above sea level, and the ocean deeps (that are mountains in reverse), which descend to as much as 10,000 meters below sea level. The continents stand as lofty platforms above the ocean floor, on the whole with very slight relief on their tops. Also significant in the table is the 8.5 percent of area between sea level and 1,000 meters below sea level. Much of this area lies at depths of less than 200 meters below sea level and forms the *continental shelves*. Although submerged, the shelves are actually parts of the continental structure; in other words, an excess of water in the ocean basins drowns the edges of the continental platforms so that, on many coasts, shallow bottoms extend many kilometers out to sea before breaking off into the ocean depths.

COMPOSITION OF CONTINENTS. Why does the earth's surface have this pattern?

Extensive geological and geophysical studies of the continents demonstrate that they consist everywhere, at relatively shallow depths, of granite-like rocks. These include true granites and such plutonic allies as granodiorites, quartz monzonites, and syenites, as well as most of the metamorphic schists and gneisses. It is true that these rocks lie at the surface over only small parts of the continents, much wider areas being covered by sediments. But the latter are a relatively thin blanket, less than two kilometers to about twenty kilometers thick at most. Besides, the sediments have been derived largely from granite-like rocks and more or less reflect the composition of their source; some sediments, such as certain sandstones, closely approach that composition.

Granites and their allies, we know, are composed dominantly of quartz and feldspar, hence are sometimes called acidic rocks. In chemical terms, their minerals are built principally of oxides of silicon and aluminum. For this granitic or continental type of earth's crust, the name *sial* has been coined by combining the abbreviations *Si* and *Al*, representing the dominant elements, silicon and aluminum. Sial has an average density of 2.7. Compare this with the average density of the earth as a whole, which is 5.5. Clearly, the stuff of continents is a skin of lighter crust lying on much denser interior material.

COMPOSITION OF CRUST BENEATH THE OCEANS. The crust beneath the oceans is evidently quite different from that beneath the continents. For example, study of earthquake waves indicates that these travel at different rates through the crust of the continents and the crust beneath the oceans. Those crossing the oceans advance more rapidly because of the greater density of the suboceanic rocks. Moreover, volcanoes in the oceans, such as those that have built up the Hawaiian Islands, erupt

3

basalt rather than lavas of granitic composition. Basalt is a dark dense rock containing such minerals as pyroxene and olivine, and is dominantly composed of oxides of silicon, magnesium, and iron. There are many reasons for believing that much of the sub-oceanic crust has a composition like that of basalt.

For this sub-oceanic type of crust, the name *sima* has been coined, as with the word sial, by combining the abbreviations *Si* and *Ma* for its two dominant elements, silicon and magnesium. Sima has an average density of 3.0, and is therefore denser than sial.

Study of the earthquake waves leads us to believe that the bottoms of the continental blocks also become more dense and probably approach the composition of oceanic sima, although there is no sharp boundary between this lower part and the thicker, overlying sialic part. Like cakes of ice floating on water, the continents are broad plates, about 37 kilometers thick, whose tops rise above the surface of the sima layer on the ocean floor and whose bases extend deeper. A cross-section of the edge of a continent may therefore be indicated diagrammatically as in Figure 1.

Deeper layers of the crust. Although sima is denser than sial, it is still not as dense as the average of the whole earth; still heavier, more compact material must lie beneath it. Moreover, study of earthquake waves indicates that both the sima of the ocean floors and the sial and sima of the continental plates have well-defined bases; they are separated from heavier underlying material by a fairly abrupt discontinuity lying at a depth of about six kilometers beneath the ocean floor, and at a depth averaging about 37 kilometers beneath the continental surface. This was first recognized about sixty years ago by a Yugoslav seismologist with the rather difficult name of Mohorovičić, hence has become known to geophysicists as the *Mohorovičić discontinuity*—for short the "M-discontinuity" and irreverently "The Moho." It is the base of the crust of the earth as we know it, and lies beneath continents and oceans alike, as shown by the lower line of our figure (Fig. 1).

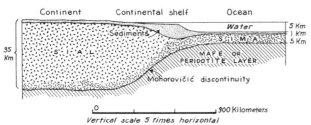

FIG. 1. Diagrammatic section across the edge of a continent into an adjacent ocean basin showing crustal layers that underlie them. After J. T. Wilson, 1954; and Ewing and Press, 1955.

A very thick layer below the M-discontinuity is known as the *mantle*, because it wraps around the central core. Its rocks lie far below our limits of observation, and although we can deduce their density from seismic properties, it is obviously difficult to translate this physical fact into terms of mineral and chemical composition. Nevertheless, certain rocks that form rare exposures at the surface—the peridotites—are thought to have been injected upward through the entire simatic and sialic crust, and to have been derived with little change from the mantle. Peridotites are even denser than basalt and its allies, with oxides of magnesium and iron dominant and those of silicon and aluminum relatively subordinate. With some hesitancy we could refer to the rocks next beneath the M-discontinuity as the *peridotite layer* or (to continue our synthetic terminology) as the *mafe*, by combining the abbreviations *Ma* and *Fe* for magnesium and iron.

Although some notion as to the character of rocks and layers still deeper in the earth is afforded by seismic evidence, we have probed deeply enough for our purpose. Let us now return to the surface features.

2. SURFACE FEATURES OF CONTINENTS

Geological classification of surface features. Our geographies of grade-school days taught us that the surface of the land is divisible into *plains*, *plateaus*, and *mountains*. This is commendably objective, as it classifies the features purely by form, without involving one in theories of their origin.

But our interest here is in origin and evolution, so that it is desirable to convert this classification into something geological. Thus, plateaus are in pretty much the same geological category as plains, the plateaus merely having been lifted higher so that they are more dissected. Moreover, there are some lowland areas, such as the Piedmont province of the southeastern United States, which share the rock structure of the adjacent mountain systems and are merely worn down parts thereof; geologically they are more properly included with the mountains. Our classification then becomes:

LOWLANDS
Shields
   Areas of exposed ancient rocks; former mountain belts that were long ago stabilized and worn down.
Interior lowlands
   Ancient rocks, covered by later sediments that remain nearly flat-lying.
Coastal plains
   Areas of young sediments along coasts, with low seaward dips; outer edges commonly submerged to form the continental shelves.
MOUNTAINS (including parts now worn down into low country)
   Folded mountains
      Made up dominantly of deformed sedimentary rocks.

Complex mountains
Made up of crystalline rocks, i.e. of plutonics and metamorphics.

Block mountains
Terranes broken by faults into blocks of various shapes and sizes, which have been raised, lowered, and tilted.

Volcanic mountains
Built by piling up of ejected material, rather than by deformation.

And various other types

Classification of mountains by origin appears to be more complex than for the lowlands yet actually is less fundamental; the varieties listed above and various others commonly occur together in disturbed regions. In the western mountains of the United States, all the varieties are present, mixed together or superposed. The disturbed regions from which mountains are produced may be called orogenic belts or deformed belts. They are products of crustal unrest, hence during the time of their formation they were mobile belts. These belts are by far the most interesting parts of the continents, and we will have much to say about them later.

SYMMETRY OF NORTH AMERICA. With respect to its surface features, North America is almost ideally symmetrical (Plate I). In the north-central part, mainly in Canada, the Canadian Shield is made up of ancient (that is, Precambrian) rocks, mostly granite but including various kinds of old folded sediments and lavas. The Shield has been worn down into a low rolling surface that passes southward and southwestward beneath sedimentary rocks of the Interior Lowlands.

Nearly encircling the Shield and Interior Lowlands are various mountain systems, formed at different times since the Precambrian. On the southeast is the Appalachian system, with a partly buried extension across the Mississippi River that closes in the Lowlands on the south. On the west is the Cordilleran system, extending the entire length of the continent along the Pacific. In the far north there are other systems of folded mountains, the Innuitian and East Greenland, along the oceanward sides of the Arctic Islands and Greenland.

Finally, along the edges of the continent, especially on the southeast, are Coastal Plains that were built after the mountains were deformed and worn down. They are made up of Mesozoic and Cenozoic sediments laid over the edges of the mountain structures.

From North America it would seem that we could make a generalization about the plan of continental structure. From the central core of the continent, proceeding outward, we would find:

SHIELD—INTERIOR LOWLANDS—MOUNTAINS—COAST-AL PLAINS—CONTINENTAL SHELVES—OCEAN BASINS

which would appear diagrammatically as in Figure 2.

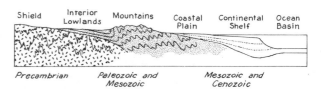

FIG. 2. Section from the center of a continent to its margin, showing ideal arrangement of lowlands and mountain belts.

COMPARISON OF NORTH AMERICA WITH OTHER CONTINENTS. Turning now to the other continents, however, we find it difficult to apply this generalization.

Asia is perhaps the most symmetrical, with a shield and interior lowlands in Siberia and great festoons of mountains surrounding them on the south and southeast, in part submerged along the edges of the Pacific Ocean.

Europe is somewhat like Asia, but curiously separated from the latter by the Ural Mountains, which run directly north across the continental block. Europe has a shield area in Scandinavia with plains on the south and east, then mountains near the Mediterranean culminating in the Alps. But Europe is cut off along its western and northwestern coasts where the shield breaks away and the mountain ranges run out into the Atlantic.

Still more anomalous are the continents in the Southern Hemisphere.

Africa is nearly all shield and plains with only fragments of mountains in the extreme north and south.

South America has only mountains along its western side, with a shield in Brazil on the east.

Australia has a shield and plains on the west and mountains in the east.

From what we know of Antarctica, it appears to be lopsided in somewhat the same manner as South America and Australia.

This rapid survey of the continents of the world suggests that, however beautiful the symmetry of North America may appear to be, it is not necessarily "normal" for all the continents. Or, if North America is "normal," most of the other continents are "abnormal."

3. CONTINENTS IN TIME

We have so far examined the continents in terms of their present substructure and surface features. Let us now examine them in terms of another dimension, that of time—geologic time, that is, which reaches back to the earth's beginning.

PERMANENCE OF CONTINENTS AND OCEANS. One of the great principles of geology, long reiterated and largely confirmed by recent research, has been the permanence of continental platforms and ocean basins. Thus, our continent of North America has never been part of the ocean, and there are no vanished continents foundered beneath the ocean waters, such as the legendary lost Atlantis.

The reader may recall that much of the record of historical geology from Cambrian time onward has been that "the seas came in and the seas went out"; that almost every part of the continent of North America has at one time been submerged beneath the seas—parts many times in successive brief transgressions, parts for very long periods. But this has little bearing on the gross history of the continent. There is scant evidence that deep sea marine deposits were laid on it, except perhaps near its edges. Most of the seas of the geological record were shallow; the term *epicontinental seas* has been used for them. They resembled the present-day seas that submerge the edge of the continent to form the continental shelves, and Hudson Bay, a great shallow downwarp in which the seas have been admitted to the heart of the continent.

It would appear, therefore, that the continents have been continental for a long time in geologic past. Moreover, the radically different compositions of continental and oceanic crusts suggest that the ocean basins have been at least as persistent as the continental platforms. It seems unlikely that any former continental areas have foundered into ocean basins, for it would have been difficult by any known geological processes to convert continental sial into oceanic sima.

A supposed corollary of the principle of permanence of continents and ocean basins has been the assumption that they have also been permanent in their present positions. But this corollary has been increasingly challenged during the last quarter of a century, and all modern evidence indicates that this was not the case.

THE THEORY OF CONTINENTAL DISPLACEMENT. On examining the geological record of the world we find that events of the past become increasingly inexplicable in terms of modern geography the farther back we go in time. During the Permian Period, for example, which was only 250 million years ago, there were extensive deserts in the Northern Hemisphere and tropical marginal seas that teemed with a varied marine life, whereas in most continents of the Southern Hemisphere (as well as peninsular India) there are indications of a vast continental glaciation. Before the Permian, there were as great or greater anomalies.

Then, too, as our survey of the continents has suggested, foldbelts, shields, and other continental structures have a disconcerting habit of extending up to the coast lines and breaking off, as though a continuation ought to exist in some other continental area, whereas nothing but ocean basins lie beyond.

Geographers for nearly two centuries have commented on the remarkable resemblance in the form of the shorelines on opposite sides of the Atlantic Ocean, as though the opposing continents could be fitted together. That this resemblance is more than accidental was emphasized around the turn of the century when oceano-

graphic soundings began to be made and showed that there was a submerged ridge in the middle of the ocean whose sinuosities matched those of the shorelines on either side.

During the latter part of the nineteenth century, when geologic exploration extended into the continents of the Southern Hemisphere, it was found that the rocks and their sequences differed significantly from the rocks and sequences in the Northern Hemisphere. One of the most peculiar features was the indication, just noted, of continental glaciation during Permian and Carboniferous time, but there were many others. For this reason, the Austrian geologist and synthesiser, Eduard Suess, postulated the former existence of a vast southern continent which he named *Gondwanaland*, after a typical example of the sequence in peninsular India, the Gondwana Series. What happened to Gondwanaland was a mystery, but it was suggested that the former connections between its fragments might have foundered to great depths, to create the modern Indian and South Atlantic Oceans (Fig. 3).

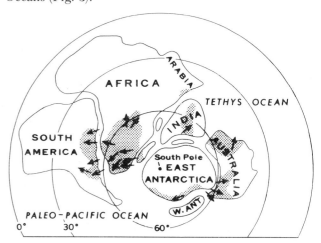

FIG. 3. The continental fragments of Gondwanaland reassembled on the assumption that they were later separated by drift. Areas covered by Carboniferous and Permian continental glaciations are shaded; observed directions of ice motion shown by arrows. Based on Hamilton and Krinsley, 1967.

All these curiosities of world geology, and many others, were brought together and explained in 1912 by the German meteorologist and geologist Alfred Wegener in his theory of continental displacement (commonly called "continental drift"). Wegener proposed that the continents have actually separated and moved across the face of the earth after the breakup of a single vast continent of Pangea early in Mesozoic time. The sialic continental plates were rafts, floating on oceanic sima that had little or no strength, and across which they were able to move, piling up mountain ranges ahead of them.

This outrageous hypothesis was met with indifference or outright hostility by most geological authorities, although it did obtain enthusiastic support from some, especially geologists working in the Southern Hemisphere and the complex Alpine chains of southern Europe. His proposed mechanism for the continental displacements was denounced as impossible by geophysicists (and was, indeed, the weakest part of his proposal). Geologists brushed aside the anomalies of world geology that he attempted to explain. They were either dismissed as remarkable coincidences or explained in other ways. Geological resemblances between widely separated continents were supposed either to have resulted from the foundering of vast intervening continental areas beneath the oceans, or the foundering of more tenuous "isthmian links."

Most of us geologists engaged in study of North America and other Northern Hemisphere continents were not so much hostile to the theory as indifferent, for it did not concern our local problems that could be explained by other means. As I wrote in the first edition of this book, "If we were dealing with one of the continents in the Southern Hemisphere we would have to say much more about questions of former land connections and of drift. North America, fortunately, is enough of a unit in itself that we need not explore the matter much further."

We were, moreover, repelled both by the enthusiasts for drift and by its more vehement opponents.

The theory had great attraction for the "lunatic fringe" of geology, who felt that any idea, however fanciful and bizarre, could be seriously proposed on the slimmest of evidence and with no real geological controls. Thus, Corsica and Sardinia were supposed to have originated off the west coast of Portugal, whence they moved through the Straits of Gibraltar to their present positions in the western Mediterranean. The Falkland Islands originated off the southeast coast of Africa, then moved across the southern oceans into the South Atlantic, rotating 180° as they did so. The modern grasses of New Zealand and coastal Chile are alike, so the two areas were originally joined in the mid-Pacific, then parted company, one half moving west, the other east. And so on, and so on.

The opponents of the theory, even otherwise distinguished geologists, seemed to feel that any adverse comment, no matter how fatuous, was a telling refutation of drift. There are glaciers on the Equator in New Guinea today, so why could there not have been glaciers in India during the Permian? The plants and insects in the southeastern United States are nearly identical with those of eastern China; the two areas could never have been contiguous, so the remarkable resemblances in faunas of former times between widely separated continents are meaningless also. And many, many others.

Despite all this, the anomalies of world geology would not go away. The theory of continental displacement languished for more than forty years, mainly because no plausible mechanism could be found that would have brought it about. Not until the great surge of oceanographic research that followed the Second World War did a vast flood of new data become available that put the matter of displacements on a firm theoretical footing—but in a somewhat different manner from that which had been proposed by Wegener.

PLATE TECTONICS. There is at least one striking resemblance between the geology of North America and Europe—their respective Paleozoic foldbelts. The Caledonian and Hercynian chains of Europe trend westward into the British Isles and run out to sea on the west coast of Ireland. The Appalachian chains of North America trend northeastward into Newfoundland, where they run out to sea on its eastern coast. Paleogeographers of an earlier day recognized the similarities in structure and history of these foldbelts and did not hesitate to connect them across the floor of the intervening North Atlantic. I remember how, in the early 1950s I waited eagerly for the results of detailed bottom surveys in this region. If the foldbelts actually existed on the floor of the Atlantic Ocean, they should be expressed in the bottom topography. But nothing of the kind materialized. The bottom topography (and presumably the structure) was nothing like that on the adjacent lands, and clearly had other origins. In fact, the dominant features trended at nearly right angles to the supposed foldbelts, and the most prominent of these was the Mid-Atlantic Ridge.

Much of the new oceanographic research in the North Atlantic concentrated on the Mid-Atlantic Ridge, whose existence had been known in a general way for three-quarters of a century. It became clear that it was one of the great mountain chains of the earth, but had features that set it apart from the mountain chains on land. On either side are abyssal plains blanketed by sediments at depths of 5,000 or 6,000 meters. From these the flanks of the ridge rise gradually, with mainly rocky surfaces, to its crest at depths of 1,500 meters or less, and in places project as volcanic islands such as the Azores. But along its crest is a rift, or deep structural valley, which seems to be the heart of the feature and which controls the structures on either side.

The rift is the scene of modern submarine volcanism and the locus of many earthquake epicenters. The volcanism was the result of upwelling of magma, and it became evident that this was creating new crust along the rift and forcing aside the rocks on either side, resulting in the rift structure. The Mid-Atlantic Ridge was thus a *spreading center*. Projected backward into the past, this spreading could conceivably have caused the separation of the opposite shores of the Atlantic. As oceanographic work proceeded, it was found that the ridge was but one segment of a world-wide system of ridges in all the oceans, and these ridges must have had a decisive role in the tectonics of the world.

7

An important line of evidence came from another direction. Studies were being carried out on the remnant magnetism of rocks on the land. When lavas were being poured out or sediments laid down, their magnetic minerals acquired an orientation controlled by the earth's magnetism of the time, and pointed toward the magnetic poles. The polar positions indicated at any particular locality were found to vary greatly with time. Still more remarkably, it was found that magnetic polarities were reversed through time at intervals of a hundred thousand or a million years, so that what had been magnetic north suddenly became magnetic south.

Surveys of magnetic anomalies were, in the meantime, being carried out at sea, and the resulting pattern was found to be a remarkable striping of alternating bands of positive and negative anomalies, which were parallel to the mid-ocean ridges. Granting that the mid-ocean ridges were spreading centers where new crust was continually being added from below, the bands of positive and negative magnetic anomalies were clearly the frozen records of successive reversals in polarity at the spreading centers, each band moving outward in turn as new crust was created behind it.

The bands of positive and negative magnetic anomalies on the sea floor were the signatures of the spreading. By various means, the age of each band could be determined or inferred, and these ages were verified by those of the sea-floor sediments that were being recovered from deep-sea drilling. This, and many other lines of evidence, indicated that all the ocean floors are rather young. At the spreading centers themselves the floor is, of course, late Cenozoic; farther out it is early Cenozoic, then Cretaceous, and toward the edges of the oceans Jurassic. No older Mesozoic or Paleozoic sea floor has so far been identified.

This at first sight seems to vitiate the principle of the permanence of the ocean basins. The Atlantic Ocean is clearly Jurassic and younger, as would be expected if the continents on the opposite sides were joined before then. But other ocean basins had existed before that elsewhere; the Pacific Ocean basin, for example, seems to have been a long-persistent feature. In the Pacific, as new crust is created at its spreading centers, the older crust moves outward and is finally thrust under (or "subducted" beneath) the edges of the bordering continents, to be consumed and reconverted into the internal material of the earth.

It came to be realized that the continents were not independent rafts, moving across the sima in the manner that Wegener had envisaged, but were parts of much larger plates that also included areas of oceanic crust. Thus, North America is one part of a great plate that extends back to the Mid-Atlantic Ridge. As new crust is added along the ridge, the whole plate moves relatively westward and, along its leading edge in western North America, impinges upon and overrides the several plates that make up the Pacific Ocean floor.

This is a very brief and inadequate sketch of the concept of plate tectonics, which fails to mention its many complications and nuances and the many interesting lines of confirmatory evidence; but it is sufficient for our purpose in this book. On the basic concept many geologists have built imposing structures of inference and speculation, partly conflicting, partly dubious. We can accept the central concept as fact and let time take care of the truth or falsity of the embellishments. The concept of plate tectonics has been called "the new global tectonics" and has been hailed as creating "a revolution in the earth sciences," but it should be realized that it is the fruition of a sequence of investigation and observation that extends back to the beginning of our century.

One matter is not as yet explained. As Wegener originally recognized, the opening of the Atlantic Ocean, the breakup of Gondwanaland, and all the other observable plate motions around the world have taken place since early Mesozoic time, and are well-documented by the magnetic striping and many other lines of evidence. But it is inconceivable that this plate tectonics regime began with the early Mesozoic. It surely extended back through the Paleozoic, and at least into the later Precambrian. For the record of these earlier times, however, most of our geological controls disappear, and the subject becomes one for inference and speculation. We will refer to some of the more plausible inferences later, but with the awareness of the very tenuous nature of the supporting evidence.

COMPARISON WITH OTHER PLANETS. Modern space exploration reveals that all the inner rocky planets of the solar system except our own Earth have a cratered landscape—the Moon, Mercury, Mars, and probably even fog-shrouded Venus. This cratering was the result of the bombardment and impact of massive swarms of meteorites large and small that occurred during the initial organization of the planets. Our landings and sampling of the rocks of the Moon indicates that the cratering event was mainly four billion or more years ago, or earlier than the oldest dates that have been obtained from the rocks of Earth. The surfaces of the Moon and Mercury have remained essentially unchanged through the eons of geologic time since this event; they are dead worlds. The surface of Mars has been modified by volcanism, by wind erosion, and probably also gullying by water, but some of the original cratering survives. What modifications may have occurred in the landscape of Venus we have yet to determine.

We can feel assured that our own Earth underwent the same massive bombardment and cratering at this long-ago time, but no obvious remnants of it now survive in the landscape—although the effects of minor, later impacts are clearly shown in many parts of the world. Our Earth has been blessed with a greater hydrosphere and atmosphere, which have produced active processes of erosion and deposition that destroyed the original landscape. Earth also has a stronger magnetic field and a more active interior that have controlled the plate tectonics regime and shuffled around the original crust beyond recognition.

ORIGIN OF THE CONTINENTAL CRUST. How did the sialic continental crust come to be separated from the prevailing simatic oceanic crust? Was it a sort of slag on the surface of the globe when its rocky crust first took form, or did it evolve later? There are few answers to these troublesome questions, and the field is wide open for speculation.

Perhaps some of the differentiation occurred as a result of the massive bombardment of four billion years ago, when the larger meteorites penetrated deeply into the Earth's interior and produced convection currents that may have aided in differentiation of patches of sialic material. If such patches existed, they would be the original granitic crust of the continents.

Much labor has been expended by geologists studying Earth's oldest rocks in a search for some trace of this original granitic crust. All such work has shown, however, that the Earth's oldest granites intrude still older rocks that were once surface lavas and sediments. Any original granitic crust on which the latter might have been laid has never been discovered. Indeed, when the oldest identifiable rocks are found, they turn out to be lavas and their sedimentary derivatives, largely basaltic in composition, hence simatic rather than sialic. These relations are observable, for example, in northern Ontario and eastern Manitoba, where the rocks are 2,500 to 3,500 million years old, or very early Precambrian in age.

That the earliest identifiable rocks of the continent are basaltic leads to the intriguing possibility that a great deal of the original crust of the continents was not sial but sima. This implies that the continental plate grew through time by accretion—that sialic material was manufactured by various processes and was built out from the original continental nuclei over the original simatic layer.

The primitive surface of the earth must have been more monotonous than the present one, and most of it was covered by ocean waters, but there were probably some protuberances. If there were patches of sialic material, they rose above the rest. Also, there were probably some build-ups of simatic or basaltic material, and the simatic material may also have been forced up along lines of buckling and fracture. Probably none of these protuberances amounted to very much, but the waters of the primitive ocean had not attained the volume of the present ocean so that even modest irregularities may well have stood above the waters as dry land.

Exposed protuberances were subject to weathering and erosion, part of the product going into solution into the sea, part being deposited as sediments along the edges of the protuberances. Much of the lime, iron, and magnesia was thus sorted out and lost by solution, concentrating as sediments what were relatively minor constituents in the source rocks—the silica and alumina.

Part of the sediments laid down along the edges of the primitive protuberances probably accumulated in the first geosynclines. We will have much to say about geosynclines later (see Chapter IV, Section 4); suffice it to say here that geosynclines were primarily areas of sedimentation, and especially areas where sediments accumulated to greater thicknesses than usual. Such an excess could occur only where a place was made for the sediments by subsidence of the crust, and this could only happen by failure along a zone of weakness; from their beginnings geosynclines were thus mobile belts. Commonly, by a continuation of crustal mobility, the geosynclinal sediments became deformed, and eventually projected as mountain ranges.

Now, it is noteworthy that all granites and allied plutonic rocks occur in deformed belts, or belts that had a history as mobile belts and geosynclines immediately prior to emplacement of the plutonic rocks. On the tectonic map of North America (Plate I) one can note the great granitic masses in the Appalachian and Cordilleran regions that had been geosynclines during Paleozoic and Mesozoic time. It is true, of course, that granites and their allies occur in other places—under the flat-lying Paleozoic and Mesozoic rocks of Kansas, for example. But we believe that such places were geosynclines and mobile belts at a far earlier period, before the flat-lying sediments were laid over them.

Be that as it may, there seems to be some causal relation between geosynclines, mobile belts, and granites. Thick sedimentation took place during the initial stages, accompanied by downwarping of the crust. Downwarping was accentuated by downfolding during deformation, the two contriving to bring the geosynclinal sediments to such depths that they were subject to the internal heat of the earth, and therefore susceptible to transformation into granite. Many petrographers believe, further, that in such belts granitic material was injected from below, from differentiates from the earth's mantle. How such differentiates could have originated is a little difficult to comprehend because of the dominantly mafic character of the peridotites of the mantle.

Let us suppose, then, that our primitive geosyncline, filled with sediments more sialic than their source rocks,

9

became deformed and raised into a mountain range, and that the most altered and heated parts were transformed into granite that penetrated widely into the higher geosynclinal material. By these processes, the former geosyncline became *consolidated* into a sialic crust that was added as land to the initial protuberance.

The cycle from geosyncline to consolidated mountain belt took place many times, and in the early stages perhaps rather rapidly. Most of the Paleozoic and later geosynclines were hundreds of kilometers broad and thousands long, and required hundreds of millions of years for their consolidation. But in primitive times the crust was probably thinner and weaker, so that individual geosynclines were smaller and had a shorter life. Although some of them were haphazardly placed, many must have been formed outside a preceding geosyncline, so that more sialic crust was added to the growing continent with each consolidation.

CONTINENTAL ACCRETION DURING RECORDED GEOLOGIC TIME. So much is fancy; whether it had any relation to actual happenings in the remote past, we can hardly say. For later geologic time, the record is plainer.

A frequently cited example of continental growth is on the southeastern side of the Canadian Shield, in Quebec, the Maritime Provinces, and New England. In the Labrador Peninsula on the northwest, near the center of the shield, are very old rocks, probably as old as two and a half billion years. These are followed on the southeast by the Grenville mountain belt, also part of the shield and thoroughly metamorphosed, granitized, and worn down; its deformation took place about one billion years ago, or twice as long ago as the beginning of the Cambrian. Still farther southeast, across the St. Lawrence River, is the Appalachian mountain belt, deformed in mid-Paleozoic time or about 300 million years ago. Since this deformation, more sediments have been accumulating on the continental shelf farther southeast. No new mountain belt has formed there, and as we cannot look with certainty into the future there is no way to determine whether one ever will.

For this side of North America we can supplement our earlier cross-section from the center of the shield to the continental margin (Fig. 2) by showing the time relations of the different parts, and thus illustrate the progressive outward growth of the continental structure (Fig. 4).

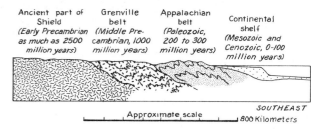

FIG. 4. Generalized section southeastward from Labrador Peninsula to Atlantic Ocean, showing age relations of the Canadian Shield, the Grenville and Appalachian belts, and the Continental Shelf.

We cannot infer, however, that the continent is visibly expanding before our eyes. In the example cited, the successive accretions were spread over two and a half billion years—a large fraction of the span of known earth history. If the process is in operation, it must be inconceivably slow.

Moreover, much of the continental area as we know it was probably consolidated by middle Precambrian time. Radiometric age determinations on Precambrian rocks exposed within and outside of the shield indicate that they were deformed and granitized during and before the Grenville mountain making just alluded to. The edges of these consolidated Precambrian rocks extend at least part way beneath the Paleozoic and Mesozoic geosynclines of the Appalachians and the Cordillera. As we will see later, however, there were certainly Paleozoic and later additions to the continent along the Gulf coast and in the western part of the Cordillera, where only oceanic crust had been before.

So far, we have touched briefly on many fundamental questions of geology. We will elaborate them further in the succeeding chapters during our discussion of the different regions of North America.

REFERENCES

1. *Layers of the earth's crust:*
   Ewing, Maurice, and Press, Frank, 1955, Geophysical contrasts between continents and ocean basins, *in* Poldervaart, Arie, ed., *The crust of the earth:* Geol. Soc. America Spec. Paper 62, pp. 1-6.
   Gilluly, James, 1955, Geologic contrasts between continents and ocean basins, *in* Poldervaart, Arie, ed., *The crust of the earth:* Geol. Soc. America Spec. Paper 62, pp. 7-18.
2. *Surface features of continents:*
   Cady, W. M., 1950, Classification of geotectonic elements: *Am. Geophys. Union Trans.*, v. 31, pp. 780-785.
3. *Continents in time:*
   Dewey, J. F., 1972, Plate tectonics: *Sci. American*, v. 226, May 1972, pp. 56-68.
   Dickinson, W. R., 1972, Evidence for plate-tectonic regimes in the rock record: *Am. Jour. Sci.*, v. 272, no. 7, pp. 551-576.

Isacks, B. I., Oliver, J., and Sykes, L. R., 1968, Seismology and the new global tectonics: *Jour. Geophys. Research*, v. 73, no. 18, pp. 5855-5899.
LePinchon, X., 1968, Sea-floor spreading and continental drift: *Jour. Geophys. Research*, v. 73, no. 12, pp. 3661-3697.
Mayr, Ernst, ed., 1952, The problem of land connections across South Atlantic, with special reference to the Mesozoic: *Am. Mus. Nat. Hist. Bull.*, v. 99, pp. 85-258.
Van der Gracht, W.A.J.M. van Waterschoot, ed., 1928, *Theory of continental drift; a symposium on the origin and movement of land masses, both inter-continental and intra-continental, as proposed by Alfred Wegener:* Am. Assoc. Petroleum Geologists.
Wegener, A. L., 1924, *The origin of continents and oceans* (trans. by J.G.A. Skerl): Methuen & Co., London.

CHAPTER II

THE CANADIAN SHIELD AND ITS ANCIENT ROCKS

1. CENTRAL STABLE REGION

Geological analysis of the continent of North America can best begin with its central part, lying within the encircling Phanerozoic mountain chains. In contrast to the latter, with their long records of crustal mobility, this part of the continent has been stable since the beginning of Cambrian time—a Central Stable Region (or more technically a *Craton*) whose subsequent deformation has seldom been greater than gentle movements upward or downward, or mild warping and flexing.

Basement of this Central Stable Region consists of Precambrian rocks. They are a prime control of its stability, as they are now strong, rigid, consolidated, and capable of resisting deformation of the crust. This consolidation was long in creation, however, as the rocks themselves bear the imprint of earlier mobility—of formation of successive orogenic belts not unlike the younger belts nearer the present continental margins. In the Interior Lowlands, or outer part of the Central Stable Region, Precambrian rocks are covered by a progressively thickening wedge of Paleozoic and younger sediments, nearly flat-lying or gently dipping. In the Canadian Shield, or nuclear area, the basement emerges and forms most of the surface. It is to the latter area that we shall turn first.

2. SURFACE FEATURES OF THE SHIELD

LOCATION AND EXTENT. The Canadian Shield makes up a sizable fraction of the northeastern part of North America (Plate I) and has an area of about five million square kilometers. It forms nearly half of Canada—the whole Labrador Peninsula, much of the provinces of Quebec and Ontario, the northeastern parts of Manitoba and Saskatchewan, much of the Northwest Territories, and part of the Arctic Islands. Along its southern edge, projections of the shield extend into the United States in the Lake Superior Region and in the Adirondack Mountains of New York state. The island of Greenland is an outlier of the shield, now separated by water and largely

covered by ice cap. On the far sides of Greenland and the Arctic Islands are the East Greenland and Innuitian orogenic belts, formed during Paleozoic time, and resembling orogenic belts elsewhere around the periphery of the Central Stable Region.

SHIELDS DEFINED. The geologic term "shield" derives from the military shields of older times, which had various forms, some roughly heart-shaped, all with a convex curvature. Lying flat, one of these might resemble a geological shield. That is, it should have a hard, convex surface, sloping away from the center in all directions, and possibly coming to a point in some direction.

TOPOGRAPHY. The Canadian Shield has many of the features of an ideal shield although the analogy is not perfect; most of its departures from the ideal shield result from damage it has suffered during Phanerozoic time.

It is most like an ideal shield along its south, southeast, and southwest borders. Here, the old surface rises gently inland away from the sedimentary rocks that cover it in the surrounding Interior Lowlands. In part, the latter form outward sloping cuestas whose scarps face toward the shield. Lower ground between the scarps and the rising shield is drowned by a remarkable chain of lakes; of these, the Great Lakes between the United States and Canada are the largest and most familiar, but the chain also includes Lake Winnipeg, Lake Athabaska, Great Slave Lake, and Great Bear Lake farther northwest in Canada. The basins of these lakes were excavated in weak rocks along the border of the shield and were accentuated late in geologic time by glacial erosion (Fig. 5).

Inland from the southern border of the shield, the sur-

FIG. 5. Idealized section across a shield to show origin of characteristic features in southern part of Canadian Shield.

11

face of the Precambrian rocks rises into low hills and rough highlands that seldom project more than 500 meters above sea level. Much of the southern part of the surface is forested, but trees play out northward and northeastward, and beyond is barren land and tundra. The surface of the Precambrian has undergone erosion intermittently since Cambrian time or even earlier. Parts may have remained bare ever since this remote period, although other parts, especially toward the edges, were covered from time to time by later sediments, most traces of which have now been eroded.

The latest vigorous erosion was during the Pleistocene period when glacial ice cleared off the accumulated soil, making the land rocky and sterile and so disordering the drainage that the surface is dotted with myriad lakes. Sterility of the land is compensated by the mineral wealth of the ancient rocks that has been revealed; they contain valuable deposits of iron, nickel, cobalt, gold, uranium, and many other metals and minerals. Mining is thus one of the great industries of Canada.

ACCIDENTS THAT HAVE MODIFIED THE SHIELD. Away from the southern border to the north and northeast, the Canadian Shield departs more from the ideal form because of various accidents that have befallen it during Phanerozoic time.

(a) Most recent damage resulted from Pleistocene glaciation, some of whose effects have just been noted. During the Pleistocene the shield was covered by great continental icecaps—one in Labrador, one in the Northwest Territories, and another in Greenland. The first two melted away 10,000 years or so ago, the third remains.

Glacial erosion beneath the icecaps and deposition of morainic material along their edges disordered the drainage, producing many lakes—the larger ones at the edge, the smaller ones in the interior. It also cleared away the surface material, and hence robbed the shield of its soil but exposed its mineral deposits.

Weight of the ice also overloaded the crust, so that in the center of the great icecaps its surface was depressed many hundreds of meters. Although much of the ice has melted, rebound of the crust has been slow, so that parts of the shield are still submerged, and its central part is still rising.

(b) One of the most conspicuous depressed areas is that of *Hudson Bay*, squarely in the center of the shield—a broad, shallow sea that fills a downwarp in the continental surface. Although the modern downwarp may be due mostly to glacial loading, the area has been one of persistent though moderate subsidence throughout Phanerozoic time. On a geologic map, one may note the Paleozoic rocks, capped in places by Mesozoic, which cover an extensive area along the southwest shore; the Paleozoic rocks of Southampton Island at the north end are also of interest. These emerged areas of stratified

rocks are the edges of a shallow structural basin that extends under much of the bay, which was filled from time to time during the Phanerozoic by the sediments of encroaching seas.

(c) Even greater modifications of the simple form of the shield have taken place to the east and northeast. Labrador faces the St. Lawrence Estuary on the southeast and the Atlantic Ocean on the northeast with bold, forbidding coasts, toward which the streams descend in canyons as much as 300 meters deep. In northernmost Labrador, in fact, peaks rise to heights of 1,500 meters above the sea, and have been called the Torngat Mountains. But while they may be mountains in a topographic sense, they are merely an uplifted and dissected edge of the surface of the old rocks of the Canadian Shield. Similar highly uplifted parts of the shield continue across Hudson Strait into Baffin Island, where some of the peaks attain heights of as much as 2,500 meters.

It is difficult to escape the conclusion that this part of the Canadian Shield has been broken by faulting late in geologic time, with the steep, straight coasts of Labrador and Baffin Island raised and the floor of the seas along their edges downdropped.

(d) The western part of the island of Greenland east of Baffin Island consists of ancient rocks like those of the shield, of which it was once a part. Greenland is, indeed, nearly connected with the rest of North America at its north end, along Nares Strait, but farther south it is separated by Davis Strait and Baffin Bay, 500 to 900 kilometers across, parts of whose floors are under 1,500 to 2,000 meters of water. Like Baffin Island, Greenland faces the strait and the bay along bold coasts. Separation of Greenland from the rest of the shield began during the Cretaceous when marine sediments were laid over what is now the western part of the island, but the main dismemberment took place later, during the Tertiary, when floods of basalt were erupted, remnants of which are preserved along the coasts of both Greenland and Baffin Island.

The separation of the part of the shield in Greenland from the parts in Baffin Island and Labrador is not a simple result of the downfaulting of an intervening block of Precambrian rocks in the water-covered area; oceanographic surveys prove that Baffin Bay and Davis Strait are not floored by continental crust but by oceanic crust. Instead, the two shores were rifted apart, pivoting in the north where they are still nearly joined, and oceanic crust has grown in the intervening area—a small-scale precursor of the opening of the North Atlantic Ocean east of Greenland somewhat later in Cenozoic time. Farther on, we will observe a similar rifting off of part of the North American continent on the Pacific Coast, to form the peninsula of Baja California (Chapter IX, section 4).

3. THE PRECAMBRIAN PROBLEM

So far, we have discussed the surface of the Canadian Shield without saying much about the rocks that compose it, except that they are ancient, strong, and rigid. We have indicated, however, that, although they are strong and rigid now, they bear the imprint of an earlier mobility—of formation of successive orogenic belts that were broadly similar to the orogenic belts formed in later times around the borders of the present continent. The shield is, then, not a monotonous expanse of indecipherable rocks, but divisible into many parts, each of which had its own eventful history.

KINDS OF PRECAMBRIAN ROCKS. Two principal kinds of Precambrian rocks occur in the shield:

Plutonic rocks, which form perhaps the greatest surface area. They are mainly granites and granite gneisses, but to the east and southeast they include quartz-poor syenites and the peculiar rock anorthosite. The plutonic rocks are never a primary crust; at one place or another each body cuts through and invades some of the supracrustal rocks, although it may form the basement of others.

Supracrustal rocks, that is, sediments and lava flows of various kinds that were laid down on the surface, with associated shallow intrusives that are mainly diabase and gabbro. Although their surface extent is less than that of the plutonic rocks, they provide more clues for interpretation of Precambrian history. They can be sorted out crudely into groups of different kinds of rock, and of different kinds of structure and metamorphism (Fig. 6).

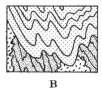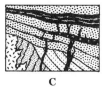

A   B   C

FIG. 6. Sketch sections showing characteristic structure of the three classes of supracrustal rocks in the Precambrian of the Canadian Shield, which are described in the text.

(A) Complex, steeply tilted, generally heavily metamorphosed supracrustal rocks that form narrow belts in the dominant granitic terrane. Most of them are poorly sorted clastic sediments, and lavas that are dominantly basaltic. Large parts of both sediments and lavas probably accumulated under water, but some may have been subaerial.

(B) Less tilted, less metamorphosed, more openly folded sediments with fewer lavas. These sediments are better sorted than the preceding and include slates, quartzites, limestones, dolomites, and iron formations; most were subaqueous and probably marine. They were laid down on a basement of earlier granites, lavas, and sediments, and are infolded with them in widely spaced orogenic belts.

(C) Gently tilted or flat-lying sediments and lavas, unaltered or only feebly metamorphosed. The sediments are mostly coarse arkosic clastics, partly of subaerial and continental origin. They form irregular patches over other rocks of the shield and occupy the smallest areas of any. Whatever their true ages, they are clearly the youngest Precambrian rocks of their respective areas.

EARLIER INTERPRETATIONS OF PRECAMBRIAN HISTORY. Some of these rocks are clearly older than others, and some are clearly younger, so that one can dimly sense a progression of events. Geologists have long sought a story of general significance—for a subdivision of rocks and time before the Cambrian into systems and periods comparable to those of the Phanerozoic rocks that overlie them. But this has not been easy because the subdivisions in the Phanerozoic are based mainly on the evidence of fossils, and fossils are scarce in the Precambrian rocks. Those which are found are the remains of primitive plants and animals that are of little value in stratigraphy; fossils of more meaningful forms of life, such as trilobites and brachiopods, only make their appearance in the Cambrian rocks. Less direct and less certain methods have therefore been resorted to in order to untangle the mysteries of the Precambrian.

There is an obvious temptation to correlate rocks from one area to another on the basis of their degree of deformation, metamorphism, and plutonism. This gave rise to a belief in Archeozoic and Proterozoic Eras of time, and of Archean and Algonkian Systems of rocks. The first was supposed to have formed during the early, chaotic beginnings of the earth so that its rocks are universally crystalline. The second was supposed to have formed when the earth had become better organized, so that sedimentation, volcanism, and other processes were more nearly like those of later times.

While there is some truth in these beliefs, they were misapplied in practice. *All* indecipherable, greatly metamorphosed and granitized rocks were assumed to be "Archean," and *all* less metamorphosed sedimentary and volcanic rocks were assumed to be "Proterozoic." For example, Sir William Logan, the pioneer Canadian geologist, recognized a complex of granitic rocks near the St. Lawrence River in the southeastern part of the shield as the Laurentian; his successors assumed that granitic complexes elsewhere in the shield were "Laurentian" also. There arose a concept that Precambrian events were marked by a succession of great cycles, each beginning with sedimentation and volcanism, followed by deformation and intrusion of granite, and terminating in a time of profound erosion before the next cycle began. Each cycle was supposed to have been universal, occurring all over the shield and perhaps the world at the same time.

Inherent in these early ideas was a misconception of the actual length of geologic time, and of Precambrian time in particular. Some inkling of the great length of geologic time was perceived by James Hutton, one of the founders of modern geology, who wrote as early as 1788, "we find no vestige of a beginning and no prospect of an end"; and by Charles Darwin three-quarters of a century later, who emphasized the great lengths of time required to accomplish organic evolution. Nevertheless, these geological and biological views were vigorously assailed by astronomers and physicists during the nineteenth century under the leadership of Lord Kelvin. Both the fiery ball of the sun and the originally molten globe of the earth must have been losing heat steadily since their creation, a finite process that eventually must end. Precise calculations proved to Kelvin that for the earth to have arrived at its present state, it could have existed no longer than 20 to 40 million years. In the face of such eminent geophysical authority, geologists themselves were reluctant to assign more than 50 to 150 million years to the age of the earth; and even when the greater length of Phanerozoic time came to be realized, the time before the Cambrian was thought not to have been much longer.

These concepts were overturned during the first decade of the present century when it became evident that the radioactive decay of some of the earth's elements that had been discovered in the laboratory some years earlier was more than a mere curiosity—that radioactive substances were widely distributed in the common rocks of the earth and provided an unfailing source of heat. The earth is not steadily losing heat; in fact, it may never have been much hotter than it is now. Lord Kelvin's formula is not a correct measure of the age of the earth.

RADIOMETRIC DATING The discovery of the widespread occurrence of radioactive minerals in the crust of the earth has an even more practical geological application, as it furnishes a means of dating the rocks. Methods of radiometric dating developed slowly, so that it is only within the last few decades that enough accurate results have been obtained to be meaningful. Radiometric dating is especially useful in rocks such as the Precambrian, for which fossil control is lacking, and it has revolutionized our thinking about Precambrian history.

We will have occasion to mention dates obtained by radiometric means from time to time in this book, so it is desirable to say something about the method (leaving the technical details to the textbooks).

Uranium, thorium, and other chemical elements of high atomic weight have the heaviest atoms and the most complex aggregates of neutrons, protons, and other atomic parts. Being heavy and complex, they are unstable and break down by loss of the various units that make up the atoms. In nature, this breakdown goes on at a constant rate, regardless of the temperature, the pressure, or other environmental influences to which the material might be subjected. Uranium goes through various transformations into daughter elements, passing first into radium and giving off the gas helium. Eventually, stability is attained in the metallic element lead, still heavy and complex, but much farther down the periodic scale. The lead derived from uranium is an isotope of the element with a slightly different atomic weight from lead derived from other sources.

Now, the age of a rock that originally contained its full quota of uranium should be obtainable from the ratio between the uranium remaining in it and the isotope of the lead formed from it. The greater the amount of this lead isotope, the older the rock should be. These calculations yield a figure indicating how many years ago a rock formed, which has been called its *absolute age* to distinguish it from the conventional age assignment to a named geological period of epoch. In terms of human history, it is as if we use a date of A.D. 300, rather than speak of the event as occurring during the later Roman Empire.

The method of "absolute" dating sounds simple enough, but there are many complications, some chemical, some geological, that prevent the results from being "absolute" in fact. Geologically, one difficulty has been that uranium and thorium occur in abundance only in certain ore minerals that are commonly found in pegmatites. The first application of radiometric methods was made on such minerals, but although the results indicated the great length of geologic time, they did little to aid in dating the common rocks for which specific ages were most desired. However, uranium does occur in minute amounts in zircon and other minerals that are minor accessories in igneous and metamorphic rocks, and exacting chemical methods for obtaining the ages of these rocks have been perfected in recent years.

Moreover, it has been found that a few of the lighter chemical elements such as potassium and rubidium also undergo transformation, producing the daughter elements argon and strontium, respectively. As potassium and rubidium are common elements in the minerals of plutonic and metamorphic rocks, and even in some sedimentary rocks, a large number of modern radiometric determinations are being made by potassium/argon and rubidium/strontium methods. Nevertheless, there are some complications; for example, argon from the potassium is not trapped in the mineral lattices until the rocks have cooled to a certain level, so that potassium/argon dates are consistently lower by small amounts than the more nearly "absolute" dates obtained by uranium/lead methods.

Even today, most radiometric determinations are being made on igneous and metamorphic rocks, and determinations on sedimentary rocks (the actual building-blocks of stratigraphy) are fewer and less reliable—especially so in the Precambrian. Commonly, the age of a Precambrian sedimentary unit is bracketed between the age of the basement rocks on which it was deposited and the time when it was metamorphosed or injected with igneous rocks. Sometimes this bracketing is within narrow limits, in others between wide limits.

IMPLICATIONS OF RADIOMETRIC DATING. Age determinations by radiometric methods now show that geologic time since the beginning of the Cambrian amounts to about 600 million years. This does not mean that Cambrian time came in with a bang—any more, say, than the Middle Ages of human history gave way overnight to the Renaissance. No trilobite (any more than some mediaeval man) awoke one morning on his seabed to the dawn of a new era and said to his neighbor, "Look, it is now 600 million years B.C., and today is the beginning of the Cambrian!" Actually, our determinations still do not permit us to know precisely the date of the beginning of the Cambrian; conditions that we associate with the Cambrian probably stole in softly, over millions of years.

Now, radiometric dating shows that Precambrian time, far from being a short prelude to Phanerozoic time, was vastly longer—at least five times as long. The oldest dated rocks in North America (and among the oldest known rocks of the World) occur in southwestern Greenland and are 3,750 million years old. Nevertheless, these rocks formed nowhere near the earth's beginning. From dating of meteorites and other evidence it now appears that the earth must be nearly 5 billion years old. The earliest history of the earth is still unrecorded.

These ages can be visualized in a diagram (Fig. 7). Phanerozoic time, or the time since the beginning of the Cambrian, becomes a narrow band at the top of the vast preceding Precambrian time, and human history at the end is infinitesimal.

MODERN CONCEPTS OF THE EARTH DURING PRECAMBRIAN TIME. Consider what this means in terms of Precambrian rocks of the Canadian Shield and elsewhere, which was the purpose of this long digression:

(a) The relatively few simple divisions of the Precambrian that have been commonly assumed must have slight relation to its true history.

(b) Instead of the few universal cycles that have been inferred, there were probably many more cycles that were local in their effects.

(c) Cycles of one area that have been correlated with those of another may very well not be correlative.

(d) With this much time available, conditions during the Precambrian become less peculiar and special than previously inferred, and easier to rationalize in terms of later conditions.

Thus, sedimentary and volcanic rocks that formed during the Precambrian have much the same appearance,

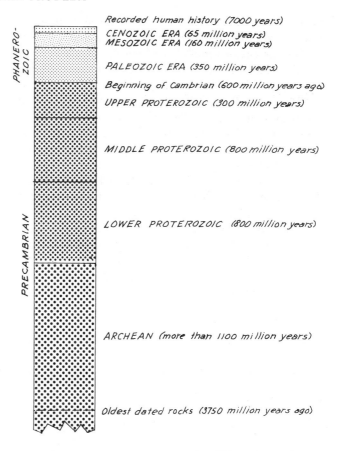

FIG. 7. Diagram showing relative proportion of different divisions of geologic time, as known from radiometric determinations and other evidence.

structure, and composition as those of later times. The sediments contain stratification, ripple-marks, cross-beds, and graded bedding; the lavas contain vesicles and pillows. Clearly, they were created by the same processes as those of later times, and can be interpreted in the same manner.

This reasoning for the small features can be extended to the larger—to sedimentary troughs, volcanic fields, plutons, and orogenic areas. As during Phanerozoic time, orogenic belts that formed during the Precambrian were probably long and narrow, and sedimentation, volcanism, deformation, and plutonism were concentrated in these belts. As during Phanerozoic time, deformation in the various belts took place at different times, while other areas were not deformed greatly; thick masses of deformed rocks in one place are thus equivalent to quite different, thinner, little deformed rocks elsewhere.

To a certain extent we can therefore apply to the Precambrian the principle of uniformitarianism (that the present is the key to the past) that has been of inestimable value in the interpretation of Phanerozoic rocks and history. But in the Precambrian we must modify this principle somewhat to take account of the slow evolution of the earth during this immensely long period.

The atmosphere must have been quite different toward the earth's beginning than now—without oxygen, for example. A modern man or other modern organism would have suffocated then, just as they would now in the atmosphere of another planet, such as Mars or Venus. The atmosphere changed gradually with time, partly from volcanic emanations, partly from life processes of plants and animals. Also, throughout the Precambrian life was primitive and confined to the seas; the lands were barren (just as they were during the early part of the Paleozoic).

These changing conditions are reflected in the rocks. The earliest sediments are poorly washed, rapidly deposited graywackes; cleanly washed quartzites and chemically deposited limestones and dolomites do not appear until later, and evaporites such as salt and gypsum are the last of all. A unique point in the evolution of the atmosphere and the seas is marked by the banded iron formations, which occur world-wide in rocks about 2,000 million years old (= Lower Proterozoic). At this time, oxygen in the atmosphere and the oceans increased to a point that ferrous iron in the ocean waters could be precipitated as layers of ferric iron, intimately interlayered with bands of silica. When this time had passed, deposition of this kind of iron formation ceased, and was not repeated in the later sediments.

4. THE PRECAMBRIAN OF THE CANADIAN SHIELD

CLASSIFICATION OF THE PRECAMBRIAN. Can we now systematize these varied facts into some kind of named subdivisions of the Precambrian? Many efforts have been made, beginning long ago in the Lake Superior Region before the advent of radiometric dating. The ages now available make a broad subdivision possible, though not approaching the finer subdivisions into periods, series, and stages that are possible in the Phanerozoic rocks.

A clue to subdivision is afforded by clustering of radiometric dates, separated by intervals with few or no dates. These express major events, frequently called "orogenies," although the spread of ages suggests that they were more properly orogenic eras, composed of a series of orogenies.

Various names have been proposed for these subdivisions, but the terms await international agreement. In this chapter and later, we will resurrect for them the traditional, originally poorly defined names *Archean* and *Proterozoic*, now given more precision by radiometric dating. This subdivision is compared below with the names presently approved by the U.S. Geological Survey and the Geological Survey of Canada:

SUBDIVISIONS OF THE PRECAMBRIAN

This book	Event (in millions of years)	Geological Survey of Canada	U.S. Geological Survey
Cambrian		Cambrian	Cambrian
Upper Proterozoic	Avalonian 570-650 m.y.	Hadrynian	Precambrian Z
Middle Proterozoic	Grenvillian 900-1,100 m.y.	Helikian	Precambrian Y
	Elsonian 1,300-1,400 m.y.		
Lower Proterozoic	Hudsonian (=Penokean) 1,700-1,800 m.y.	Aphebian	Precambrian X
	Kenoran (=Algoman) 2,500-2,700 m.y.		
Archean		Archean	Precambrian W

Base undefined; probably includes unrecognized subdivisions; oldest dated rocks about 3,750 m.y.

PROVINCES OF THE CANADIAN SHIELD. One of the parts of the shield longest known is that in the Lake Superior Region, on both sides of Lake Superior in southern Canada and northern United States. It has been intensively studied because of its mineral wealth, especially of iron and copper. Its long sequence of supracrustal rocks (with a cumulative thickness of about 50,000 meters), punctuated by orogenic and plutonic events, has inspired many generalizations about Precambrian history, on the assumption that it is a "standard" with which Precambrian rocks in other regions could be compared.

Until the last few decades, however, large areas of the remainder of the shield were poorly known or even unexplored geologically. Mapping and age dating in other parts of the shield now show that different parts have had different histories, reflected by differences in dominant radiometric ages of their basement rocks and by their structural patterns. The shield can therefore be divided into provinces, many of which are separated by major faults, some of them thrusts, others transcurrent and produced by lateral shifting between crustal blocks (Fig. 8).

The *Superior province*, lying between Lake Superior and Hudson Bay, is composed of old Archean rocks, with ages of 2,500 million years or greater. It is a domain of ancient gneissic granites, crossed by numerous subparallel belts of steeply tilted supracrustal rocks, frequently called "greenstone belts" (type A of Fig. 6). A smaller replica, the *Slave province*, lies in the far northwest, between Great Slave and Great Bear Lakes.

Between the Superior and Slave provinces in parts of

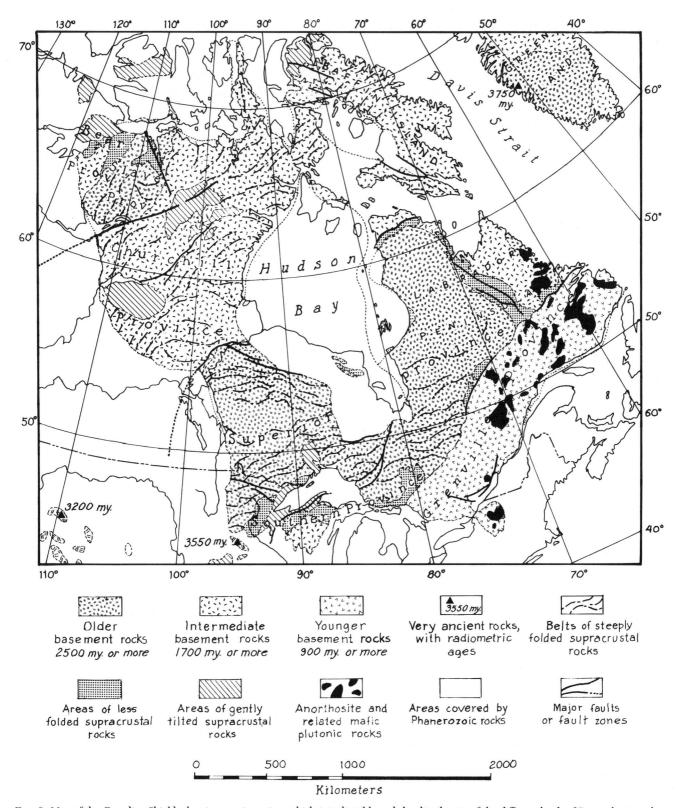

Older
basement rocks
2500 my. or more

Intermediate
basement rocks
1700 my. or more

Younger
basement rocks
900 my. or more

3550 my

Very ancient rocks,
with radiometric
ages

Belts of steeply
folded supracrustal
rocks

Areas of less
folded supracrustal
rocks

Areas of gently
tilted supracrustal
rocks

Anorthosite and
related mafic
plutonic rocks

Areas covered by
Phanerozoic rocks

Major faults
or fault zones

Kilometers

FIG. 8. Map of the Canadian Shield, showing provinces into which it is divisible and the distribution of the different kinds of Precambrian rocks. Compiled from Geologic and Tectonic Maps of Canada (1969) and other sources.

Manitoba, Saskatchewan, Alberta, and Northwest Territories, is the *Churchill province*, again a domain of granites and gneisses with belts of supracrustal rocks, but with different structural trends from those of the first two. Some of the belts of supracrustal rocks are again Archean, but others are Lower Proterozoic, and the province was not consolidated until after the first two provinces, as its dominant radiometric dates are between 1,700 and 1,800 million years. Extensions of the province occur east of Hudson Bay in the Labrador Peninsula and northward in Baffin Island. This part of the shield has long been stable, as large areas of nearly flat-lying Middle Proterozoic clastic rocks (type C of Fig. 6) overlie the basement south of Lake Athabaska and elsewhere, and have ages of about a billion years.

Northwest of the Slave province is the *Bear province*, resembling the Churchill province, but passsing westward beneath the Paleozoic cover so that its full extent is unknown. South of the Superior province is the *Southern province*, which includes the Lake Superior Region referred to above, with extensive Lower Proterozoic rocks and ages of 1,700 to 1,800 million years, but overlain along Lake Superior by the synclinal volcanic and sedimentary mass of the Keweenawan Series with Middle Proterozoic ages of about 1,100 million years.

Southeast of the Superior province along the southeastern margin of the shield is the *Grenville province*, also with a highly deformed and plutonized basement, but consolidated later than the others, with ages of about a billion years. Note that these crystalline rocks were being created at about the same time that supracrustal rocks were accumulating in the Southern, Churchill, and other provinces farther northwest in the interior of the shield, which by that time had already been consolidated and stabilized.

ARCHEAN ROCKS OF THE SUPERIOR PROVINCE. The Archean rocks of the Superior province, north of Lake Superior, form a terrane of linear belts or island-like areas of supracrustal rocks, interspersed with or surrounded by a more extensive sea of intrusive granitic gneisses (shown in pink on most geologic maps).

The belts of supracrustal rocks in the province trend generally east-west, and vary from mere wisps in the gneisses to belts as much as 700 kilometers long. One of the largest, the Abitibi belt on the border of Ontario and Quebec, is 650 kilometers long and as much as 200 kilometers broad, and includes the great gold-mining camps of Porcupine, Timmins, Kirkland Lake, and Noranda. The belts preserve the earliest supracrustal rocks known in the shield, with sequences 10,000 to more than 30,000 meters thick. They accumulated in island arcs or submarine trenches between and bordering the early proto-continents. Radiometric dating indicates that those in northern Minnesota accumulated between 2,700 and 2,750 million years ago; older dates have been reported from some of the belts farther north, but never younger.

The supracrustal rocks include great thicknesses of lava, largely basaltic, but sometimes passing upward into rarer flows of more silicic composition; most of the flows were spread out under water and are marked by pillow structure. The associated sandstones are characteristically "dirty" or poorly sorted, of the type called *graywacke*. Unlike the more familiar sandstones, which are made up of well-rounded quartz grains with a little cement, fragmental material in the graywackes is of all kinds, shapes, and sizes, and includes many rock fragments largely derived from the volcanics. Associated with the graywackes are thin beds of iron formation; and lenses of conglomerate, some of great thickness but very local, largely made up of volcanic clasts but with a small though significant number of granite.

The graywackes are products of rapid erosion of the source area and of transportation directly to the site of deposition without washing or reworking, where they were dumped into the water and settled helter-skelter to the bottom. Graywackes younger than the Precambrian, such as those in the Franciscan Group along the Pacific Coast (see Chapter IX, section 4), occur only in the earth's mobile belts, where mountains were uplifted and troughs subsided so rapidly that the sediments could not be modified by any sorting. In Archean time such conditions appear to have been universal, rather than special and local.

These supracrustal rocks have been called by various names—Keewatin for lavas, Coutchiching for sediments beneath lavas, Timiskaming and Knife Lake for sediments above lavas. In places, structural unconformities between the different units have been claimed, sometimes with granite injected into the older unit and not into the younger. But all these names are very local in application and there is no assurance that a rock called by one of the names is of the same age at all places; also, sequences may be unconformable in one place and conformable in another. The lavas are now known to occur at different levels in the sequences, so that sediments beneath or above them may be high or low in the section, depending on locality.

Contrary to what might be expected from their extreme age, the supracrustal rocks for the most part are only slightly metamorphosed—of greenschist facies or a little higher. Probably the Superior province was so thoroughly consolidated during the Kenoran orogeny that it has resisted deformation and has remained stable since this remote period.

The granitic rocks (the pink areas of the maps) are largely gneisses poor in potash—granodiorite, quartz diorite, and quartz monzonite; true granites are rare. Much of the granitic rock seems to have welled up in the geanticlines between the belts of supracrustal rocks. All, so far as known, intrude the supracrustal rocks, but they might have been remobilized from an earlier basement. A hint of such a basement occurs along the Minnesota River valley southwest of the Lake Superior Region, where ancient gneisses have yielded ages of 3,550 million years.

The rocks of the Superior province are typical of the Archean world-wide, and all have common characters that distinguish them from those of later ages, as they formed at a time when the atmosphere and oceans were unlike the present, and before the organization of the crust into well-defined cratons and geosynclines. Andrew C. Lawson, who worked and thought much about the rocks of the Canadian Shield at an earlier time, expressed the contrast vividly and poetically: "On the far side of the Eparchean Interval we encounter the vestiges of an archaic world."

LOWER PROTEROZOIC OF SOUTHERN PROVINCE. Along the southern border of the Superior province the Archean rocks are overlain with right-angled unconformity by several assemblages of Lower Proterozoic rocks.

To the east, extending for 400 kilometers along the north side of Lake Huron is the *Huronian Series*, first observed years ago by Sir William Logan, pioneer geologist of Canada. To the south, where the series is considerably folded, it is more than 6,500 meters thick and divisible into a number of groups and formations. The lower units are argillites, graywackes, and subarkoses, with some interbedded volcanics; higher up are units of limestone and quartzite as well as the prevailing argillites and subarkoses. The highest Cobalt Group spreads northward for more than 100 kilometers, overstepping the earlier strata and lying nearly flat on the deeply eroded Archean rocks. At its base is the remarkable *Gowganda Conglomerate*, composed of heterogeneous clasts of all sizes, some of them striated and with striated pavements beneath in places, which is almost certainly a glacial tillite (similar lesser tillites occur in some of the units lower down in the Huronian). They express a very ancient time of lowered temperatures and refrigeration of the earth.

To the west, around Lake Superior and separated from the Huronian by Paleozoic cover, is the Animikie Series, formerly correlated with the Huronian and likewise sedimentary, but otherwise quite different. The two are now known to be of different ages; the Huronian formed before intrusion of the Nipissing Diabase, whose age is 2,150 million years; the Animikie has been dated at about 1,800 million years or a little earlier, and formed during a later part of Lower Proterozoic time.

North of Lake Superior in Minnesota and Ontario, the Animikie dips gently southward toward the Keweenawan Series in the Lake Superior syncline, with a thickness of about 2,000 meters, and consists, above a basal conglomerate, of a thick bed of iron formation followed by a mass of argillite and graywacke not unlike the sediments of the earlier Archean sequence. Folding of the Animikie rocks increases southward, and where they reappear beyond the Lake Superior syncline in Michigan and Wisconsin they have been thrown into large folds by the Penokean (= Hudsonian) deformation, which brings up Archean rocks on their crests. Here, the sequence increases to 16,000 meters and includes strata both older and younger than the equivalent of the type Animikie (hence has been called the Marquette Range Supergroup). The lower units include a thick basal quartzite, followed by an equally thick dolomite. The middle unit includes persistent iron formations probably equivalent to those north of Lake Superior, which are again followed by argillite and graywacke, but here containing some thick though impersistent bodies of pillow lava.

The most distinctive of the Animikie rocks are the beds of banded iron formation—the local representatives of the world-wide accumulation of iron formation about 2,000 million years ago which was referred to earlier. The iron formations are an alternation of ferruginous chert (called "taconite"), slate, and stromatolite beds, whose weathering has produced the high-grade iron ore of the "iron ranges": on the north side the great Mesabi Range and the Gunflint and Cuyuna Ranges on strike to the east and west, and on the south side the Gogebic, Menominee, Marquette and other ranges. An elaborate economy has grown up around them: the great iron mines where ore is taken out of open cuts by power shovel: the railroads to Lake Superior, where the ore is loaded into ships; ship transport down the lakes to ports on Lake Erie, where the ore is again carried by rail to steel mills in Pennsylvania and Ohio.

Vast though these iron deposits are, they are not inexhaustible. The high-grade ore of even the great Mesabi Range will soon be mined out, and technological problems have been overcome so that mining can begin on the leaner taconite beneath. As a substitute, mining has also begun on nearly identical iron formations of the Labrador trough, which extends southward through the Labrador Peninsula, and the product is being shipped by rail to ports on the Gulf of St. Lawrence, for eventual delivery to the steel mills.

MIDDLE PROTEROZOIC OF SOUTHERN PROVINCE. Above the Lower Proterozoic rocks in the trough of the Lake Superior syncline is the *Keweenawan Series*, a great body of land-laid volcanics and sediments with associated mafic intrusives. The Keweenawan forms the north and south shores of the lake, as well as its floor, and extends for long distances farther southwest and southeast, partly under cover of the Paleozoic rocks.

Within this restricted area the Keweenawan accumulated to a thickness greater than 16,000 meters; much of the lower half is basaltic lava, the upper half is coarse, red feldspathic sandstone derived from erosion of the older rocks of the shield roundabout (Fig. 9). To make a place for this enormous body of supracrustal rocks, their floor subsided rapidly during accumulation, producing a synclinal basin with about the same proportions as the modern Lake Superior and its shores; very likely neither the lavas nor the sediments were spread very far beyond their present limits. During and after accumulation the rocks were gently to steeply tilted toward the lake and were broken by great faults, yet they have been neither folded nor metamorphosed.

While the flows were being poured out on the surface the underlying part of the succession was being filled with mafic intrusives. The largest of these is the great floored lopolith of the *Duluth Gabbro* along the north shore of the lake, 250 kilometers long and as much as 16,000 meters thick. Radiometric determinations on the mafic intrusives indicate that they were emplaced between 1,120 and 1,140 million years ago.

The Keweenawan contains copper deposits, notable as having been the first to be mined in the United States. Copper occurs as flecks and masses of various sizes in the lavas and conglomerates of the series; the copper is native rather than being combined in sulfides as it is in the great copper deposits of the West, discovered later. Being pure metal, it can be extracted and used without smelting, and hence was even dug on a small scale by the Indians long before the coming of the white man. Copper artifacts are found in burial mounds and other Indian remains throughout the Mississippi Valley, whither they had arrived by trading from tribe to tribe.

The Keweenawan formed long after the Animikie Series of the same area, as indicated by the respective dates of 1,100 and 1,800 million years for the two. In places the unconformity between the Animikie and the Keweenawan is not very marked, but this is because of the variable deformation of the former—greatest on the southeast, less on the northwest.

In the trough of the Lake Superior syncline, the Keweenawan sandstones are overlain by another, thinner body of sandstones, still red and unfossiliferous but finer grained and more cleanly washed and quartzose—known from place to place by such names as the Jacobsville, Bayfield, and Hinckley Sandstones. As they

are stratigraphically high above the mafic rocks with 1,100-million-year dates, they may belong to the Upper Proterozoic. Both the Keweenawan and these overlying sandstones are succeeded with low-angle unconformity by marine Upper Cambrian sandstones of the Croixan Series, which are the initial deposits of the Paleozoic sequence of the Interior Lowlands.

We have mentioned that the Keweenawan rocks and the Lake Superior syncline extend far in each direction from the Lake Superior basin beneath the cover of Paleozoic rocks. On the southwest, gravity and magnetic anomalies indicate that the trough and its mafic igneous rocks extend another 980 kilometers into eastern Kansas, and somewhat vaguer geophysical data suggest that the trough also extends southeastward into the lower peninsula of Michigan. The whole structure thus has a curious arcuate form, concave to the south, which was evidently the site of a great rift in the continental crust that opened during the Middle Proterozoic, and was filled by the Keweenawan lavas and sediments.

ROCKS AND STRUCTURES OF GRENVILLE PROVINCE. The Grenville province borders the Superior province on the southeast, forming a belt 400 kilometers wide peripheral to the central part of the shield from Lake Huron through Ontario and Quebec to the Atlantic Coast in Labrador. Rocks like those of the Grenville province also occur, as noted, in the Adirondack uplift of New York state. The name Grenville originates in Grenville township in southwestern Quebec; this is the type locality of the supracrustal rocks of the *Grenville Series*, which is one of the components of the province.

The boundary between the Grenville province and the Superior province is the *Grenville front*, where there is an abrupt change from the Archean and Lower Proterozoic supracrustal rocks with low-grade metamorphism into higher-grade granitic gneisses of upper amphibolite or granulite facies, and in some places a zone of faulting. Northeast-trending structures along the Grenville Front abruptly truncate the easterly-trending Archean structures of the Superior province. The Grenville province is also a coherent radiometric domain whose metamorphism and deformation occurred between 1,170 and 1,250 million years ago, or much later than that of the rest of the shield, which by then had

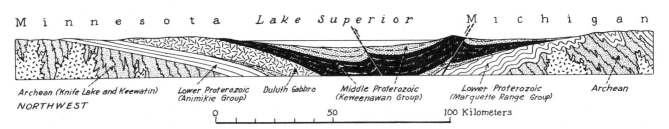

Archean (Knife Lake and Keewatin)   Lower Proterozoic   Duluth Gabbro   Middle Proterozoic   Lower Proterozoic   Archean
NORTHWEST   (Animikie Group)   (Keweenawan Group)   (Marquette Range Group)

0   50   100 Kilometers

FIG. 9. Generalized section across Lake Superior syncline showing structure and relation of Keweenawan Series and the Lower Proterozoic rocks. Compiled from Leith, Lund, and Leith (1935).

been stabilized—as indicated, for example, by the 1,100-million-year radiometric dates in the little deformed Keweenawan rocks of the Southern province.

The Grenville Series itself is preserved only in the southeastern part of the province. It is a Middle Proterozoic supracrustal sequence as much as 8,200 meters thick of marble, quartzite, and aluminous paragneiss with minor interbedded volcanics, strongly deformed and of medium metamorphic grade. Streaks of graphite occur, derived from original carbonaceous sediments, and small amounts of natural gas, a hydrocarbon, have been detected. The deposits contrast notably with Precambrian supracrustal rocks northwest of the Grenville Front. Their abundant marbles were originally limy or dolomitic carbonate deposits, their quartzites cleanly washed sands, and their aluminous gneisses shales; except for their extreme metamorphism they are closely akin to the Paleozoic and Mesozoic miogeosynclinal deposits laid down in the Appalachian and Cordilleran geosynclines.

The remaining 60 percent of the province, mainly to the northwest, is a domain of gneisses and plutonic rocks, mostly of higher metamorphic grade. The gneisses are dominantly feldspathic and granitic, but with more mafic streaks, whose layering forms gently dipping, large-scale domes and basins, the whole producing a terrane of great monotony. A few remnants of highly altered supracrustal rocks like those of the Grenville Series occur, but for the most part the gneisses appear to be older and to be the basement on which the series was deposited, now reworked and altered by the Grenvillian orogeny. Greatly altered remnants of Archean and Lower Proterozoic supracrustal rocks can be traced for some distance southeast of the Grenville Front; they were originally deformed by the Kenoran or Hudsonian orogenies, or both, and have been deformed again during the Grenvillian orogeny.

True granitic plutons directly related to the Grenvillian orogeny are rare in the gneiss complex, whose granitic gneisses originated earlier. Much more distinctive are the anorthosites, which, with associated syenites, occur in great bodies. The most famous is the Mount Marcy body in the Adirondack Mountains, but others of comparable size extend thence northeastward across the Grenville province in Quebec, and beyond the province into the older crystalline rocks of eastern Labrador. In the latter area, outside the region of Grenvillian influence, they have been dated radiometrically at 1,400 million years, hence are a product of the pre-Grenvillian Elsonian event. The anorthosites within the Grenville province probably formed at the same time and have been reworked by the Grenvillian orogeny.

Anorthosite is made up almost exclusively of plagioclase, or soda-lime feldspar. If any other minerals occur, they are mafic silicates, the pyroxenes and amphiboles. It is difficult to picture how anorthosite could have been derived from an igneous magma, and its origin has been much debated. Be that as it may, the formation of anorthosite appears to have been a unique event in earth history during Middle Proterozoic time; anorthosite is less common in Precambrian rocks of other ages, and is unknown in the Phanerozoic.

The Grenville province thus appears to be an orogenic belt built against the previously stabilized older part of the Canadian Shield, that is more nearly comparable to the more familiar orogenic belts of Phanerozoic times. The chief difference is that the orogenic belt is so ancient that it has been more deeply eroded, so that its highly metamorphosed and reworked basement is more widely exposed, and its original geosynclinal accumulation, the Grenville Series, has been reduced to remnant patches in the deeper downfolds. The Grenville orogenic belt is much more extensive than its exposed segment in the southeastern part of the Canadian Shield. As we shall see later, parts of it emerge in the higher uplifts in the northwestern part of the Appalachian orogenic belt, and it has been traced in subsurface thence into Texas, and even eastern Mexico. It breaks off eastward at the Atlantic Coast, but must have continued into western Europe before separation of the continents.

REFERENCES

Greenland and Arctic Islands:
  Berthelsen, Asger, and Noe-Nygard, Arne, 1965, The Precambrian of Greenland, *in* Rankama, Kalervo, ed., *The Precambrian,* v. 2: Interscience Publishers, New York, pp. 113-362.
  Haller, John, 1971, *Geology of the East Greenland Caledonides:* Wiley-Interscience, New York.
  Thorsteinsson, R., and Tozer, E. T., 1970, Geology of the Arctic Islands, *in Geology and economic minerals of Canada:* Canada Geol. Survey Econ. Geol. Rept. 1, 5th ed., pp. 548-590.
  Trettin, H. P., and others, 1972, The Innuitian province, *in* Price, R. A., and Douglas, R.J.W., eds., *Variations in tectonic styles in Canada:* Geol. Assoc. Canada Spec. Paper 11, pp. 83-279.
Precambrian Chronology:
  Goldich, S. S., 1968, Geochronology in the Lake Superior Region: *Canadian Jour. Earth Sci.,* v. 5, no. 3, pt. 2, pp. 715-724.

Holmes, Arthur, 1965, *Principles of physical geology:* Chapter 13, Dating the pages of earth history: Ronald Press Co., New York, pp. 346-385.
Knopf, Adolph, 1957, Measuring geologic time: *Sci. Monthly,* v. 85, pp. 225-236.
Stockwell, C. H., 1968, Geochronology of stratified rocks of the Canadian Shield: *Canadian Jour. Earth Sci.,* v. 5, no. 3, pt. 2, pp. 693-698.
Precambrian General Problems:
  Cloud, Preston, 1972, A working model of the primitive earth: *Am. Jour. Sci.,* v. 272, no. 5, pp. 537-548.
  Cloud, Preston, and Gibor, Ahron, 1970, The oxygen cycle: *Sci. American,* v. 223, no. 3, pp. 110-123.
  Engel, A.E.J., and others, 1974, Crustal evolution and global tectonics: *Geol. Soc. America Bull.,* v. 85, no. 6, pp. 843-848.

Glaessner, M. F., 1968, Biological events and the Precambrian time scale: *Canadian Jour. Earth Sci.*, v. 5, no. 3, pt. 2, pp. 585-590.

Precambrian Rocks of the Shield:

Engel, A.E.J., and Engel, C. G., 1953, Grenville Series in the northwest Adirondack Mountains, New York, (1) General features of the Grenville Series: *Geol. Soc. America Bull.*, v. 64, pp. 1015-1048.

Goldich, S. S., and others, 1961, Precambrian geology and geochronology of Minnesota: *Minnesota Geol. Survey Bull.* 41.

Goodwin, A. M., 1974, Precambrian belts, plumes, and shield development: *Am. Jour. Sci.*, v. 274, no. 9, pp. 987-1028.

James, H. L., 1960, Problems of stratigraphy and correlation of Precambrian with particular reference to the Lake Superior Region: *Am. Jour. Sci.*, v. 258-A (Bradley vol.), pp. 104-114.

King, P. B., 1976, Precambrian geology of the United States; an explanatory text to accompany the Geologic Map of the United States: *U.S. Geol. Survey Prof. Paper* 902, pp. 13-29.

Pettijohn, F. J., 1943, Archean sedimentation: *Geol. Soc. America Bull.*, v. 54, no. 7, pp. 925-972.

Stockwell, C. H., and others, 1970, Geology of the Canadian Shield, *in Geology and economic minerals of Canada*: Canada Geol. Survey Econ. Geol. Rept. 1, 5th ed., pp. 44-150.

Wynne-Edwards, H. R., 1972, The Grenville province, *in* Price, R. A., and Douglas, R.J.W., eds. *Variations in tectonic styles in Canada*: Geol. Assoc. Canada Spec. Paper 11, pp. 264-334.

CHAPTER III

THE INTERIOR LOWLANDS AND
THE SCIENCE OF GENTLY DIPPING STRATA

1. GEOGRAPHY

We pass now to that other part of the Central Stable Region, the Interior Lowlands, where the Precambrian basement is concealed beneath younger, little disturbed rocks—a region about as extensive as the Canadian Shield itself, lying mainly to the south, southwest, and west, forming the vast central part of the United States, as well as a wide band in western Canada between the shield and the Cordillera (Plate I).

In the United States the Interior Lowlands are the region drained by the Mississippi River and its tributaries—the Ohio, Missouri, Arkansas, and others—which flow into the Gulf of Mexico. In Canada it is the region drained by the Nelson and Mackenzie Rivers and their tributaries, which flow, respectively, into Hudson Bay and the Arctic Ocean.

The Interior Lowlands are largely plains country, mostly standing only a few hundred meters above sea level, widely masked by drift and morainal deposits, and leveled in the north by continental glaciers. Eastward toward the Appalachians and in the Ozarks of Missouri and adjacent states the surface rises into plateaus that have been intricately dissected. Westward the surface rises across the Great Plains also, but with little dissection, and attains altitudes of nearly two kilometers above sea level at the foot of the Rocky Mountains.

2. GEOLOGICAL INVESTIGATIONS

The rather monotonous geologic features of the Interior Lowlands would seem of less interest than the complex rocks and structures of the Canadian Shield, the Appalachians, or the Cordilleras, nor can we, in this book, devote space to them commensurate with their surface area. But millions of our fellow citizens live in the Interior Lowlands and earn their livelihood from the land, either directly or indirectly—from the glacial drift and soils by agriculture and forestry, or from its rocks by exploitation of their fuels and mineral deposits. The lowlands have yielded a sizable fraction of the nation's oil production; coal measures of Pennsylvanian age are preserved in many of its structural basins; the same basins and others farther west are mined for salt; veins in the upper Mississippi Valley, the Illinois-Kentucky district, and the Tri-State district (Missouri, Kansas, and Oklahoma) contain deposits of lead, zinc, fluorspar, and other valuable minerals.

Much patient labor has been expended to learn the geology of the Interior Lowlands, partly for the sake of research, partly to discover and develop the mineral deposits. A body of special knowledge has thus accumulated that we might call the science of gently dipping strata. The lowlands have, in fact, shared with the states of the eastern seaboard in the birth of American geology, and it is of interest to sketch some of its beginnings.

The first real account and map of the geology of the United States—or any part of North America, for that matter—was published in 1809 by William Maclure, a Scotch immigrant who had become a prosperous merchant in Philadelphia. Although Maclure traveled widely about the country east of the Mississippi to assemble his information, today his results seem generalized and primitive.

For the next twenty years various other men interested in geology nibbled away at the subject in different areas. There were no true professional geologists in those days, only enthusiastic amateurs—men who had received some education in the professions of the ministry, law, or medicine, and who were curious about their surroundings. For the most part their studies were labors of love, but the various states began to realize the need for an appraisal of their resources as an aid to growth and development, and by the third decade of the century their legislatures were granting funds to geologists to make official surveys. Some of these surveys left an enduring mark on earth science, others are now forgotten; of them all, certainly the most notable was that of New York state.

In 1836 the state of New York set up a geological survey. It was organized along rather peculiar lines, the state being divided into four districts, each assigned to a geologist who operated more or less independently of the rest. The man and their assignments were:

W. W. Mather	southeastern district
Ebenezer Emmons	northeastern district
Lardner Vanuxem	central district
Timothy A. Conrad	western district

The first three districts, nearest the centers of population and with the most varied geology, were considered the choicest assignments. The western part of the state, which was rough pioneer country at the time and a region of gently dipping strata, was considered a poor fourth. At the end of the first year Conrad gave up the western district for other duties and it was assigned to a twenty-five-year-old assistant of the survey, James Hall.

Out of this seemingly unpromising area, Hall forged a career that was to occupy much of the remainder of his life. For here he found the Paleozoic strata to be unaltered and richly fossiliferous, sloping gently to the southwest and laid out in a series of gigantic steps that ascended from Ordovician on the northeast through Silurian and Devonian into Mississippian on the southwest. Here was found the stratigraphic key not only of the more complex and puzzling rocks elsewhere in the state but of rocks in much of the adjacent part of the Interior Lowlands as well. For many years the western New York section thus became a standard of reference for the whole region. Hall's work on this section and his study of its innumerable fossils has given him an enduring place among the founders of American geology. That he was also perceptive to other geologic problems we will see presently when we discuss the subject of geosynclines (Chapter IV, section 4).

It was Hall and his colleagues of the New York Survey who began the custom, now universal in American stratigraphy, of naming rock units after geographic localities where they are typically exposed, instead of using the earlier quaint and often misleading descriptive or mineralogical designations. "Calciferous sandrock" thus became Beekmantown, "Birdseye limestone" be-

came Lowville, and "Corniferous limerock" became Onondaga.

The other geologists of the New York Survey labored valiantly on their supposedly choicer districts, but with less enduring results. They are little remembered today, except perhaps poor Emmons whose strange delusions still have a place in the annals of American geology. Some of the geology of the eastern part of the state has proved to be so difficult that there is little agreement on it even yet.

3. PRECAMBRIAN BASEMENT OF THE LOWLANDS

STRUCTURE OF THE BASEMENT. Before saying farewell to the Precambrian on which we have dwelt in the Canadian Shield, let us remember that the Interior Lowlands differ from the shield merely in possessing a sedimentary cover; that throughout the lowlands the sediments are underlain by Precambrian rocks. Of course we know less about them here than in the shield because they are largely concealed, but some little patches do emerge—in the Sioux uplift of southeastern South Dakota, the Ozark uplift of Missouri, the Arbuckle and Wichita Mountains of Oklahoma, and the Llano uplift of Texas. At the western edge, also, Precambrian emerges in the Black Hills of South Dakota and the Front Range of the Rocky Mountains in Wyoming and Colorado. Besides, Precambrian rocks have been reached in many of the deeper drill holes put down for oil and gas in the intervening plains and have been cored for samples. Some notion of buried Precambrian structures has been obtained from geophysical data as well. From these data, admittedly incomplete, it is posssible to construct generalized maps of the Precambrian geology of the Interior Lowlands.

We can anticipate that the Precambrian beneath the lowlands is divisible into provinces like those in the Canadian Shield—extensions of those in the shield and various new provinces—and this inference is justified by the drill records. A belt of ancient Archean rocks extends southwestward from the Superior province in Minnesota into the Rocky Mountains of Wyoming and adjacent states. South of it, a large area, both beneath the plains and in the southern part of the Rocky Mountains, consists of supracrustal and metamorphic and plutonic rocks that yield Lower Proterozoic dates like the Churchill province in the shield; and along the southeastern side of the United States, from the Appalachians into Texas, are metamorphic rocks that yield Middle Proterozoic dates and are extensions of the Grenville province. In addition there are various new elements, such as the unaltered and little deformed Middle and Upper Proterozoic rocks of the Cordilleran region, and a peculiar belt of late Precambrian and early Cambrian volcanic rocks and shallow intrusives that extends through the Wichita Mountains of southern Oklahoma.

SURFACE OF THE BASEMENT. The gentle surface of the Canadian Shield, cut on Precambrian rocks, passes beneath the Cambrian and younger rocks along its edges and, in the Interior Lowlands, forms the floor on which these younger rocks were laid. Much of the plantation of the Precambrian was thus accomplished before the Cambrian. In most places in the Interior Lowlands the surface has been reduced to a nearly level plain before sediments were laid over it; a few places retained considerable relief, as in parts of the Ozark area of Missouri, so that knobs and peaks project as much as 500 meters into the cover of sedimentary rocks (Fig. 10B).

Aside from this local relief, the top of the Precambrian is broadly undulating, rising toward the crests of domes in the later rocks and descending deeply beneath their basins. These undulations result from later warping of the Precambrian; in fact, they represent the total of all deformation that has affected the region since the beginning of the Cambrian.

In most places undulations of the top of the Precambrian are very gentle, but in others the surface is sharply bent or broken. Extending southward across Kansas into Oklahoma is a narrow strip where Precambrian projects to within a few hundred or thousand meters of the surface. This is the "granite ridge" of Kansas, or Nemaha uplift, not shown on the surface geology maps and buried entirely by later Paleozoic rocks. The ridge is a block of Precambrian rocks that was raised in early Pennsylvanian time (Fig. 10A).

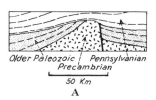
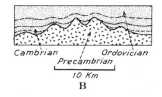

FIG. 10. Sections showing exceptional relief features of the Precambrian surface in the Interior Lowlands: (A) Nemaha uplift, or "granite ridge" of Kansas, produced by uplift and faulting of the surface in early Pennsylvanian time. (B) Buried hills in the Ozark area of Missouri, which represent erosional topography of the surface prior to burial by Paleozoic rocks. Note difference in horizontal scales; vertical scales exaggerated. Adapted from Lee (1956) and Bridge (1930).

4. SEDIMENTARY COVER OF THE LOWLANDS

Let us now consider the rocks of the Interior Lowlands that overlie the Precambrian floor. These, we find, are mainly sedimentary and of relatively small thickness—a hundred or a thousand meters in most places, but exceeding 3,000 meters in the deeper basins. Basal sedimentary deposits are Cambrian, or if not that, younger Paleozoic. Paleozoic rocks form the surface as far west as the hundredth meridian, beyond which they are covered by Cretaceous and Tertiary strata. A few

lava caps occur along the western edge of the Great Plains; igneous intrusions are widely scattered through the lowlands but are small, sparse, and inconsequential.

INITIAL, OR CAMBRIAN DEPOSITS. Events that took place in the Interior Lowlands during Cambrian time had an important influence on the evolution of the continent as we know it and are worth considering at some length.

Cambrian time appears to have been very long—perhaps 80 million years, or longer than all time back to the beginning of the Tertiary. Where sedimentation was nearly continuous through the period, its deposits reach great thickness; in the Inyo Mountains of eastern California they amount to nearly 5,000 meters (Chapter VIII, section 2). But these thick Cambrian deposits are all outside the Interior Lowlands, in areas that were geosynclines through long periods of Paleozoic and Mesozoic time and later were raised into mountain belts.

In considering these thick Cambrian deposits it is convenient to divide them into a Lower, Middle, and Upper Series, each characterized by distinctive history and fossils. The terms Waucoban, Albertan, and Croixan have been used for the same subdivisions, but are not necessary for our purpose.

In contrast to these thick Cambrian deposits of the geosynclinal areas, those of the Interior Lowlands are 300 meters thick at most, and in many places much thinner; with a few exceptions they are all Upper Cambrian. Typical Cambrian deposits of the lowlands are exposed along the edges of the shield in Wisconsin and Minnesota, hence the alternate term "Croixan" for the Upper Cambrian, named for the St. Croix River between the two states. They are mainly sandstones, probably derived from erosion of the Precambrian of the shield; the sandstones are marine—at many places they contain fossil trilobites, brachiopods, and other sea-dwelling animals.

In Cambrian time the sea thus covered first the geosynclines along the edges of the Central Stable Region, and all through Early and Middle Cambrian time the Central Stable Region (Interior Lowlands and Canadian Shield) was still land consisting of exposed Precambrian rocks. It was thus not until Late Cambrian time that marine waters began to spread over the central region and to cover large parts of the Interior Lowlands and even some of the shield. These relations of Lower, Middle, and Upper Cambrian to the geosynclines and the Central Stable Region show that by the beginning of Cambrian time the latter had developed into a continental platform (Fig. 11).

Abrupt thinning and wedging out of Lower and Middle Cambrian toward the edge of the Central Stable Region (continental platform) has been proved by exposures and drill records, both along the front of the Appalachians on the southeast and along the front of the Rocky Mountains in Canada on the west.

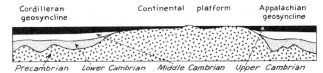

Precambrian   Lower Cambrian   Middle Cambrian   Upper Cambrian

FIG. 11. Section from west to east across the middle part of North America at end of Cambrian time, showing overlap of Lower, Middle, and Upper Cambrian Series, and how the Central Stable Region acquired the character of a continental platform. Length of section about 4,000 kilometers; vertical scale grossly exaggerated. Adapted from Kay (1951).

But there is an exceptional area along the southwestern side of the Central Stable Region. The map shows that here the front of the Rocky Mountains extends southeast through Wyoming and south through Colorado into New Mexico. This part fails to obey the rule that younger mountain belts formed where troughs of greatest sedimentation existed. Where the Cambrian is turned up along the edges of the ranges, it is thin Upper Cambrian, nearly like that in the Interior Lowlands of Wisconsin and Minnesota. The boundary between thin Cambrian and thick Cambrian lies well west of the mountain front near the western edge of the Colorado Plateau in central Utah.

In terms of continental history, this means that the continental platform of Cambrian time extended westward beyond the present Interior Lowlands and included what are now the Southern Rocky Mountains and Colorado Plateau. It thus appears that the mountain structures of these provinces were created by dismemberment or reactivation of a corner of the continental platform after Cambrian time. We will return to this important inference later (Chapter VII, sections 1 and 2).

CONTINENTAL BACKBONE. Another feature, partly the result of Cambrian overlap, partly a later development, is found in a belt extending southwest from Minnesota to New Mexico; here relatively young rocks generally lie on the Precambrian. This is not a structural feature in the usual sense, and it cannot be seen on any ordinary map; it is known mostly from comparison of stratigraphic sections shown either on surface outcrops or well records. It has been called the continental arch, or continental backbone.

For example, behind El Paso, Texas, rise the Franklin Mountains, an uplift that exposes a section that consists, above the Precambrian basement, of sedimentary rocks of Cambrian, Ordovician, Silurian, Devonian, Mississippian, Pennsylvanian, and Permian ages—in other words, representatives of all the Paleozoic systems (Fig. 12A). But 400 kilometers to the north near Albuquerque, New Mexico, rise the Sandia Mountains, consisting of Precambrian rocks nearly to their crests, overlain unconformably on their tops by Pennsylvanian rocks (Fig. 12B). All the intervening Paleozoic systems are missing; in ranges between El Paso and Albuquerque the earlier systems gradually thin and disappear northward. In exposures within 150 kilometers of Albuquerque even the Pennsylvanian is missing, so that Permian rocks lie directly on the Precambrian.

This illustrates conditions near the southwest end of the continental backbone and how they are obtained from surface outcrops. Outcrops and drill records indicate similar conditions elsewhere along this feature to the northeast. Cambrian or younger Paleozoic rocks were never deposited over parts of the belt, so that there was a tendency for it to persist as land through successive transgressions of the seas. Parts of the belt are marked by later uplifts along the same trend, so that, if any rocks were deposited on it earlier in the Paleozoic, they have been removed later by erosion.

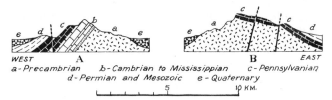

WEST   A   B   EAST

a - Precambrian   b - Cambrian to Mississippian   c - Pennsylvanian
d - Permian and Mesozoic   e - Quaternary
           5   10 KM.

FIG. 12. Sections of Franklin Mountains (A) and Sandia Mountains (B) near El Paso, Texas, and Albuquerque, New Mexico, respectively, showing difference in sequence of Paleozoic formations above Precambrian basement rocks, to illustrate stratigraphic relations on south margin of continental backbone. Sections are about 400 kilometers apart. After Richardson (1909) and Darton (1928).

OVERLAP FEATURES. By the gradual spreading of Cambrian and later seas, their deposits *overlapped* the Stable Region (Fig. 13A). Each younger layer extended farther inland than the one before, deposits farthest inland being sandy near-shore deposits; these became progressively younger the farther inland the seas advanced. Sand bodies along the edges of the advancing seas are more porous than sediments farther out, and form *wedge belts of porosity* in which fluids such as oil or water can accumulate (Fig. 13D). Some of the overlapping deposits thus form stratigraphic traps for oil, and have resulted in oil fields more extensive than those in the more familiar anticlinal traps, although they are more difficult to locate by ordinary means of exploration.

After Cambrian time, successive advancing Paleozoic seas spread their deposits over the earlier strata that had been somewhat tilted and eroded. Toward the positive

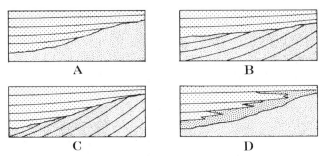

A   B

C   D

FIG. 13. Sketch sections illustrating: (A) Overlap. (B) Overstep. (C) Combination of overlap and overstep. (D) Wedge belts of porosity.

or domal areas these deposits were thus laid across the truncated edges of successively older strata that they *overstep*, lying with small hiatus on rocks a little earlier on the flanks, and with great hiatus on much older rocks on the crests (Fig. 13B).

LATER PALEOZOIC DEPOSITS. Paleozoic deposits of the Interior Lowlands were products of shallow, ephemeral, constantly shifting seas, whose inferred outlines produce an intricate pattern on the paleogeographic maps contained in textbooks of historical geology.

The Paleozoic deposits produced during the many little transgressions and regressions of the seas can be generalized into larger sequences, which have little relation to the largely artificial periods and systems. Commonly these sequences each extend over a large part of the Central Interior and into the geosynclines on each side, and are bounded below and above by regional unconformities (as distinguished from local unconformities that do not extend very far). It is thus possible to recognize a *Sauk sequence* from the base of the Cambrian to the top of the Lower Ordovician; a *Tippecanoe sequence* from the Middle Ordovician into the Lower Devonian; a *Kaskaskia sequence* from Middle Devonian to the top of the Mississippian; and an *Absaroka sequence* from the Pennsylvanian into the Lower Jurassic. Other sequences have also been recognized in the Mesozoic and Cenozoic rocks, in regions mostly outside the Interior Lowlands.

The lower half of the Paleozoic deposits, of Ordovician to Mississippian age, was of marine origin and includes much limestone, but has subordinate layers of sandstone and shale. The only conspicuous clastic layer is the St. Peter Sandstone of Middle Ordovician age, as much as 100 meters thick, which covers an area of more than 1,800,000 square kilometers in the north-central states; it lies on an eroded surface of earlier carbonates, the local representative of the regional unconformity at the base of the Tippecanoe sequence. Much of the upper half of the Paleozoic deposits was non-marine and continental, including coal-bearing Pennsylvanian east of the Mississippi River and Permian redbeds west of it.

Several exceptional but significant sorts of deposits are worth noting. Some of the marine deposits contain reefs, which are mound-like or wall-like masses of limestone or dolomite built up by lime-secreting corals, algae, sponges, bryozoans, and other sessile organisms so that they projected above the sea floor on which contemporaneous deposits were accumulating. Reefs are common in the Middle Silurian (Niagaran Series) through a wide area in the northeastern states, and are mound-like or atoll-like bodies (Fig. 14A). Devonian reefs occur in Alberta and Pennsylvanian reefs in central Texas, but the greatest reefs of all are those in the Permian of west Texas—barrier reefs or great walls built around the edges of subsiding basins (Fig. 14B). We will discuss them in more detail later in this chapter (section 6).

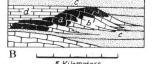

a-Reef core   b-Reef talus   c-Fore-reef or inter-reef deposits
d-Back-reef or lagoonal deposits

FIG. 14. Sketch sections showing limestone reef structures of the Interior Lowlands: (A) Mound type, characteristic of Silurian of Great Lakes region. (B) Barrier type, characteristic of Permian of West Texas region. Note differences in horizontal scales; vertical scales somewhat exaggerated. Adapted from Cumings and Shrock (1928) and King (1948).

Reef structures arouse increasing interest because some of them, or deposits associated with them, are reservoirs for oil—a form of stratigraphic trap different from the one previously mentioned, but equally difficult to locate by ordinary means of exploration. Oil is thus produced from the reef complexes of all the ages mentioned—Silurian, Devonian, Pennsylvanian, and Permian.

Other exceptional deposits are the evaporites or deposits of gypsum, anhydrite, rock salt, and various potash minerals formed from sea water by precipitation of its dissolved constituents during evaporation. As with reefs, they are not confined to any particular part of the column. In general they occur at the farthest edge of any sea when barriers of some sort caused part of the sea to be cut off from free access to the ocean. Thickest evaporites are known only from drilling, as their outcropping edges dissolve and weather back so that they are concealed by younger deposits. Evaporites of the Permian are well known and extend from Texas to Kansas. Thick evaporites also occur in the Upper Silurian (Salina Series) in the northeastern states, notably in New York and Michigan. Others in the Devonian and Mississippian have recently been discovered by drilling to the northwest from Montana into Alberta.

MESOZOIC AND TERTIARY DEPOSITS. We will say little here about the Mesozoic and Tertiary rocks of the Interior Lowlands, as it is more appropriate to consider them in connection with the Gulf Coastal Plain and the Cordillera (Chapters V and VII).

In the eastern half of the lowlands the highest deposits in the sequence in a few places, as in the center of the Michigan basin, have been proved by plant spores to be of Jurassic age. Farther south, Cretaceous and Tertiary deposits fill the Mississippi Embayment, a sag extending into the lowlands along the Mississippi River, which allowed Coastal Plain deposits to encroach inland as far as southern Illinois. East and northeast of the Mississippi Embayment no Cretaceous or Tertiary deposits are preserved in the lowlands, and it is doubtful whether any part of them was submerged or covered during these later times.

Cretaceous deposits are extensive in the western part

of the lowlands, however, forming a wide tract along the front of the Rocky Mountains from Texas into Canada. They are products of a sea that encroached inland from the Gulf of Mexico to the Arctic Ocean, and spread eastward from the Cordilleran geosyncline as far as Kansas, Iowa, and Minnesota. In places the Cretaceous is succeeded by continental or lacustrine early Tertiary deposits, and the whole is covered by a thin blanket of later Tertiary sands and gravels that forms the surface of the Great Plains.

5. STRUCTURES OF THE SEDIMENTARY COVER

DOMES AND BASINS. So much for the rocks of the Interior Lowlands—now, what of the structures in the region? In single outcrops, the strata appear flat-lying or so gently inclined that their dip is difficult to detect with the eye. Actually, they slope at very low angles in different directions for long distances, as one will find when he views the outcrops of a larger area. Patterns of their structures come into focus on small-scale geologic maps, such as those of the United States or of North America.

In general, one would expect the dip of the strata to be away from the Canadian Shield and toward the bordering mountain belts, with sedimentary cover thinnest close to the latter. Broadly speaking, this is true. Cambrian and Ordovician rocks are exposed around most of the edges of the shield, whereas Pennsylvanian and Permian rocks lie along the Appalachians on the southeast, and Cretaceous and Tertiary rocks along the Cordillera in the west.

But the outward dip of the strata from shield to mountain belts is complicated by a series of domes and basins, well displayed in the map pattern (Plate I).

To the north near the shield are the *Wisconsin* and *Adirondack domes* in which Precambrian rocks emerge due to stripping of the sedimentary cover that once arched over their crests. Farther south the large *Ozark dome* of Missouri and adjacent states and the small *Llano uplift* of central Texas bring smaller areas of Precambrian to the surface, surrounded by outcrops of Cambrian and early Ordovician rocks. East of the Mississippi River are the *Cincinnati* and *Nashville domes* in which neither Precambrian nor Cambrian are exposed but which reveal wide areas of Ordovician rocks on their crests.

The basins include the nearly circular *Michigan basin*, which occupies the lower peninsula of that state and preserves Pennsylvanian and Jurassic rocks in the center (Fig. 15A), closer to the edge of the shield and farther north than one would anticipate. The *Illinois basin* to the south also retains a wide area of Mississippian and Pennsylvanian rocks in the center (Fig. 15B and C).

AREAS OF UNUSUAL DEFORMATION. Very rarely areas of unusual deformation are found in the lowlands. The

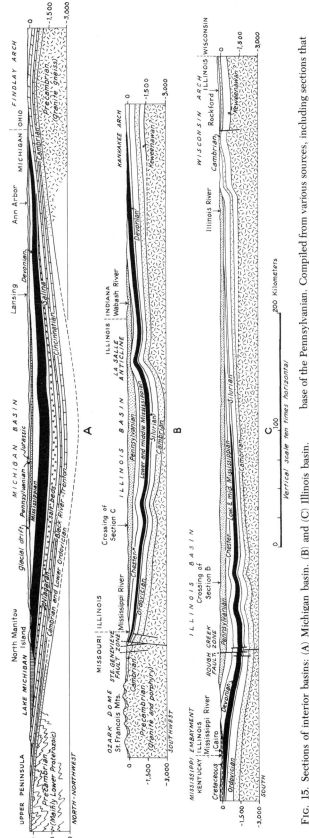

FIG. 15. Sections of interior basins: (A) Michigan basin. (B) and (C) Illinois basin. Compiled from various sources, including sections that accompany the state geologic maps. Note thickening of units into the basins, and in (B) and (C) the unconformity at the base of the Pennsylvanian.

most notable is the zone of faults that extends westward from West Virginia, across Kentucky, and into southern Illinois and Missouri. Its most complex part is in the Illinois-Kentucky fluorspar district near the head of the Mississippi Embayment, where several sets of faults trending in different directions cross and intersect (Fig. 16). Along the fault zone, the Precambrian basement is offset by greater amounts than the surface Paleozoic strata, so the zone is a long-persistent feature, possibly a potential rift in the continental plate. The faulted Paleozoic rocks are truncated by Cretaceous and younger deposits of the Mississippi Embayment, yet two disastrous earthquakes occurred with magnitudes as great as 8 in the embayment near New Madrid, Missouri, in 1811 and 1812, and minor shocks still continue,

thus testifying to the continued tectonic instability of the area.

FORELAND BASINS. So far we have not spoken of the larger and more extensive basins that follow the edges of the mountain belts. Because of their special relations to the latter, they are called foreland basins (or foredeeps). The relation of these basins to mountain belts is twofold:

(a) During early stages of growth, when initial mountain ridges were being uplifted and eroded, clastic sediments were spread away from them over the foreland, tapering inland like wedges (Fig. 17B).

(b) During the final stages of mountain building, the forelands themselves were mildly folded and were downwarped into basins parallel to the mountain front (Fig. 17C).

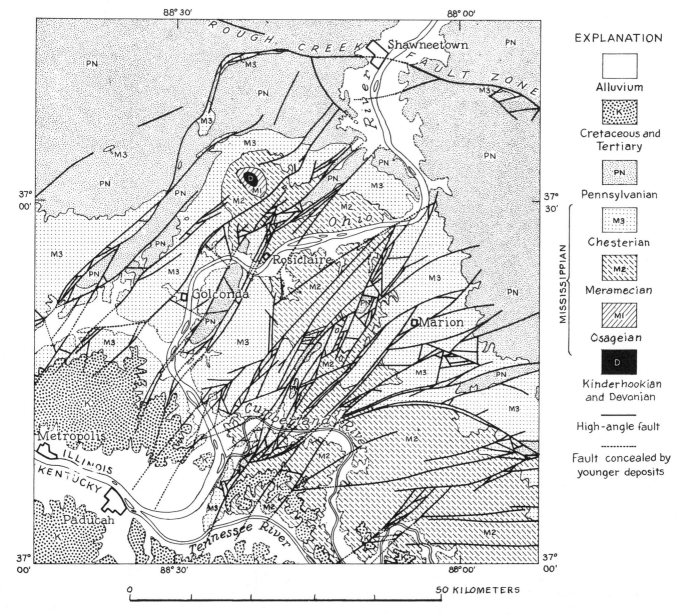

FIG. 16. Map of the fluorspar district in southern Illinois and adjacent Kentucky, showing complex faulting of the Paleozoic rocks and their truncation by the Cretaceous deposits of the Mississippi Embayment. Compiled from geologic maps of Illinois and Kentucky, and other sources.

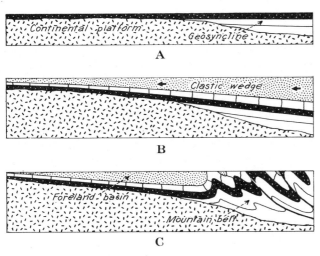

Fig. 17. Sequential sections showing development of a foreland area: (A) At end of Cambrian time, showing overlap from geosyncline toward continental platform. (B) After initial phase of mountain growth and deposition of clastic wedges derived from erosion of early mountain ridges, to right of end of section (arrows indicate direction of transport of sediments). (C) At close of mountain making, when a foreland basin developed in front of mountain belt. Length of sections about 500 kilometers; vertical scale greatly exaggerated.

On the map the most conspicuous foreland basin on the southeast is the *Allegheny synclinorium*, which extends along the front of the Appalachians from New York to Kentucky and preserves Pennsylvanian and early Permian continental beds and coal measures in its trough (Fig. 18). The most conspicuous foreland basins on the west are the *Williston basin* of North Dakota and adjacent states and the *Alberta basin* to the northwest in Canada. Other basins occur farther south along the edges of the Interior Lowlands, but they are more overlapped by younger deposits and less conspicuous in the map pattern.

The foreland basins contain notable quantities of mineral fuels. The Allegheny synclinorium preserves the great coal deposits on which the industrial complex of Pittsburgh and surrounding areas is based. It was the site of the first oil test in the United States, the Drake well of 1859. Here also John D. Rockefeller, in the latter part of the nineteenth century, put together his Standard Oil Company, which later spawned a whole family of corporate giants. The foreland basins of Oklahoma and Texas have likewise been established as oil provinces for many years, and the Williston and Alberta basins have become so since the Second World War.

MEANS OF ANALYSIS OF DOME AND BASIN STRUCTURE. The domes and basins of the Paleozoic rocks, so strikingly shown on the geologic maps, are clearly of pre-Mesozoic age; where the latter overlie them, they truncate their eroded surfaces.

It has been assumed that the Appalachian mountain belt farther southeast was created by an Appalachian revolution toward the close of the Paleozoic time; we will

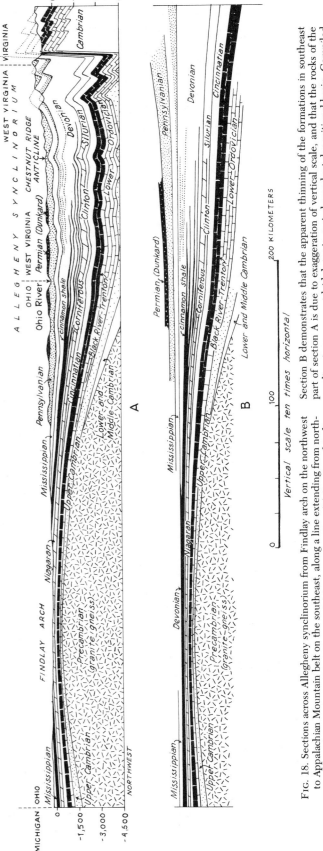

FIG. 18. Sections across Allegheny synclinorium from Findlay arch on the northwest to Appalachian Mountain belt on the southeast, along a line extending from northwest... Section B demonstrates that the apparent thinning of the formations in southeast part of section A is due to exaggeration of vertical scale, and that the rocks of the synclinorium were not laid down in an independent depositional basin. Compiled

see later that this idea will require modification (Chapter IV, section 5). But granting for a moment that it is so, did the more gently dipping structures in the Paleozoic rocks of the Interior Lowlands similarly originate in one great period of movement?

Various means have been devised for analysis of this and various other structural problems of gently dipping strata:

(A) Structure contour maps show configuration of the surface of a stratum. Imagine instead of a normal land surface, that all the overburden had been stripped off down to a single stratum, and that all its eroded parts had been restored. Contours on such a surface would show its topography, which would also be its structural configuration. In practice, of course, it is unnecessary to strip away or restore the surface of the stratum. Altitudes on the stratum from which contours can be constructed are obtainable from surface outcrops, from well records, and by calculations based on underlying strata where the stratum has been removed by erosion.

The accompanying Figure 19 shows structure contours on successively higher strata in the Michigan basin. All bring out the nearly circular form of the basin; some hint of its evolution is afforded by progressive flattening of the structure in each younger and higher stratum.

(B) A more subtle form of analysis is the isopach map, which shows variations in thickness of a given sedimentary unit. Here we are no longer contouring any real surface, but are representing graphically a body of statistics. Thickness of the unit is determined in various places from outcrop sections and drill records, and contours are drawn from these figures.

Our next illustration (Fig. 20) shows isopach lines drawn on successive rock units in the Michigan basin. In general, deposits are thicker in the center of the basin than toward its margins, showing that it subsided progressively during Paleozoic time. But isopach lines on some of the units have little relation to the shape of the modern basin—some show no basinal features at all. On the other hand, isopach lines for the Upper Silurian or Salina Series (Fig. 20E) perfectly reflect the basin shape, and suggest that a significant phase of its growth took place during this epoch.

(C) Another form of analysis is the paleogeologic map. This should not be confused with the more familiar paleogeographic map, which shows inferred geography of former lands and seas. The paleogeologic map shows areal geology of an ancient surface over which younger deposits have been laid.

For demonstration let us shift from the Michigan basin to the state of Iowa. Iowa lies on the flank of the Wisconsin arch, and its strata dip gently in a broad homocline southwestward toward the Forest City basin and southward toward the Illinois basin.

In the western part of the state Cretaceous strata spread across all the earlier rocks and their structures, from the Precambrian on the northwest to the Pennsylvanian on the southeast (Fig. 21A). This is to be expected, as we have already noted that Mesozoic rocks bevel the Paleozoic of the Interior Lowlands. Let us extend the contacts between the different Paleozoic units that appear in surface outcrops westward beneath the Cretaceous, marking them with dotted lines to show the areal geology of the surface on which the latter was deposited (Fig. 21B). The patch of Precambrian on the northwest now comes into focus as the Sioux uplift, another structurally high area like the Wisconsin arch, away from which the Paleozoic rocks are tilted.

But observe, too, that the Pennsylvanian is discordant on the Mississippian (a part of the sub-Absaroka regional unconformity referred to earlier). In central Iowa and farther east in Illinois, its basal contact cuts across the subdivisions of the latter; outliers of Pennsylvanian in the eastern part of the state lie as well on the Devonian and Silurian, with all the Mississippian missing. The southwestward-dipping homocline of Paleozoic rocks in the state is thus composite, part of it formed after and part before Pennsylvanian time. Let us extend beneath the Pennsylvanian by a dotted line the contacts between subdivisions of the Mississippian.

Descending lower in the section, we observe how the Devonian truncates the Silurian in the northeastern part of the state, overstepping northward onto Ordovician rocks (a part of the sub-Kaskaskia regional unconformity referred to earlier). Again, the southeast-dipping homocline is composite—part formed after, part before Devonian time. Let us extend beneath the Devonian the contact between the Silurian and the Ordovician.

By this demonstration we have not actually made any paleogeographic maps; we would need more data than are afforded by the surface geologic map of the state alone. But we have made a start on three such maps—of the sub-Cretaceous, sub-Pennsylvanian, and sub-Devonian surfaces—and have shown how paleogeologic maps are compiled.

In Iowa our demonstration has indicated that there is a major unconformity above the Paleozoic and two other major unconformities within it, the structures under each being steeper and different from the structures above. A. I. Levorsen, the petroleum geologist, has aptly termed this relation *layer-cake geology*. In Iowa, according to our analysis of the map, the "cake" above the Precambrian has four bodies of rock of different structure, each one bounded by unconformities. (Actually, there are five layers, as another unconformity, not apparent on the map, separates Mississippian and Devonian rocks; this acquires greater importance in the states to the south.)

GROWTH OF DOMES AND BASINS. These methods of

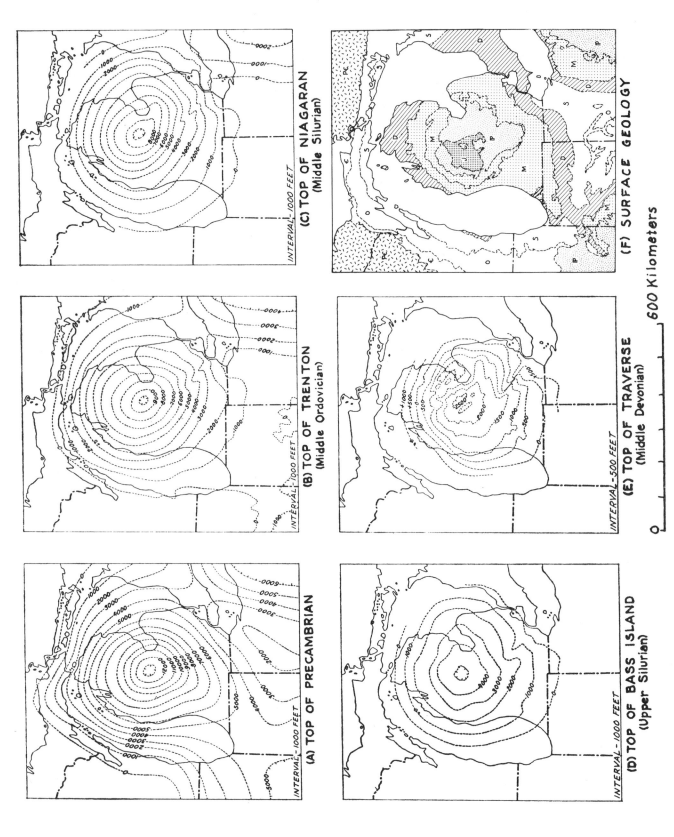

FIG. 19. Maps of Michigan basin and adjacent areas, showing structure contours on successively higher horizons (A to E) and distribution of geologic systems at surface (F). Contours after Cohee and Landes (1945, 1947, 1948); surface geology from Geologic Map of United States (1974).

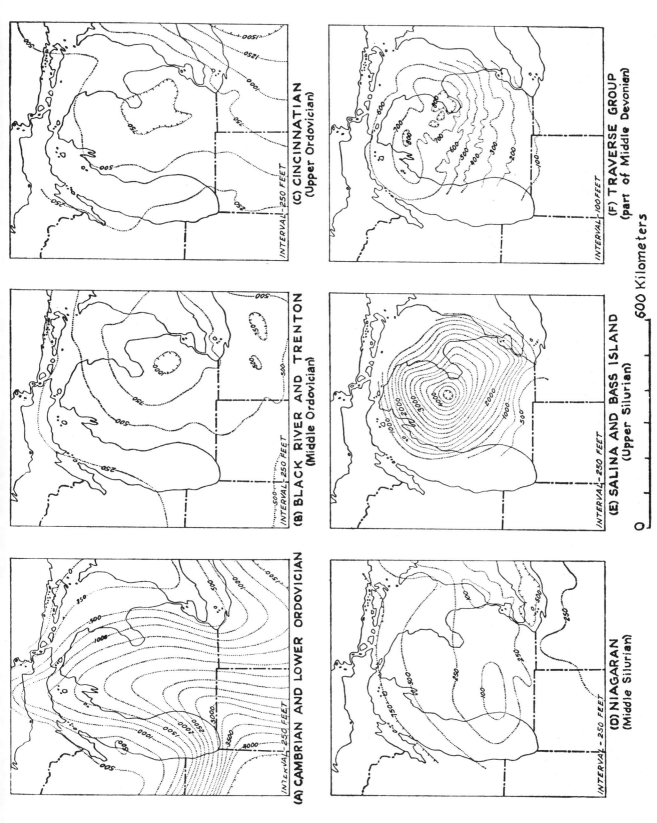

Fig. 20. Maps of Michigan basin and adjacent areas, showing by isopachous lines the variations in thickness of strata laid down there during certain Paleozoic epochs. Note the well-marked basin structure developed there during some epochs (E) and its absence from others (D). Contours are in feet. After Cohee and Landes (1945, 1947, 1948).

(A) CAMBRIAN AND LOWER ORDOVICIAN
INTERVAL - 250 FEET

(B) BLACK RIVER AND TRENTON
(Middle Ordovician)
INTERVAL - 250 FEET

(C) CINCINNATIAN
(Upper Ordovician)
INTERVAL - 250 FEET

(D) NIAGARAN
(Middle Silurian)
INTERVAL - 250 FEET

(E) SALINA AND BASS ISLAND
(Upper Silurian)
INTERVAL - 250 FEET

(F) TRAVERSE GROUP
(part of Middle Devonian)
INTERVAL - 100 FEET

0   600 Kilometers

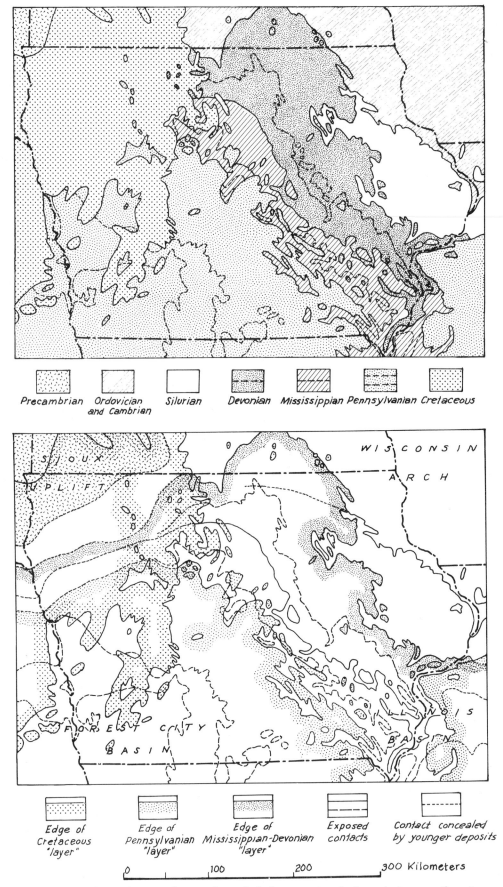

Precambrian   Ordovician   Silurian   Devonian   Mississippian   Pennsylvanian   Cretaceous
          and Cambrian

Edge of   Edge of   Edge of   Exposed   Contact concealed
Cretaceous   Pennsylvanian   Mississippian-Devonian   contacts   by younger deposits
"layer"   "layer"   "layer"

0   100   200   300 Kilometers

FIG. 21. Maps of state of Iowa to illustrate the method of construction of paleogeologic maps. Above is a conventional geologic map. The map below shows the same exposed geologic contacts, and also contacts that are covered by unconformably overlying deposits. The rocks of the state above the Precambrian are thus divisible into four "layers" of a "layer-cake"—Cretaceous rocks, Pennsylvania rocks, Mississippian and Devonian rocks, and Silurian and Ordovician rocks. After Geologic Map of Iowa (1969) and other sources.

analysis indicate that the domes and basins in the Paleozoic rocks of the Interior Lowlands, far from having been created by a single period of deformation late in Paleozoic time, have grown progressively through much of the era. Structure contour maps indicate that inclination of the strata steepens as one proceeds downward in the section; isopach maps show that many of the units thicken into the basins and thin toward the domes; paleogeologic maps prove that many of the younger units overstep the older toward the domes on surfaces of regional unconformity.

Growth of domes and basins is a form of *epeirogeny*, a term used to distinguish this rather passive process from the more positive processes of orogeny or mountain building. It has two guises (Fig. 22):

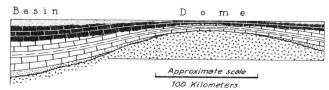

FIG. 22. Idealized section of a dome and basin in the Interior Lowlands, showing thinning of all units away from the basin and toward the dome. This results partly from deposition of a greater thickness of each unit in the basin than on the dome, and partly from truncation and overlap along unconformities.

(a) Greater subsidence of basins and less subsidence of domes, indicated by variable thickness of sediment laid down from place to place in a given period (see isopach maps of Michigan basin, Fig. 17). This process was secular; that is, it went on more or less without interruption through the Paleozoic era.

(b) Actual uplift of domes during relatively brief periods, which brought about erosion of the earlier units and overlap and overstep of the younger on surfaces of unconformity. (See the paleogeologic map of Iowa, Fig. 18; it is also well illustrated on the Ozark and Nashville domes, from which Fig. 19 is generalized.) Some of these times of uplift may correspond to periods of more intense deformation in the mountain belts roundabout; for example, the pre-Mississippian unconformity corresponds roughly to the Acadian orogeny in the Appalachians.

All that we have done here is to furnish some simple examples of the growth of the structures of the Interior Lowlands. The story has been worked out in much detail, especially in the western part, where extensive oil drilling has provided subsurface information. Such drilling has always brought forth surprises; subsurface structure cannot, certainly, be predicted from outcrops. Gentle surface structures steepen downward due to progressive growth with time. Other structures are encountered, such as the "granite ridge" of Kansas, for which there is no surface indication; they formed early, were eroded and buried, and were little disturbed again.

6. THE WEST TEXAS BASIN

In this book we have sketched the foreland basins briefly, but I cannot close the present chapter without saying more about the basin with which I have been most concerned personally—that in West Texas. Some years ago I had an opportunity to return to West Texas, take part in a field trip, and revisit old geological localities, some of which I had not seen for fifteen or twenty years. On the trip, one of the younger men said to me, "You must be pretty smart to know so much about this country and to have worked all this out." My reaction was, "Hells Bells! I was in this country on and off for twenty years. In that time even a simpleton should have figured out something about it!"

This brought home to me something of the handicap all younger geologists face in coming into an established geological province, where the great principles that control it have all been worked out by geologists who have gone before, in ways they cannot know. During the years of which I spoke, we geologists who had come early to West Texas had an opportunity to "grow up with the country" just as truly as James Hall had "grown up" with the geology of New York state a century earlier. We saw a major oil province when there were few oil wells and little subsurface information, and when all its complex geology was still a mystery. We were able to probe these mysteries and learn the geological laws of the province the hard way—by slow process of trial and error.

Here, I will depart from the style of the rest of the book and indulge in personal reminiscence for the purpose of recreating the spirit of the times in which the modern ideas on the region developed.

WEST TEXAS "PERMIAN" BASIN. The West Texas basin, as the name implies, lies mainly in western Texas, although one corner extends into southeastern New Mexico. For the most part it lies beneath the southern end of the Great Plains, east of the Texas and New Mexico mountains beyond the Pecos River. Southward it is bordered by older mountains—the Ouachita chain of Paleozoic time (Fig. 20)—but these are now little evident at the surface, being mostly buried by Cretaceous rocks and emerging only briefly in the Marathon country, which we will discuss later (Chapter IV, section 6). The basin structure of West Texas is indicated at the surface by opposing dips of Paleozoic rocks off the trans-Pecos Mountains on the west and off the exposed Paleozoic in north-central Texas to the east, but the basin itself is masked by Triassic, Cretaceous, and Tertiary deposits.

The West Texas basin is known in all the trade journals and to all the local people as the "West Texas Permian basin." Coupling the word Permian with that of the province connotes the great thickness of Permian rocks there—more than 5,000 meters in places—and the prolific oil production they have yielded. Permian rocks were the first in the province to produce oil, and although deeper and older oil-bearing horizons have since been found, the former still accounts for more than half the total production.

In fact, our Texas friends have pretty much taken over the word "Permian." In Midland, the oil headquarters town, there is a "Permian Building" and a "Permian Oil Company"; some of the national technical societies have "Permian Basin sections," and there is a "University of Texas of the Permian Basin." As the reader may recall, the Permian System was established in 1841 by Sir Roderick Impey Murchison, who named it for the city and province of Perm, west of the Ural Mountains in European Russia. For a time the name "Perm" disappeared from Russian maps, and was replaced with "Molotov" for a Soviet dignitary. Since then, now that the "cult of personality" has faded, the name Perm has happily been restored to its rightful place in Russian geography.

EARLY YEARS. Like any other college graduate in 1924, I was anxious for a job and uncertain of my future. My professors had written to various alumni of the school in behalf of us graduates. For me, in the week of graduation, came the heartening telegram from one of them, "Report at once to the Marland Oil Company in Dallas." This I shortly did, being not quite twenty-one at the time. After a few weeks with the company in Dallas I was sent to join geological field parties that were being organized by the company in West Texas.

The West Texas country in those days was quite different from what it is now—a backwash of the frontier that had never quite attained prosperity, a land of great cattle ranches joined by ungraded dirt tracks with the raw towns along the railroads. The oil companies were certain that the region had possibilities. It was a sedimentary basin little tested even by the wildcatters, in which oil had already been found in a few places—at Big Lake in Reagan County and Westbrook in Mitchell County to the east and south, and at Artesia, New Mexico, on the west, where oil was produced, and in widely scattered test holes where intriguing "oil shows" had been encountered.

But later I came to realize that West Texas at the time was also the "Siberia" of oil geologists—a place where companies sent misfits and amateurs with whom they did not know what else to do. I was certainly one of these; I still remember with embarrassment my foolish errors at the plane table and alidade, my inability to close traverses within allowable limits of error. Needless to say, West Texas is a "Siberia" no longer, but an established oil province in which technical employment is an honor rather than a stigma.

I spent a year or so with the oil company, helping to survey structures of the Cretaceous rocks that covered the whole surface. This was all we knew how to do, although we realized that proven oil production was in the Permian, many thousands of feet below the surface, and separated from the surface rocks by at least two unconformities. But the region was one of the first to be explored for oil in which producing horizons were markedly unconformable beneath surface rocks—it was perhaps the first encounter of the oil geologist with "layer-cake geology."

Many theories existed as to the structure of the subsurface rocks—some mere fantasies, others with the weight of scientific authority—but all proved to be wrong. One of the most respectable of these was the theory of the "Marathon fold," propounded by Johan August Udden, Director of the Texas Bureau of Economic Geology. The Ouachita folds, as exposed in the Marathon country, strike northeast beneath the Cretaceous. Therefore, he reasoned, these folds and their cover rocks on their northeastward extension might contain oil-bearing strata. The "fold" was projected by him and his assistants across north-central Texas along the east side of the Permian basin, and many drilling locations were made upon it—including those at Westbrook and Big Lake, which resulted in the first sizable oil fields in the basin. The results were happily correct, but for the wrong reasons. Actually, the oil fields have nothing to do with any "Marathon fold." East of the Marathon country, beneath the Cretaceous cover, as we now know, the northeastward trend of the Ouachita folds is not maintained; instead, they bend around to the east, and even the southeast!

All that we actually knew of subsurface stratigraphy and structure was from drillers' logs, written by men untutored in the fine arts of geology. The logs were sufficiently baffling, as one would report thousands of meters of limestone, and another only a few kilometers away indicated great thicknesses of salt and gypsum or a great thickness of sandstone. A testimony of those days is a Geological Survey Bulletin on the potash resources of the region. (No. 780, 1926, p. 33-126) which discusses at length the meaning of these logs; it makes curious reading today. Actually, the drillers' logs were not mendacious; they gave a blurred impression of the different kinds of rocks penetrated and would probably be meaningful to a modern West Texas stratigrapher. The real difficulties were with the rocks themselves, which obeyed no laws with which we were familiar at the time.

While we were struggling with the surface structures of the region, the Gulf Oil Company was leasing great blocks of West Texas territory at low prices and under long-term contracts. Even at terms of a few cents an acre, such contracts meant riches to the local ranch people, each of whom owned hundreds of square miles of barren country, but were "land poor" because of a disastrous succession of droughts and slumps in the cattle market that followed the First World War. There seemed to be no sense or system in land leasing by Gulf; some of the blocks were in areas that other geologists of the time did not suppose had any possibilities. Years later I learned that the leasing was based on real scientific study, not aimless guessing, by O. C. Harper and a crew of able assistants. From the data available, they made isopach maps of the Permian formations of the basin, so far as they had been penetrated by drilling, and especially of salt thicknesses. If salt was thin, land was leased; if salt was thick, the area was rejected. As things turned out, this was as good a rough and ready means of blocking out promising territory as one could find at the time. In later years the Gulf Oil Company found itself in possession of leases on some of the most favorable land in the basin.

CENTRAL BASIN PLATFORM. From surface indications and drillers' logs, we believed that the deepest part of the West Texas basin was in Winkler County, midway between opposing dips on the east and west sides. Oil should be trapped, we thought, in structures marginal to such a basin; Winkler County, in the center of the basin, should offer the least possibilities of any. But about this time a wildcatter without geological inhibitions began to drill here with no encouragement from the companies (except perhaps the Gulf). He struck oil—spectacularly—irrevocably overturning all previous theories about the West Texas Permian basin. The reader can picture the excitement—provisions that had to be made for the unexpected flow of oil, the new town of "Wink" hurriedly laid out by land promoters, and the readjustment that geologists had to make in all their thinking.

As drilling in Winkler County progressed, it became evident that oil occurred here on a limestone "high," and geologists began to realize that the West Texas basin was composite. Instead of being a single great geological depression, it consisted of several subbasins separated by structural ridges. One of these, the "high" in Winkler County, came to be known as the Central Basin platform; it divided the larger West Texas basin into the Delaware basin on the west and the Midland basin on the east (Fig. 23).

THE REEF THEORY. But this broad structural pattern did not explain all the anomalies of the region. The geology revealed by drilling was not merely a matter of simple folding or warping of previously deposited strata, but one in which the strata themselves changed character from one unit to another (Fig. 24). Different rock sequences thus occurred in each unit beneath the surface rocks:

Delaware basin. A thick body of salt underlain by a body of anhydrite, and this underlain by sandstone.
Central Basin platform. A nearly solid sequence of limestone down to basement rocks, which had been reached in a few places by 1929.

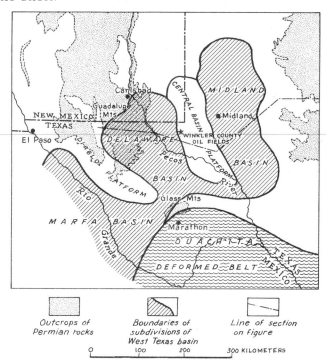

FIG. 23. Map of West Texas basin showing subsidiary basins and platforms into which it is divided. After King (1942).

Midland basin. Interbedded salt, anhydrite, and redbeds, underlain by shales and thin limestones.

About this time I left the oil company and began work on the outcrop areas of Paleozoic rocks southwest and west of the basin—first as a graduate student for the Texas Bureau of Economic Geology in company with R. E. King, later for the U.S. Geological Survey. This work was not as remotely related to the geological work by the oil companies as one might suppose. The modern West Texas basin, it is true, is blocked off by mountain uplifts on the west, but these are of Laramide or later age; during Permian time when the critical features of the basin developed, it extended much farther west.

My first work was in the Glass Mountains on the southwest, where Permian rocks emerge at the edge of the basin (Fig. 23). Later I worked in the Marathon lowland to the south, in folded earlier Paleozoic of the Ouachita orogenic belt. Still later, I worked in the Sierra Diablo and Guadalupe Mountains west of the basin, where Permian rocks again come to the surface.

On the outcrops we began to find the same stratigraphic puzzles as in the subsurface sections. In the Glass Mountains, lateral changes in the Permian stratigraphy were extreme; the rocks in the section on the west were almost totally unlike those on the east—on the west interbedded shales, sandstones, and limestones; on the east nearly solid thin-bedded limestone.

Professor Charles Schuchert, who was supervising our work, told me that the geologists who had been in the area earlier—Johan August Udden and Emil Böse—had

37

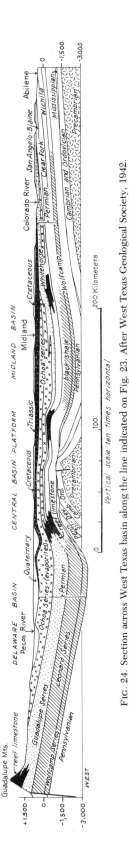

FIG. 24. Section across West Texas basin along the line indicated on Fig. 23. After West Texas Geological Society, 1942.

talked of an idea that the thick limestone bodies might be reefs; apparently they did not know quite how, and the idea was so vague that it had never appeared in any of their publications. Schuchert urged me to look into the possibility. I was unimpressed, and to bolster my objections I looked up the subject of fossil reefs in Grabau's *Principles of Stratigraphy.* There, a drawing that I had merely glanced at before—a view of Triassic reef structures in the Tyrolean Alps—suddenly took on new meaning. The lay of the strata on the Alpine mountainside was a near replica of oddities we had seen on the slopes of the Glass Mountains and for which we had not found an explanation. Perhaps the odd structures were marginal to a great reef! Perhaps (but the idea seemed too outrageous) reef barriers were responsible for the unlike stratigraphic sequences at the two ends of the Glass Mountains!

Amazingly, as has happened with many other great scientific discoveries, nearly every geologist who was working in West Texas came independently to the same conclusion at about the same time; by 1929 the "reef theory" as an explanation of the Permian stratigraphy of the region was in full flower. Through the years that followed, further evidence has accumulated, so that reef theory has become reef fact, and is now established as one of the controlling principles of West Texas Permian geology.

PERMIAN OF GUADALUPE MOUNTAINS. Although we could sense the dominant control of reefs on the stratigraphy of the Glass Mountains, structural complications and the remoteness of the area from country that was being intensively drilled prevented us from grasping the regional implications. Other geologists had better success, notably E. Russell Lloyd, who was examining the same rocks in the Guadalupe Mountains farther northwest. It was my privilege to work in these mountains much later.

The Guadalupe Mountains begin near the Pecos River in New Mexico and extend southwest into Texas with steadily increasing altitude, terminating in a great point or cliff. On this is exposed a wonderful section of about 1,300 meters of strata (right-hand end of Fig. 25B), all of Permian age and highly fossiliferous. This was first discovered by George G. Shumard, one of the geological explorers before the Civil War, at the time of the Pacific Railroad Surveys. It consists of the following, in descending order:

Capitan Limestone. White, massive or poorly bedded.

Delaware Mountain Formation (or Group). Sandstone, mainly fine-grained and thin-bedded with some coarser and more massive layers, interbedded with shaly sandstone and thin-bedded dark limestone.

Bone Spring Limestone. Black, thin-bedded limestone, shaly in part.

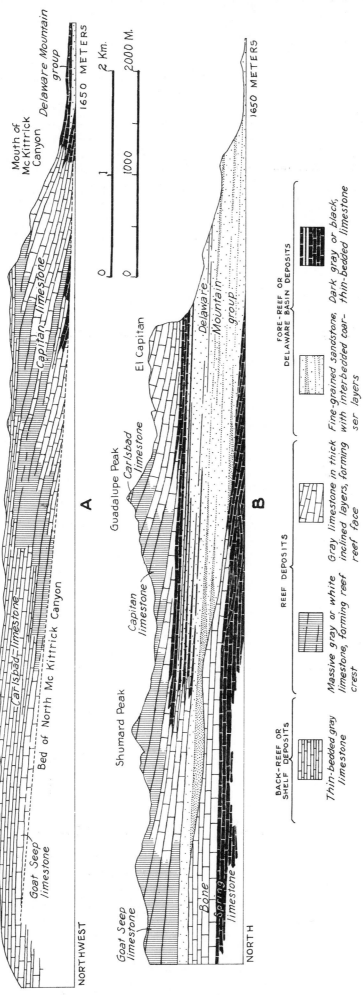

FIG. 25. Two sections showing reefs and related structures in Permian rocks of Guadalupe Mountains, West Texas. (A) Along a canyon wall in the mountains, showing upper part of succession. (B) Along escarpment on west side of mountains, showing lower part of succession. After King (1948).

But this fine sequence, which one would think should provide a stratigraphic key to the mountains, does not extend far in any direction. Bone Spring Limestone and Delaware Mountain Formation continue to the southeast, but the latter is overlain by Castile Gypsum. Where is the Capitan Limestone? Sands of the Delaware Mountain Formation extend only a few miles to the northwest, beyond which most of the section is limestone, but limestone that has lost the distinctive features of the Capitan and Bone Spring (left-hand end of Fig. 25B).

Despite its short extent to the southeast and northwest, the Capitan Limestone forms a massive front or escarpment that can be followed 80 kilometers northeastward to the Pecos River, where it plunges beneath the surface. But it can be traced by drilling beyond, curving in a semi-circle around the north end of the Delaware basin, to pass through the Winkler County "high" and thence into the Glass Mountains. The sands of the Delaware Mountain Formation are thus a body confined in their extent to the Delaware basin and are surrounded by partly contemporaneous limestone deposits (Fig. 23).

Geologists imbued with the reef theory began to discover strange things about the Capitan Limestone. Instead of being a well-behaved, flat-lying deposit, all its layers are inclined to the southeast toward the Delaware basin (Fig. 25A). At their lower southeastern ends each flattens and thins abruptly, changing from white massive limestone into thin-bedded limestone or sandstone of the facies of the Delaware Mountain Formation. At their upper ends, the layers pass into exceedingly massive limestone that, farther northwest, intergrades with flat-lying, thin-bedded limestone. Structures of the Capitan are thus very much like an ideal diagram of a delta, with topset, foreset, and bottomset beds (Fig. 14B).

We now know that the massive limestone at the top of the slope was a growing barrier reef built by sponges, algae, bryozans, and other wave-resistant lime-secreting organisms. The inclined beds below were reef talus, and the sands at their bases were laid down on a sea floor in front of the reef, probably in 600 meters or more of water.

The thin-bedded limestones to the northwest were laid down in a shallow lagoon behind the reef barrier. Farther in this direction, they intertongue with dolomites, evaporites, and redbeds formed in evaporating pans toward the shore. The Castile Gypsum, which lies at the same level as these back-reef deposits, is a later evaporite formed after the Capitan was deposited, when the Delaware basin itself was cut off from free access to the sea.

The substructure of the Capitan reef is laid bare in cross-section on the great fault scarp on the western side of the mountains (Fig. 25B). A short distance back from the foot of the Capitan reef, the middle part of the Delaware Mountain Formation changes into a massive limestone of reef facies, just as the upper part has changed into Capitan. This precursor of the Capitan reef (or Goat Seep Limestone) also has its reef talus and growing reef and rises to the same height as the crest of the Capitan deposits, but lies several miles behind it.

But the lower third of the Delaware Mountain disappears northwestward in another manner. The top of the black Bone Spring Limestone rises in this direction in a flexure, crowned at its upper end by a bank of gray limestone. The top of the flexed Bone Spring is a local unconformity within the Permian, and the sands of the lower Delaware Mountain overlap and wedge out against its sloping surface.

This assemblage of complex stratigraphic and structural features—barrier reefs, banks, and flexures—has caused the contemporaneous deposits in front of, within, and behind the reef zone to be very different. Also our sections (Fig. 25) show the features *the way they really are*. In other sketches and figures in this book it has been necessary to represent features on an exaggerated vertical scale, or to assemble the items from exposures scattered over a considerable distance. Here, the features are shown on true scale, and all are laid bare in cross-section on single canyon walls and mountainsides.

RELATION OF PERMIAN STRATIGRAPHY TO OIL ACCUMULATION. All this is interesting enough, the reader may say, but how does it relate to the oil of the West Texas basin? Remember, however, that our cross-sections (Fig. 22) are exposed samples of a structure traceable for hundreds of kilometers around the rim of the Delaware basin, the eastern half of which, in Winkler and adjacent counties, is buried, and followed by a chain of oil fields along the west edge of the Central Basin Platform. The same substructure, or something very much like it, must underlie the oil fields.

The Capitan reef has not itself entrapped oil in this eastern segment, but deposits adjacent to it and controlled by it have done so; many of the fields are in porous lagoonal beds behind the reef. One should remember, too, that the reef, a narrow barrier, is not the only Permian deposit in the West Texas basin, but merely the most spectacular part of a complex of deposits spread over a vast area. Many different parts of this complex, when porosity and structure were right, have beome oil reservoirs.

As exploration of the West Texas Permian basin continued, the more venturesome test wells were extended through the Permian into earlier Paleozoic strata, and these strata were found to contain oil reservoirs down into the Lower Ordovician. In the earlier Paleozoic rocks we have entered several lower slabs of the West Texas "layer cake," slabs with their own primitive sets of structures that were the foundation on which the reefs and other Permian deposits were built.

At present, the only foreseeable downward limit of oil possibilities in the region is the last and deepest slab of the "layer cake," the Precambrian floor of the basin (Fig. 21). The Precambrian has been reached by the deepest test wells and consists of granitic plutonic rocks, roofed in places by altered lavas and continental sediments; these would not have generated oil in any event, even if they had been much younger.

Now the West Texas basin has been probed to its depths, and perhaps we can be content. We have learned that it is a great depression whose construction occupied much of Paleozoic time. It was covered by successive seas, each of whose organisms generated oil that was caught in a myriad of stratigraphic and structural traps, where it was ultimately discovered by the eager search of man.

REFERENCES

2. *Geological Investigations*

Merrill, G. P., 1924, *The first one hundred years of American geology*: Yale Univ. Press, chaps. 3 and 4, pp. 127-292, especially pp. 223-235.

3. *Precambrian Basement of the Lowlands*

Dake, C. L., and Bridge, Josiah, 1932, Buried and resurrected hills of the central Ozarks: *Am. Assoc. Petrol. Geol. Bull.*, v. 16, pp. 629-652.

Flawn, P. T., 1956, *Basement rocks of Texas and southeast New Mexico*: Texas Univ. (Bur. Econ. Geol.) Publ. 5605.

Goldich, S. S., Muehlberger, W. R., and others, 1966, Geochronology of the Midcontinent Region, United States: 1. Scope, methods, and principles. 2. Northern area. 3. Southern area. 4. Eastern area: *Jour. Geophysical Res.*, v. 71, no. 22, pp. 5375-5438.

King, E. R., and Zietz, Isadore, 1971, Aeromagnetic study of the Midcontinent gravity high of central United States: *Geol. Soc. America Bull.*, v. 82, no. 8, pp. 2187-2208.

4. *Sedimentary Cover of the Lowlands*

Dake, C. L., 1921, *The problem of the St. Peter Sandstone*: Missouri School of Mines and Met. Tech. ser., v. 6, pp. 1-228.

Cloud, P. E., Jr., and Barnes, V. E., 1948, *The Ellenburger Group of central Texas*: Texas Univ. (Bur. Econ. Geol.) Publ. 4621.

Lowenstam, H. A., 1950, Niagaran reefs of the Great Lakes area: *Jour. Geology*, v. 58, pp. 430-487.

Sloss, L. L., 1953, The significance of evaporites: *Jour. Sed. Petrol.*, v. 23, pp. 143-161.

———, 1963, Sequences in the cratonic interior of North America: *Geol. Soc. America Bull.*, v. 74, no. 2, pp. 93-114.

Weller, J. M., 1930, Cyclical sedimentation of the Pennsylvanian Period and its significance: *Jour. Geology*, v. 38, pp. 97-135.

5. *Structures of the Sedimentary Cover*

Ham, W. E., and Wilson, J. L., 1967, Paleozoic epeirogeny and orogeny in the central United States: *Am. Jour. Sci.*, v. 265, no. 5, pp. 332-407.

Kay, Marshall, 1942, Development of the Allegheny synclinorium and adjoining regions: *Geol. Soc. America Bull.*, v. 53, pp. 1601-1658.

Levorsen, A. I., 1927, Convergence studies in the Midcontinent Region: *Am. Assoc. Petrol. Geol. Bull.*, v. 11, pp. 657-682.

———, 1933, Studies in paleogeology: *Am. Assoc. Petrol. Geol. Bull.*, v. 17, pp. 1107-1132.

Powers, Sidney, 1931, Structural geology of northeastern Oklahoma: *Jour. Geology*, v. 39, pp. 117-132.

Wilson, C. H., Jr., and Born, Kendall, 1943, Structure of central Tennessee: *Am. Assoc. Petrol. Geol. Bull.*, v. 27, pp. 1039-1059.

6. *The West Texas Basin*

Adams, J. E., and Frenzel, H. N., 1950, Capitan barrier reef, Texas and New Mexico: *Jour. Geology*, v. 58, pp. 289-312.

Dunham, R. J., 1972, *Capitan reef, New Mexico and Texas; facts and questions to aid interpretation and group discussion*: Soc. Econ. Paleontologists and Mineralogists, Permian Basin section Publ. 72-14.

King, P. B., 1948, *Geology of the southern Guadalupe Mountains, Texas*: U.S. Geol. Survey Prof. Paper 215.

Lloyd, E. R., 1929, Capitan Limestone and associated formations of New Mexico and Texas: *Am. Assoc. Petrol. Geol. Bull.*, v. 13, pp. 645-658.

Myres, S. D., 1973, *The Permian basin, petroleum empire of the southwest; era of discovery*: Permian Press, El Paso, Tex.

Newell, N. D., and others, 1953, *The Permian reef complex of the Guadalupe Mountains region, Texas and New Mexico*: W. H. Freeman & Co., San Francisco.

West Texas Geological Society, 1942, Resume of geology of south Permian basin, Texas and New Mexico: *Geol. Soc. America Bull.*, v. 53, pp. 539-560, with cross-section. (Other and more detailed cross-sections of the West Texas basin have been issued later by local societies, but are not in readily accessible periodicals, and do not greatly change the general picture here presented.)

CHAPTER IV

APPALACHIAN AND RELATED SYSTEMS; PALEOZOIC STRUCTURES SOUTHEAST AND SOUTH OF CENTRAL STABLE REGION

1. TOPOGRAPHY AND STRUCTURE

We pass now to the younger mountain belts that border the Central Stable Region, to which we will devote much of the remainder of this book. Attention will be given first to those structures formed during Paleozoic time that lie southeast and south of the stable region (Plate I).

TOPOGRAPHIC MOUNTAINS. We have referred to these Paleozoic structures as a "mountain belt," but this is true more in a geological than a geographical sense; more properly, it is an orogenic belt. While the system was once truly as mountainous as the Cordillera of the west is today, that was long ago. Since then, deformation of the region has been inconsequential; parts have gone through several cycles of uplift and erosion; other parts of subsidence and burial beneath younger deposits. The mountains we see today are only the deeply eroded stumps of a fraction of the original mountain belt.

The word "Appalachians" can be used broadly for that segment of the former mountains east of the Mississippi River, although topographically the term "Appalachian Mountains" applies more strictly to high ridges that extend along its axis from Pennsylvania to Alabama. The New England Upland is also geologically part of the Appalachians, although it is largely separated from the part to the southwest by a depressed segment near New York City, partly covered by younger deposits and partly by the sea. Canadians again use the term "Appalachians" for ridges northeast of New England in southeastern Quebec and in the Maritime Provinces, i.e. New Brunswick, Nova Scotia, and Prince Edward Island.

West of the Mississippi River in Arkansas and Oklahoma, other stumps of the once lofty system project as the Ouachita, Arbuckle, and Wichita Mountains; a final fragment emerges far to the southwest in the Marathon Region of western Texas. The fragments west of the Mississippi are now so widely scattered that their original plan is no longer apparent either from surface topography or exposed structures; we will reserve analysis of them for the last part of this chapter (section 6).

MOUNTAINS WORN DOWN TO PLAINS. Parts of the system have been so deeply eroded that they are no longer topographic mountains.

Between the present Appalachian ridges and the edge of the younger deposits on the southeast in the Atlantic Coastal Plain is a belt of low country about 160 kilometers broad which has been called the Piedmont Plateau. This is not even a very good topographic "plateau," as much of it in Virginia, the Carolinas, and Georgia is as featureless and heavily farmed as the Interior Lowlands of the Middle West in Illinois and Iowa. Unlike the latter, which are underlain by glacial drift and gently dipping bedrock strata, the lowlands of the Piedmont are formed on the edges of steeply upturned and altered rocks that were originally parts of the Appalachian mountain system.

BURIED MOUNTAINS. Elsewhere the system is not only worn down but lost to view, as it is buried by Mesozoic and Tertiary deposits of the Atlantic and Gulf Coastal Plains (Fig. 33). These deposits were laid over the eroded edges of the ancient mountain structure, and dip seaward with little deformation. Although they are of much interest in themselves, for our purpose they are merely an inconvenient cover that must be probed by drilling and other means to determine the substructure.

Southeastward across the strike of the southern Appalachians, the worn down rocks of the Piedmont Plateau pass beneath deposits of the Atlantic Coastal Plain; the southeastern edge of the Appalachian system, whatever it was, is now no longer visible. Also, southwestward along the strike, the whole mountain structure plunges beneath deposits of the Gulf Coastal Plain. It is thus not possible to determine exactly the relations of the Appalachians to the similar Ouachita system across the Mississippi Embayment on the west. Much of the Ouachita and other systems in Oklahoma and Texas are similarly buried by Cretaceous or even by later Paleozoic deposits.

SUBMERGED MOUNTAINS. Other parts of the former Paleozoic mountain chain are still less accessible, as they lie submerged beneath the sea under the continental shelves.

Much of the connection between the Central Appalachians and the part in New England is thus submerged in the segment near New York City. Northeastward beyond New England the Appalachian folds of Gaspé and the Maritime Provinces also run out beneath the Gulf of St. Lawrence. They emerge briefly again in the island of Newfoundland, but on its northeastern side they pass beneath the waters of the Atlantic Ocean; they extend across the continental shelf to the edge of the deep ocean where they are broken off and are gone from our sight for good (Plate I).

The deep water of the Atlantic Ocean is floored by oceanic crust rather than continental crust; this has a structure very different from that of the Appalachian Mountains. However, 4,000 kilometers to the east, in Great Britain and elsewhere in western Europe, are the Caledonian and Hercynian mountain systems that formed in early and late Paleozoic time, respectively, whose rocks and structures closely resemble those of the Appalachians. Another fragment of the Caledonian mountain system occurs in eastern Greenland to the northeast. Increasing evidence now indicates that all these far-separated fragments of Paleozoic mountain systems were originally adjacent and continuous, and that they were rifted apart during the opening of the North Atlantic Ocean during Mesozoic and Cenozoic time.

STRUCTURAL PATTERN. So much for preservation of the old mountain system in modern topography and its possible extensions overseas. Let us consider its pattern in North America.

On the surface the Appalachians extend with interruptions from Newfoundland to Alabama, a distance of nearly 3,200 kilometers, disappearing northeastward under the Atlantic and southwestward under the Gulf Coastal Plain. In this long expanse the course of the system is sinuous rather than straight, so that it forms a series of salients and recesses, each salient being 600 to 900 kilometers across (Plate I).

One salient occupies most of New England and the Maritime Provinces; to the northeast is a recess in the Gulf of St. Lawrence and to the southwest another near New York City. The structures in Newfoundland northeast of the Gulf of St. Lawrence are part of another salient. Southwest of New England less strongly convex salients are visible on the map, one centering in Pennsylvania, another in Tennessee and the Carolinas.

West of the Mississippi the pattern of salients and recesses continues, although more obscured by cover of younger deposits. The Ouachita Mountains of Arkansas and Oklahoma seem to lie on the apex of one salient, the Marathon area of western Texas on another, with a deep recess east of the Ouachita salient beneath the Mississippi Embayment and another between the Ouachita and Marathon areas southeast of the Llano uplift in central Texas.

There has been much speculation as to the meaning of these salients and recesses. They might be accidental sinuosities of the former mountain chain, or they might have deeper meaning. Some geologists have suggested that the salients were the loci of most active deformation of the system and of greatest crowding of its rocks northwestward toward the continental interior. Perhaps this is so, yet the evidence adduced for the existence of such loci can be otherwise interpreted.

WIDTH OF EXPOSURE. Recall that east of the Mississippi River not only does the Appalachian system pass from view at its ends but its southeastern edge is either buried or submerged, so that a variable width of the former structure is now visible.

The broadest exposure is toward the northeast in Gaspé and the Maritime Provinces, where a section 650 kilometers wide is exposed. Southwestward the visible section narrows toward New York City, but widens again in the salient of Tennessee and North Carolina, where a section 400 kilometers wide is exposed (Fig. 33B). To the southwest, exposures narrow once again toward the Gulf Coastal Plain, but in Georgia, Alabama, and Florida drilling has been carried through the coastal plain deposits in so many places that we know much about a cross-section, exposed and buried, that is nearly 550 kilometers wide.

2. GEOLOGICAL INVESTIGATIONS

Before going further, let us say a few words on the birth of our knowledge of the Appalachian region:

A century and a half ago, in the days of William Maclure, the meaning of steeply inclined strata was only imperfectly understood. Ideas of the eighteenth-century German "geognocist" Abraham Gottlob Werner were still in vogue—that the inclination of strata originated during formation of the sediments, when they were precipitated from waters of a universal ocean onto the slopes of the "primitive" or initial mountains. Inclined strata of this sort were supposed to have formed during a "transition" era, and most of the sedimentary rocks of the Appalachians were assigned to this era by Maclure.

Realization of the true state of affairs came slowly.

While the nature of rock deformation had been apprehended by James Hutton and his colleagues in Scotland in the latter part of the eighteenth century, it was also worked out independently by various American geologists in the decades immediately succeeding Maclure's pioneer publication, as a result of patient field work in the Appalachian chain.

We have said that James Hall and his colleagues of the New York Geological Survey laid the groundwork for American stratigraphy. Fundamentals of American structural geology were being established at about the same time by state surveys to the south, especially in the beautifully folded Appalachian region of Pennsylvania. Here in 1838 Henry Darwin Rogers, state geologist of Pennsylvania, and his assistants found the stratigraphic key of the region—a sequence of formations in their proper order, laid out on one mountain side—and used this to unlock the structure of rocks that elsewhere had been disordered by folding and faulting. The same methods were extended by his brother William Barton Rogers into Virginia (which at that time included West Virginia). Results of their work were presented in an epoch-making paper of 1842, in which the Appalachian structures were likened to a series of wave-like undulations moving from the southeast toward the little-deformed continental interior. Details of the structure as there described are still valid—the great linear extent of the folds, the manner in which they are overturned and broken by faults, and the meaning of slaty cleavage.

On this foundation many other geologists have built. This account is too brief to give them the honor they deserve. Of the many we can mention several briefly: J. Peter Lesley, ordained Presbyterian minister turned geologist and engineer, who carried forward the work of Rogers as state geologist for the Second Pennsylvania Geological Survey, and whose maps are models of technical skill; James Merrill Safford, who laid out single-handedly the geology of Tennessee during the trying times of the Civil War period; and Arthur Keith, who in the latter part of the century produced a great series of geological folios of the southern Appalachian region for the U.S. Geological Survey. It was Keith and his colleagues of the Geological Survey (Bailey Willis, C. W. Hayes, and M. R. Campbell) who discovered the one remaining major feature of Appalachian structure that had escaped the Rogers brothers—the great low-angle thrust faults.

An outstanding pioneer in the Northern Appalachians was Sir William Logan, who, as part of his duties as first director of the Geological Survey of Canada, made many observations in the Canadian part of the mountains, and recognized the profound structural and stratigraphic discontinuity between the Appalachians and their foreland, which is still commemorated as "Logan's Line." Edward Hitchcock, his son Charles H. Hitchcock, and B. K.

Emerson did notable work in Massachusetts, Vermont, and New Hampshire in the nineteenth century and the first part of the twentieth, but the difficult geology of New England defied general interpretation until Marland K. Billings and his students began their investigations in the 1930s.

3. APPALACHIAN CROSS-SECTION

Let us now examine the characteristic structures of the Paleozoic mountain system. These can best be illustrated by a cross-section of the Appalachians from northwest to southeast—from the little-deformed rocks of the continental interior to the complex, highly altered rocks nearer the coast.

Treatment in terms of such a cross-section is more appropriate for the Appalachians than for many other mountain systems. The Appalachians have been little confused or modified by later structures and maintain a close similarity throughout their length; they are characteristically divisible into several narrow belts of like rocks and structures that are very similar from Canada to Alabama. My presentation will admittedly be biased toward the Southern Appalachians, with which I am most familiar. This is appropriate for the northwestern parts, which are best displayed there. It is less appropriate for the southeastern parts, as structural elements are missing in the Southern Appalachians that are well displayed farther north, so later on more reference will be made to the Northern Appalachians.

FORELAND AREA. To begin our cross-section, let us recall the features of the foreland area to the northwest (Fig. 17)—that this is part of the Interior Lowlands and became the edge of the continental platform early in Paleozoic time by inland overlap of the Cambrian deposits; that during growth of the mountain system the foreland was covered by wedges of sediments eroded from the system; that during closing stages of the deformation the foreland was mildly folded and warped down into a basin.

Largest of these foreland basins is the Allegheny synclinorium (Fig. 18), which extends southwestward from Pennsylvania into Kentucky. Topographically it forms the Allegheny Plateau and its extension to the southwest, the Cumberland Plateau—a broad, high-standing region, everywhere deeply cut by rivers and streams, the intervening ridges rising to accordant heights and without pattern other than that imposed by erosion. These plateaus, much more than the ridges of the true Appalachian Mountains on the southeast, were the great barrier to westward expansion of the colonists along the eastern seaboard. Here, as before, we can point out the discrepancy between "topographic mountains" and "geological mountains."

Surface rocks of the plateau and synclinorium are largely Pennsylvanian continental and coal-bearing strata. They lie conformably above Mississippian and Devonian strata and are succeeded conformably in the central part of the synclinorium in West Virginia by a small thickness of similar strata of early Permian age. The Pennsylvanian and associated rocks have been warped into a series of anticlines and synclines by the Appalachian movements, but most of the deformation is so light that over wide areas the strata appear to lie nearly flat. Presence of the early Permian rocks in this conformable sequence is of interest because it demonstrates that at least the northwestern part of the Appalachian area was deformed later than early Permian time. This fact has led to a further widely held assumption that the whole Appalachian orogeny occurred toward the end of the Paleozoic era—in a grand "Appalachian Revolution." We will see later in the chapter why this idea should be discarded (section 5).

On the southeast the Allegheny Plateau breaks off along the *Allegheny Front* (Fig. 28A), an imposing escarpment that overlooks the more varied, linear ridges and valleys of the true Appalachians. The front marks an abrupt change in style of deformation; the strata now turn up abruptly, and beyond they are heavily folded and faulted; we pass here from the foreland into the main deformed belt.

SEDIMENTARY APPALACHIANS (VALLEY AND RIDGE PROVINCE). Broadly speaking, the deformed belt of the Appalachians is divisible into two parts, which I will call, for want of better terms, the sedimentary Appalachians and the crystalline Appalachians; the former is encountered first on proceeding to the southeast.

The sedimentary Appalachians are built exclusively of sedimentary rocks of Paleozoic age, a mass that was laid down in the Appalachian geosyncline southeast of the continental platform; this geosyncline will be discussed later in the chapter (section 5). The Paleozoic begins with Lower and Middle Cambrian deposits, which, as we have seen, wedge out toward the continental interior. Most of the first half of the succession, up to the middle of the Ordovician, consists of carbonate rocks (that is, limestone and dolomite); higher parts above the middle of the Ordovician are mainly sandstones and shales—the significance of this arrangement will be seen farther on.

In the humid climate of the eastern states, the limestones and dolomites are more susceptible to erosion than are the sandstones and shales; wherever deformation has raised them to view they are worn down to low ground, whereas the adjacent sandstones and shales project in ridges. Characteristic topography of the sedimentary Appalachians is thus a succession of parallel valleys and ridges which form the *Valley and Ridge province*. As the underlying limestones and dolomites are raised highest on the southeast, they occupy their widest surface extent in this direction and form a broad expanse of lowland, the *Appalachian Valley*.

Strata of the sedimentary Appalachians have been flexed into a succession of anticlines and synclines, each several kilometers across, one fold crowded closely against another. Most folds are asymmetrical and have been pushed over to the northwest relative to the rocks beneath them, so that on this side of each anticline the strata are steep or overturned, whereas on the southeast side they dip gently. With increase of the northwestern push the strata on the steeply dipping sides have been broken by southeast-dipping faults on which the rocks above have been thrust toward the northwest.

Folds dominate the structure of the Valley and Ridge province in Pennsylvania, but southwestward across Virginia into Tennessee, faults increase in number and magnitude until few unbroken folds remain (Fig. 26B). Many of the faults are more than simple breaks on the flanks of anticlines and are great low-angle thrusts that have carried sheets of rock for miles northwestward over the rocks beneath—as shown where the thrust sheets have been warped and breached by erosion, revealing the overridden rocks in windows. Some great thrusts, such as the *Saltville* and *Pulaski faults*, are traceable for hundreds of kilometers along the strike, although they eventually die out at their ends.

Like the folds, the low-angle thrusts result from a relative push of the rocks toward the northwest during the Appalachian deformation. The thrusts were formed by tearing loose of higher parts of the mass of sedimentary rocks from the lower parts along weak, shaly layers interbedded in the succession.

This principle is illustrated by a great thrust block in the Cumberland Mountains area near the common corners of Virginia, Tennessee, and Kentucky; the block lies along the boundary between the Valley and Ridge province and the Allegheny Plateau, and its initial structures are better preserved than those of the more complex thrusts to the southeast (Fig. 27A). The block was separated from the rocks beneath along two zones of weak strata: shales in the Lower and Middle Cambrian (Rome and Conasauga Formations), and shales at the base of the Mississippian (Chattanooga Formation) (Fig. 27C). When a relative push of the rocks toward the northwest occurred, the stronger intervening and overlying strata moved over the shales and also internally along more steeply dipping shear planes; eventually the system of fractures united to form a single low-angle thrust, the *Pine Mountain fault*. During northwestward movement along this fault of five or six kilometers (in the segment shown in Fig. 27) rocks of the overlying thrust block of the Cumberland Mountains became warped as they passed over its irregular, steplike surface (Fig. 27B).

In the more complex Valley and Ridge province to the southeast, it is found that apparent simple folds in the

45

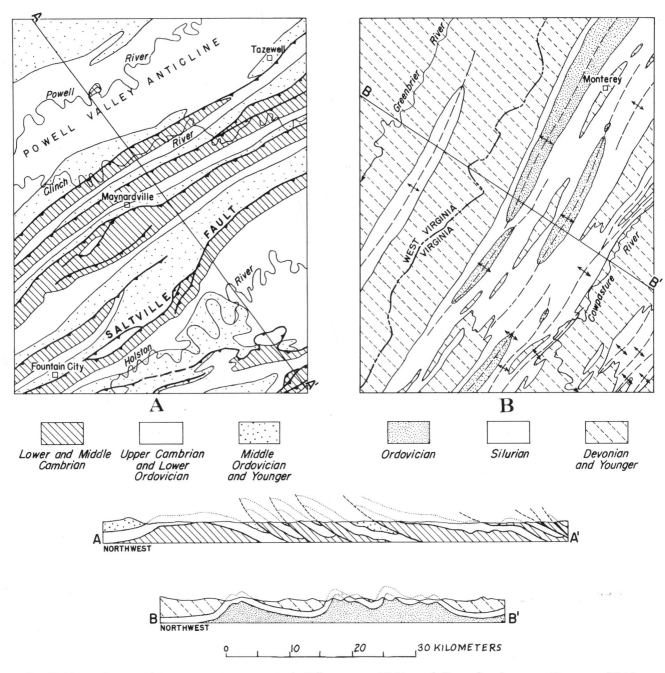

FIG. 26. Maps and sections showing contrast in structure in the Valley and Ridge province between the Southern Appalachians where faulting dominates, and the Central Appalachians where folding domi- nates. (A) Maynardville quadrangle, eastern Tennessee. (B) Monterey quadrangle, Virginia and West Virginia. After Keith (1901) and Darton (1899).

surface rocks turn out, when drilled, to be the result of piling up of thrust slices beneath which have moved along various weak layers in the succession (Fig. 28). In the southern part of the Valley and Ridge province, where faulting dominates at the surface, thrust slice after thrust slice brings up weak shaly rocks of the Rome and Conasauga Formations but fails to reveal any older Cambrian or Precambrian rocks. Apparently the thrusts originated at the level of the Rome and Conasauga, so that the underlying Cambrian strata and their basement

have been little disturbed—or at least were deformed into some different kind of structure.

Thrusting and probably also folding in the sedimentary Appalachians was thus relatively shallow, confined to the body of sedimentary rocks above the Precambrian basement. It could not have developed independently, but was marginal to other structures on the southeast in the Blue Ridge and in the crystalline Appalachians, whose growth provided a driving force; these we will now examine.

46

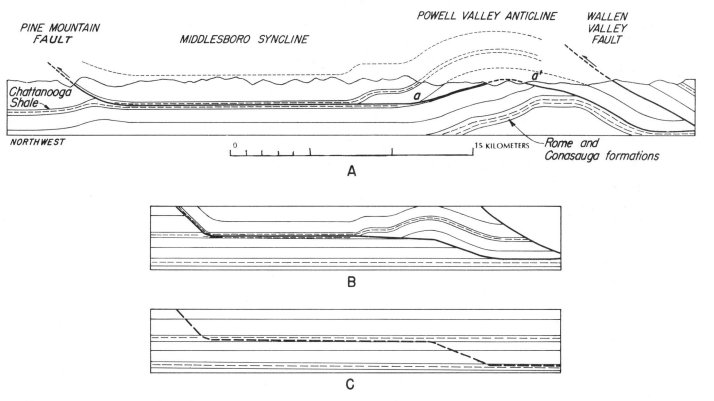

FIG. 27. Sections across Cumberland Mountain thrust block, Virginia and Kentucky. (A) Present structure, with displacement on Pine Mountain fault indicated by points *a–a'*. (B) The same, with folding in overridden block eliminated. (C) Area before faulting, showing initial course of break that later became Pine Mountain thrust. Compiled from Butts (1927), Rich (1934), and Miller and Fuller (1947).

We can summarize that part of the Appalachians so far covered by means of two generalized cross-sections (Fig. 29).

BLUE RIDGE PROVINCE. Southeast of the Appalachian Valley rise other mountains known as the *Blue Ridge*, which runs from Pennsylvania southwest to Georgia. The Blue Ridge narrows northeastward and ends in Pennsylvania as South Mountain, but it widens south-

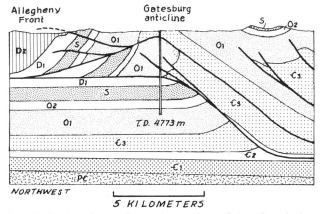

FIG. 28. Section of a simple anticline in the surface rocks, which is shown by drilling to be complexly thrust-faulted at depth, but without disturbing the basal layers of the succession. The well boring started in Cambrian rocks and ended in Ordovician rocks at a total depth of 4,773 meters, after passing through two or three thrust faults on the way. Gatesburg anticline on Nittany arch of central Pennsylvania. After Gwinn (1970).

westward into Tennessee and North Carolina, where it is a massive highland 120 kilometers across (Fig. 33B). This includes Mount Mitchell, with an altitude of 2,037 meters the highest summit in the eastern United States, and many other peaks almost as high. These altitudes may not seem impressive by western standards; nevertheless the Blue Ridge is a good, rugged mountain area in which relief from ridge top to valley bottom is nearly two kilometers in many places. The Great Smoky Mountains, popular in song and legend, are part of the Blue Ridge, although the name is restricted by geographers to a small segment in Tennessee and North Carolina. In New England the *Green Mountains*, and in Newfoundland the *Long Range* lie in the same position as the Blue Ridge in the cross-section and have a similar structure (Fig. 33A).

A structural tendency in the Valley and Ridge province continues into the Blue Ridge—a progressively higher uplift toward the southeast. Here, therefore, rocks beneath the carbonates of the Appalachian Valley emerge in an anticlinorium—Lower Cambrian quartzites, arkoses, and conglomerates that form the bottom of the Paleozoic geosynclinal column, and various stratified Upper Proterozoic rocks beneath. The latter are mainly basaltic lavas in Virginia, but farther southwest are a great mass of graywackes and other clastics less cleanly washed than the Paleozoic deposits (the

47

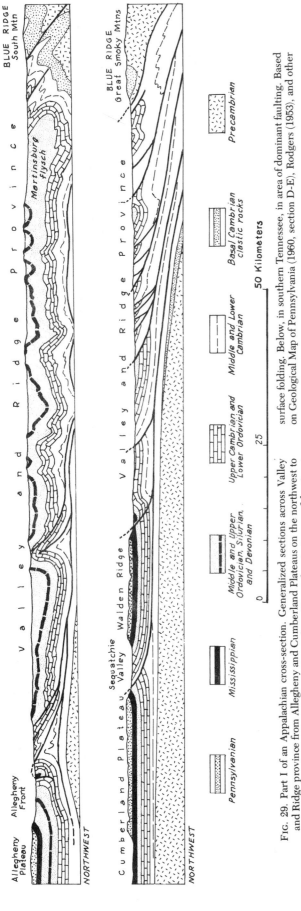

BLUE RIDGE
South Mtn

BLUE RIDGE
Great Smoky Mtns

Allegheny Plateau

Allegheny Front

A l l e g h e n y   a n d   R i d g e   P r o v i n c e

Mortinsburg Flysch

Sequatchie Valley

Cumberland Plateau

Walden Ridge

V a l l e y   a n d   R i d g e   P r o v i n c e

NORTHWEST

NORTHWEST

Precambrian

Basal Cambrian clastic rocks

Middle and Lower Cambrian

Upper Cambrian and Lower Ordovician

Middle and Upper Ordovician, Silurian, and Devonian

Mississippian

Pennsylvanian

0   25   50 Kilometers

FIG. 29. Part I of an Appalachian cross-section. Generalized sections across Valley and Ridge province from Allegheny and Cumberland Plateaus on the northwest to Blue Ridge on the southeast. Above, in southern Pennsylvania, in area of dominant surface folding. Below, in southern Tennessee, in area of dominant faulting. Based on Geological Map of Pennsylvania (1960, section D-E), Rodgers (1953), and other sources.

Ocoee Series). These stratified rocks—Early Cambrian and later Precambrian—lie on a basement of earlier Precambrian granites and gneisses that has been forced up as a welt in the midst of the Appalachian structure (Fig. 33B). These yield Middle Proterozoic dates of about 1,000 million years, indicating that they are an extension of those of the Grenville province of the Canadian Shield.

Significant changes in style of deformation appear in the Blue Ridge province that foreshadow the kind of deformation in the main crystalline belt of the Appalachians beyond. Folds of the sedimentary Appalachians formed in the strata mainly by flexing, distortion being taken up by gliding between the layers with little development of slaty cleavage. On passing into the Blue Ridge, folding is mainly by shear, or penetrative deformation, so that the rocks have been deformed by laminar flow, with great thickening along the axes and thinning along the flanks of the folds, and with extensive development of slaty cleavage, as well as increasing metamorphism. Distinctions between stratified overburden and basement become blurred, and the whole mass of rocks has been deformed as a unit.

In places deformation of this kind resulted merely in folding, but in others it produced low-angle thrusts that differ from those in the sedimentary Appalachians because they extend as great shears deep into the basement. Such thrusts dominate the border of the Blue Ridge from southwestern Virginia into Tennessee and beyond; their northwestward movement provided a driving force that probably assisted in the marginal deformation in this segment of the sedimentary Appalachians.

There is also a significant change in gravity. The southeastern part of the sedimentary Appalachians shows a prominent gravity minimum throughout its length (as much as 100 milligals in places), which changes abruptly in the Blue Ridge and southeastward to positive gravity anomalies, producing a striking gravity gradient. In many places the gradient follows the northwest edge of the Blue Ridge, but in others it drops back behind it—in places where the Blue Ridge rocks are known to be overthrust over the sedimentary rocks. Part of the positive anomalies may be due to the presence of mafic intrusions, but to a large degree they reflect genuine differences in the nature and thickness of the crust—probably an approach to a thinner, more oceanic crust, rather than a thick continental crust.

Along the southeastern border of the Blue Ridge and its extensions, the rocks in many places merely bend over and pass beneath those of the crystalline Appalachians, but in others the border is faulted. From southern Virginia to the Coastal Plain in Alabama, especially, the boundary is the *Brevard zone*, a remarkably straight lineament and zone of faulting that cuts directly through the more irregular structures on either side, and juxtaposes contrasting rock assemblages. Late in its history it seems to have been a zone of strike-slip displacement, but it had a complex earlier history that is poorly understood. We will explore some of the possibilities later (section 5).

CRYSTALLINE APPALACHIANS (NEW ENGLAND UPLAND AND PIEDMONT PLATEAU). Southeast of the Blue Ridge are the main crystalline Appalachians. Some of the crystalline area projects in mountains quite as high as the Blue Ridge—the New England Upland extends eastward from the Green Mountains; the summit of the White Mountains beyond in New Hampshire is Mount Washington with an altitude of 1,916 meters, the highest peak in the northeastern states. But farther southwest, because of relatively rapid erosion of the crystalline rocks in the humid climate, wide areas have been worn down to low ground in the Piedmont Plateau, as we have seen.

The crystalline Appalachians are made up of metamorphic schists and gneisses and of various plutonic (or deep-seated igneous) rocks, mainly felsic or granitic, but partly mafic or even ultramafic.

Because the crystalline complex resembles similarly altered Precambrian rocks in the Canadian Shield, it was formerly inferred that it is also of ancient age; but it is now known to be mostly younger. Some of the Middle Proterozoic Grenvillian gneissic basement comes up in domes a short distance southeast of the Blue Ridge belt (as east of the Green Mountains in Vermont, near Baltimore, Maryland, and in the Sauratown Mountains on the North Carolina-Virginia border), but the remainder of the complex is altered from younger supracrustal rocks, which were originally argillites, sandstones, tuffs, and lavas—largely contemporaneous with the Paleozoic rocks of the sedimentary Appalachians to the northwest but of different facies and formed in a quite different environment. In Canada and New England enough fossils have been found to demonstrate that the crystalline rocks include a sequence of Cambrian, Ordovician, Silurian, and Devonian ages. In the Central and Southern Appalachians most of the younger components are missing, and the altered supracrustal rocks are largely Cambrian and Upper Proterozoic. We will analyze the complex history of the crystalline rocks later (section 5).

Scattered through the metamorphic rocks are small pods and lenses of ultramafic plutonic rocks—peridotites, pyroxenites, dunites, and serpentines. Although individual bodies are small, they are characteristically grouped in belts or swarms; in both New England and the Southern Appalachians, the most prominent belts are in the northwest part of the crystalline area, in or near the Green Mountain and Blue Ridge uplifts. Probably the ultramafic rocks did not arrive in their present positions as molten magmas; instead, they are shreds of material from the mantle that were carried high above their source by a complex combination of tectonic processes.

Of much greater extent are the felsic plutonic rocks, the granites and their allies, which permeate the altered supracrustal rocks so widely that few areas are wholly devoid of them; in part they replaced or engulfed the supracrustal rocks to such an extent that not much of the latter remains.

The felsic plutonic rocks have a wide variety of relations to the metamorphosed supracrustal rocks (Fig. 30). Some are thoroughly gneissic and form thin to thick lenses or beds concordant with the foliation of their hosts; they fade out into them at their ends as streaks and lit-par-lit injections. At the opposite extreme are massive granitic rocks that break through and cut off the ends of the metamorphic rocks and granite gneisses, forming bodies of various shapes and sizes up to scores of miles across, and including in northern New England a spectacular array of ring dikes.

But these extremes in the felsic plutonic rocks are not sharply separated; between are many bodies that are partly concordant and weakly gneissic yet that break through the enclosing rocks in many places. The whole assemblage developed during a long period of time—from the late Precambrian through the Paleozoic and (in norther New England) into the Jurassic—and at deep levels in the crust.

We will examine later the significance of the plutonic rocks—ultramafic to felsic (section 5).

The metamorphic and plutonic rocks of the crystalline Appalachians have a highly complex structure, so that their pattern on the geologic map is one of swirls and knots that is sometimes difficult to resolve into any orderly system of folding. Foliation frequently stands at high angles, but in places it rolls over the crests of domes or arches, and in other places it dips at low angles over wide areas. Detailed studies in both New England and the Southern Appalachians indicate that in many places these apparent features are actually parts of nappes, or great recumbent folds kilometers across, and these may prove to be more widespread than is now realized. Where the structure has been worked out in detail, it is found to be very different from that in the sedimentary Appalachians in that it involves much flowage of the rocks and thickening and thinning of the units with little breaking or faulting. Nearly all the faults of the crystalline area formed after the rocks had been deformed and congealed. Deformation of the crystalline Appalachians must have taken place under greater overburden and at greater pressures and depths than the folding and faulting of the sedimentary Appalachians, in a realm where large supplies of heat and magmatic juices were available.

Conditions in this realm are suggested by various

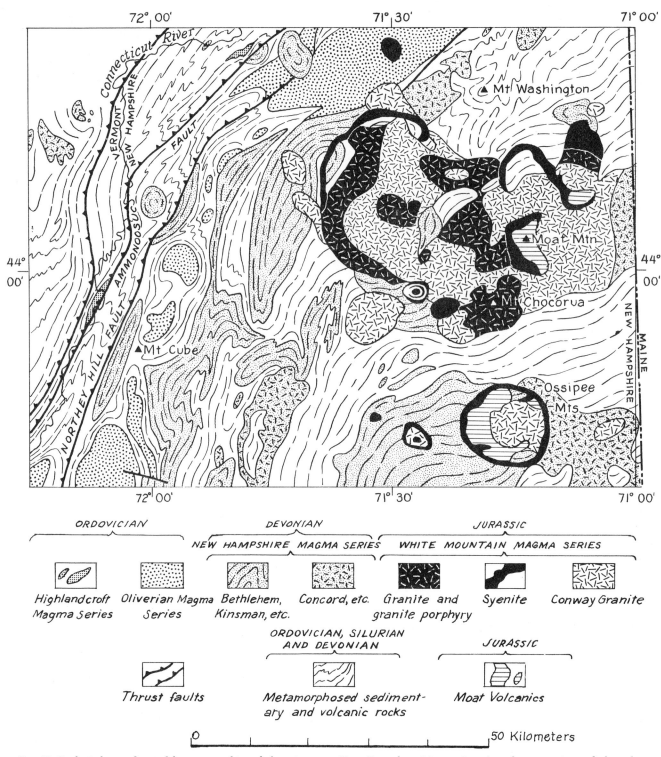

Fig. 30. Geological map of part of the metamorphic and plutonic complex of central New Hampshire, showing granitic plutons lying in host rocks that were originally eugeosynclinal sediments and volcanics. The plutons have various structures ranging from early foliated and concordant bodies (Highlandcroft, Oliverian, and part of New Hampshire Magma Series) to later massive and through-breaking bodies (mainly White Mountain Magma Series); and a range in age from Ordovician to Jurassic. Compiled from Geologic Map of New Hampshire (1955) and other sources.

50

index minerals that grow from the rock materials with increasing temperature and pressure. First traces of metamorphism are indicated by chlorite; progressively higher metamorphic rank is shown by biotite, garnet, staurolite, kyanite, and finally by sillimanite. (A still higher rank called the "granulite facies" occurs mainly in the Grenvillian basement of the crystalline Appalachians, and was produced prior to the Appalachian deformation.) Commonly the metamorphic rank increases near larger felsic plutonic bodies—obvious local sources of heat—but this cannot be the whole story. The metamorphic mineral assemblages as well as the degree of physical metamorphism progresses regionally from the edges toward the interior of the crystalline belt; regional metamorphism seems to result from a combination of all conditions at work in the axial zone of the orogenic system: depth, pressure, heat, and plutonism.

Within the crystalline Appalachians, metamorphic rank increases progressively from the sedimentary Appalachians and the Blue Ridge, but it does not continue to do so to the southeastern exposures of the system. In New England the kyanite zone is attained in central Vermont and western Massachusetts and the sillimanite zone forms a wide area along the White Mountains and east of it in New Hampshire and Massachusetts. But there is a curious zone of low-grade metamorphism along the Connecticut Valley west of the White Mountains, which is historically interesting because it contains many localities of Silurian and Devonian fossils, that provided the key which unlocked the stratigraphic mysteries of much of the surrounding area. Also, southeast of the sillimanite area in southeastern New Hampshire and eastern Massachusetts, metamorphic grade drops off in the remarkably short distance of a few kilometers into low-rank metamorphic rocks.

Similarly, in the Southern Appalachians the metamorphic climax in the sillimanite zone occurs in the Blue Ridge and, more extensively, in a belt about midway between the Blue Ridge uplift and the Coastal Plain (between the Brevard and Kings Mountain belts), southeast of which metamorphism again decreases into the Carolina Slate Belt, where most of the rocks are of lower rank.

Metamorphism also decreases northeastward along the strike. The high-grade metamorphic rocks do not extend much beyond southwestern Maine; and beyond into Canada metamorphism is generally low, or even non-existent—so that the term "crystalline Appalachians," which we have applied to the belt, is no longer appropriate. As in the case of the low-grade belt along the Connecticut Valley (but to an even greater degree), the low-grade rocks of northeastern Maine and southeastern Canada provide the geologist with abundant stratigraphic data that assist in unraveling the more

complexly metamorphosed crystalline rocks farther south.

POSTOROGENIC DEPOSITS. Besides the foundation of crystalline rocks, the inner parts of the Appalachians contain patches of sedimentary and igneous rocks that are partly or wholly younger than the principal deformation. The sedimentary rocks lie unconformably on the eroded folds of the older rocks, and contain fragments of their metamorphosed and plutonized products; they are, therefore, postorogenic.

From Nova Scotia to South Carolina, rocks of the *Newark Group* of late Triassic age form long strips in the crystalline area; similar rocks have been encountered in wells under the Coastal Plain deposits as far south as Florida and as far west as Arkansas. Newark sediments are all non-marine and are mainly arkosic red sandstones, but include conglomerate, dark shale, and thin beds of coal. They probably accumulated in downfaulted troughs of little greater dimensions than their present outcrops, after the great deformation of the crystalline foundation had ceased but while the region still possessed considerable relief. The sediments are not metamorphosed or even folded, but have been tilted, warped, and broken by normal faults produced by crustal tension (Fig. 31). Sedimentation was accompanied by igneous and volcanic activity; in places the sediments are interbedded with basaltic lavas and intruded by masses of diabase. Diabase dikes of the same age also penetrate the crystalline foundation widely, even far from any areas of Triassic sediments (Fig. 32).

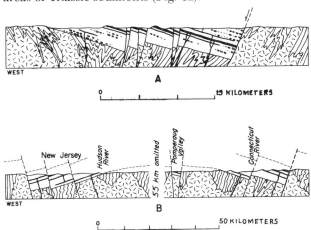

FIG. 31. Sections showing structure of Triassic rocks (Newark Group) in southern part of Northern Appalachians: (A) Section across Connecticut Valley near Hartford, Connecticut. (B) Regional section from Connecticut to New Jersey. After Barrell (1915) and Longwell (1932).

The Triassic rocks provide a significant terminal date beyond which no Appalachian deformation could have taken place; hence, Appalachian deformation is definitely older than late Triassic. For the present, let us conclude that deformation of the crystalline rocks on which

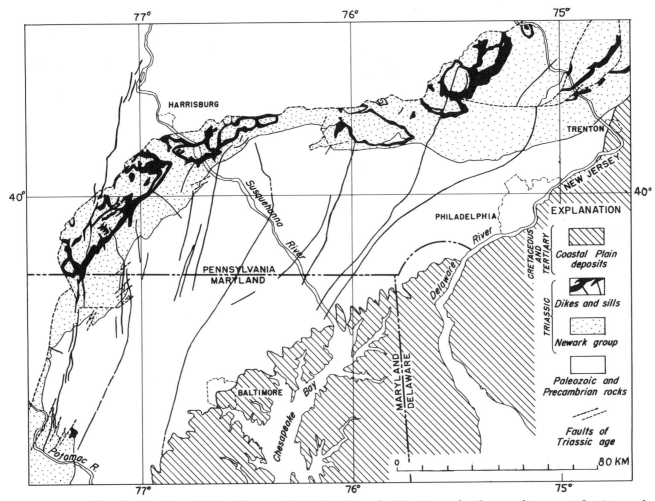

FIG. 32. Map of southeastern Pennsylvania and eastern Maryland showing sedimentary rocks of Newark Group, and dikes and sills of diabase that intrude both the Newark Group and the earlier crystal-line and sedimentary rocks of surrounding areas. After Stose and Stose (1944).

they lie might have been only a little earlier than late Triassic, or might have been much earlier; we will return to the problem later (section 5).

Postorogenic deposits that bridge, to some extent, the lost interval between Triassic deposition and the deformational climax occur in the northeastern part of the Appalachian system in the Maritime Provinces of Canada. Here are extensive areas of Mississippian and Pennsylvanian sedimentary rocks that are less deformed than the Devonian and earlier rocks beneath, and show no trace of their metamorphism. Although some marine beds occur in the Mississippian, most of the deposits are continental, and the Pennsylvanian contains beds of coal that are mined on Cape Breton Island and the mainland of Nova Scotia; the highest strata are Permian continental redbeds on Prince Edward Island. These later Paleozoic rocks are nearly flat-lying in places, but in others are mildly to steeply tilted. The structure of the late Paleozoic rocks indicate that the major deformation of the northeastern segment of the crystalline Appala-

chians had been completed before Mississippian time, although milder deformation continued nearly to the end of the Paleozoic Era. The Mississippian, Pennsylvanian, and Permian postorogenic deposits, like those of the Triassic, are basinal and mainly continental, but they differ in that they bear the marks of the last crustal compression.

We have now carried our exposition of the Appalachian system far enough to present a second part of our cross-section (Fig. 33).

SOUTHEASTERN BORDER OF APPALACHIAN SYSTEM. What happens on the southeastward side of the Appalachians?

As we have seen, the folded, metamorphosed, and plutonized parts of the crystalline Appalachians pass from view in this direction beneath deposits of the Atlantic Coastal Plain and continental shelf, so that this flank of the orogenic system is concealed. But the system cannot continue indefinitely southeastward, as beyond the

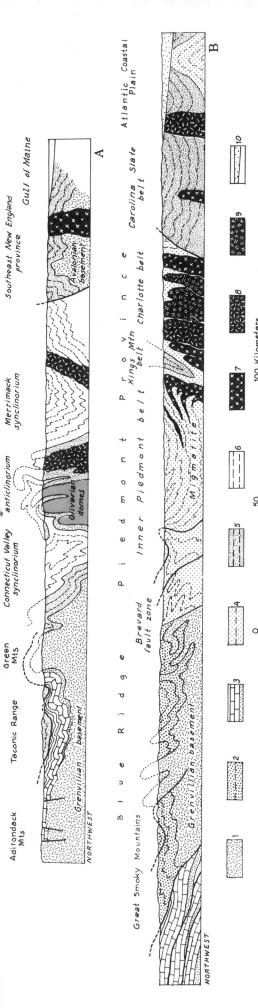

FIG. 33. Part II of an Appalachian cross-section: Sections across the crystalline Appalachians. (A) In New England (New York, Vermont, and New Hampshire). (B) In Tennessee and North Carolina. Note that these sections are on a smaller scale than Part I of the cross-section (Fig. 29). Compiled from many sources, including sections on Geologic Maps of Vermont (1961) and New Hampshire (1955), Hadley and Nelson (1971), and Griffin (1974).

Explanation of symbols: 1–Precambrian basement rocks, Middle Proterozoic to northwest, Upper Proterozoic to southeast. 2–In section B, altered sedimentary rocks of Upper Proterozoic age (Ocoee Series). 3–Paleozoic quartzite, limestone, and shale, formed in miogeosynclinal area. 4–In Section B, metamorphic complex, mainly of Upper Proterozoic age (schist, gneiss, migmatite, and amphibolite). 5–Older eugeosynclinal rocks (Cambrian and Ordovician in section A, Upper Proterozoic and Cambrian in section B). 6–Younger eugeosynclinal rocks (Silurian and Devonian). 7–Older Paleozoic granitic rocks (mainly Ordovician). 8–Younger Paleozoic granitic rocks (Devonian and younger). 9–In section B, Paleozoic mafic intrusives. 10–In section B, Cretaceous and Tertiary deposits of Atlantic Coastal Plain.

continental shelf is the deep Atlantic Ocean, floored by simatic crust—a quite different structural element.

Although much of the southeastern border of the Appalachian system is not visible, we nevertheless can make many educated guesses about it from various lines of evidence—from rocks and structures exposed immediately northwest of the edge of the Coastal Plain, from wells that have been drilled through the Coastal Plain deposits, and from geophysical surveys on the land and at sea.

Surface outcrops indicate that the axis of greatest deformation and highest grade of metamorphism lies well inland, within the exposed areas in Newfoundland, New England, and the Piedmont—southeast of which the rocks are less deformed and metamorphosed. These areas are not truly the southeastern border of the whole system but represent new structural elements with a different history, which we will explore later. In eastern Massachusetts Upper Proterozoic granites are widespread, overlain by fossiliferous Cambrian and some later Paleozoic, cut by a few early Paleozoic granites (Fig. 33A). In the Piedmont from Virginia to Georgia near the edge of the Coastal Plain is the *Carolina Slate Belt*, formed of slates graywackes, and volcanics of Upper Proterozoic and Cambrian age, which are only moderately folded and metamorphosed (Fig. 33B). Beyond this, in the Coastal Plain, similar rocks are penetrated by drilling.

Southeastward, the Appalachian rocks and structures are covered by a seaward-thickening wedge of younger deposits in the Coastal Plain, the continental shelf, and the continental slope, about which much has been learned from drilling and from geophysical surveys. Pioneer geophysical surveys by seismic refraction methods were made of these deposits two or three decades ago by Maurice Ewing and his associates of Lamont Geological Observatory of Columbia University, but since then knowledge has greatly proliferated.

As would be anticipated, the Tertiary and Cretaceous rocks of the Coastal Plain form wedges that thicken seaward, eventually reaching a thickness of 3,300 to 5,000 meters near the edge of the continental shelf. The lower part of the deposit, however, has much greater complexity, and there are one or more sedimentary troughs beneath the shelf and beyond where the fill attains 10,000 to 12,000 meters—geosynclinal in their own right. Marine Lower Cretaceous wedges in beneath the Upper Cretaceous, and below that is Jurassic, and possibly even some Triassic at the base. Unlike the ordinary clastic Coastal Plain deposits above, the Jurassic is largely carbonate rocks and salt (Fig. 34).

These lower beds probably formed during the initial rifting open of the Atlantic during Mesozoic time, when only a narrow trough separated North America from the trans-Atlantic continents. The higher beds accumulated

53

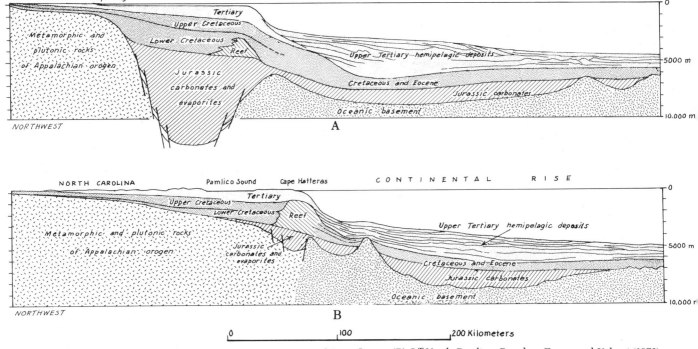

FIG. 34. Part III of an Appalachian cross-section. Sections across the Atlantic Coastal Plain, the continental shelf and slope, and the continental rise, based on drilling and geophysical surveys. (A) Off New Jersey. (B) Off North Carolina. Based on Emery and Uchupi (1972) and Sheridan (1974). Vertical scale ten times horizontal.

as an embankment on the edge of the continent after the Atlantic began to widen. Most of the Coastal Plain deposits, even the Jurassic, were originally laid down in rather shallow water, so that there has been a progressive downbending of the edge of the continent toward the Atlantic Ocean floor.

The Coastal Plain deposits lie on the truncated surface of the Appalachian system, formed by subaerial erosion, which now lies at depths of 10,000 meters or more at the outer edge. Somewhere on the continental slope, or a little beyond, the continental rocks of the Appalachian system give place to simatic oceanic crust. Probably the junction was originally a rift along which the Atlantic continents have separated during Mesozoic time. Southeastern extensions of the Appalachian system, if they exist, must therefore be sought across the present Atlantic Ocean, in northwestern Africa and southwestern Europe, where Paleozoic orogenic systems are known.

SUMMARY. We have now reviewed the topographic provinces and structural units of the Appalachians. Later we will consider the sedimentary and tectonic environments in which these different units were formed. It is our misfortune that it is necessary to use for each of these—the topographic, structural, and sedimentary units—a different set of names, many of which are hallowed by usage. To prevent confusion and make clear how these are interrelated, the following table is included for reference. The terms given for "rock facies" are defined in section 5 of this chapter.

COMPARISON BETWEEN DIFFERENT NAMES FOR LARGER UNITS IN THE APPALACHIAN AREA

Geomorphic province:	Structural unit:	Rock facies:
Allegheny and Cumberland Plateaus	Allegheny synclinorium	Foreland
Valley and Ridge province	Sedimentary Appalachians (folded and faulted sedimentary rocks)	Miogeosyncline (see section 5)
Blue Ridge province (including Green Mountains in north)	Anticlinorium in some places, faulted uplift in others	Exposures of basal Paleozoic and of Precambrian basement
New England Upland and Piedmont province	Crystalline Appalachians (metamorphic and plutonic rocks)	Eugeosyncline (see section 5)
Atlantic Coastal Plain and continental shelf	Cretaceous and Tertiary sediments, lying on crystalline rocks of eugeosynclinal origin.	
Atlantic Ocean basin	Sea floor at depths of 5,000 meters with simatic crust not far beneath sedimentary cover.	

4. GEOSYNCLINES

In preceding parts of this chapter we have placed the Appalachians in space by summarizing their surface form and plan, and their cross-section. Although we have been able to draw some inferences, we have not yet presented a comprehensive story, and many of the facts given may have seemed unrelated. The next step in our analysis will be to arrange these facts in a sequence and review the Appalachians in time—how they originated, how they grew, and how they were built into the structures we see today. None of this story took place overnight, or even in a geological period or two; deformation was preceded by a long time of preparation.

During much of the time of preparation the Appalachian region was a geosyncline. Before we discuss the growth of the system itself, it will be profitable to discuss geosynclines in general—a subject to which we have alluded briefly in several of the earlier chapters.

HALL'S IDEAS. First, it is worth setting forth how the idea of geosynclines originated in the minds of geologists.

The notion of what we now call a geosyncline probably began with James Hall, whom we encountered as one of the pioneers of American paleontology and stratigraphy (Chapter III, section 2). In making his observations on strata and fossils, Hall traveled widely in New York state, both in the folded rocks of the Appalachian area and farther west. In addition, he extended his studies into the Interior Region, where he at one time made a geological survey of Iowa. From these experiences he came to significant conclusions regarding the lay of the strata and their bearing on the formation of geologic structures, which he summarized in an address in 1859.

In brief, Hall observed that Paleozoic sediments in the Interior Region are thin, whereas those of the Appalachian area are thick; yet he observed that each had formed during about the same span of time. He reasoned that there must be some relation between the greater thickness of sediments in the Appalachians and their mountainous character, and concluded that all large mountain chains must represent areas of greatest accumulation of sediments.

Sediments in the part of the Appalachians which Hall had studied, like those of the Interior Region, were laid down in shallow water. The greater thickness of shallow water sediments in the Appalachians was due to a greater subsidence of the crust there than in the interior; this, in turn, must have resulted from gradual yielding of the crust beneath the weight of the sediments themselves. Later, these great sedimentary accumulations were uplifted, then eroded into the mountain belts we see today.

Mountain formation was thus largely a matter of thick accumulation of sediments, subsidence of the crust, and subsequent uplift. Deformation was incidental to the accumulation and a consequence of the subsidence. Along the axis of the subsiding area, sediments became folded and in places were so ruptured as to allow the ascent of igneous magmas. Here, then, was a theory of mountain formation in which the great transformation on and

within the crust was ascribed to slow surficial processes—those of erosion and sedimentation.

DANA'S IDEAS. The significance of Hall's observations and speculations gradually came to be appreciated among geologists, but so far the ideas were a theory without a name.

It remained for another geologist, James Dwight Dana, to give these concepts a terminology. Dana was a contemporary of Hall's, and for many years was professor of geology at Yale University. He originated the name geosyncline (which he called a "geosynclinal"), as well as the less commonly used term geanticline (in the form "geanticlinal"), applied to the opposite of a geosyncline—a part of the crust that is gradually rising and being eroded, rather than subsiding and being covered by sediments.

While Dana agreed with the facts as presented by Hall, he was more critical of Hall's explanation, and appraised it as "a theory of the origin of mountains with the origin of mountains left out." Dana had theories of his own and was one of the first geologists to point out the fundamental differences in character between continents and ocean basins and to suggest the possibility of continental accretion—matters we have discussed earlier (Chapter I, section 3). The earth's crust he thought to be under compression because of general contraction of the earth's interior; greatest yielding to such compression was between the continents and the oceans along belts warped down to form the "geosynclinals." Here, thick masses of sediments accumulated because a place was made for them by forces within the earth. Eventually the "geosynclinals" were destroyed by "a catastrophe of plications and solidifications."

To summarize, both Hall's and Dana's theories were based on parts of the Appalachian area; hence, the Appalachians are the site of the type geosyncline; also, although certain implications of mountain formation were inherent in both theories, emphasis was primarily on the sediments themselves; finally, the opinions of the two men diverged greatly as to the nature of the forces involved—whether thick accumulations of sediments resulted from loading of the crust, or whether the crust was bent down by other processes to form a receptacle in which the sediments could accumulate. We will see that each interpretation has its adherents to this day.

LATER IDEAS. Since the time of Hall and Dana, nearly all geologists have given some thought to geosynclines, but there has been a wide range of opinion as to what geosynclines are, what caused them, and what their effect has been on the subsequent history of an area.

Some geologists have rejected the idea entirely, preferring to consider what it seeks to explain in other ways and by other terms. Several decades ago, when the concept of the "tectogene," or great crustal downfold, was a popular explanation for mountain formation, its proponents found no use for geosynclines. But "tectogenes" have gone the way of many good geological theories and are now no longer seriously invoked. Within the last decade the theory of "plate tectonics" has come to the fore, and geosynclines are being challenged again, perhaps with more reason. However, I fancy that the geosynclinal concept will survive this new onslaught, perhaps modified and strengthened, and that it will continue to be viable and useful.

To some, a geosyncline is almost any area of relatively thick sedimentation, including not only sedimentary troughs that later became deformed mountain belts, but also sedimentary basins in the interior of the continents that were never more than slightly deformed, and basins where sedimentation is now actively in progress. This view has the virtue of treating sedimentary accumulations for their own sake, without implications as to what caused them or what they might evolve into; possibly only in this way can we discover any modern analogues of geosynclines, a topic we will consider in Chapter V. To most geologists, nevertheless, the problem of geosynclines is inextricably interwoven with that of orogenic belts and the origin of mountains. What were the unique qualities of the sedimentary accumulations and their subcrust that conditioned them for such severe folding later on?

These elusive qualities have been widely sought. Some geologists, such as those who have labored long in the European Alps, believe that geosynclinal sediments are fundamentally different from sediments in other areas—that they are bodies now found only in heavily deformed regions made up of shaly and slaty rocks rhythmically interbedded with sandstones, and associated peculiar limestones, cherts, and submarine volcanics. We will see presently that this facies is a genuine component of the mass of sediments in geosynclines, but only part of it. Such special definitions of geosynclinal sediments (amusingly enough) would make it necessary to exclude from the geosyncline an important part of the sediments of the Appalachian area—the typical and original geosyncline as envisioned by Hall and Dana.

Some geologists have elaborated on Hall's belief that geosynclines originated from loading of the crust by weight of the sediments themselves. Arguments have been brought forward, based especially on the Gulf Coast, that the great thicknesses of Cenozoic sediments preserved there resulted from an inordinate volume of material brought down from the land by its many rivers; it is thought that such material could only have been entrapped near the river mouths if the crust were depressed by the sediments. It has been suggested, besides, that sediments can accumulate only up to a limiting thickness before they become folded; hence, that "drainage patterns determine the future course of mountains."

In extreme form such ideas are rather bizarre, but at least they have a partial basis in isostasy. We know that the crust has limits of strength beyond which it will subside under load—we have seen this in our discussion of the Pleistocene ice caps of the Canadian Shield (Chapter II, section 1). Great bodies of sediments must therefore depress the crust to some extent, but most geologists do not believe that light, unconsolidated sediments can displace an equal volume of heavier consolidated crust beneath.

Instead, these geologists seek the formation of geosynclines and subsequent mountain building in forces deeper within the crust. The geosyncline is, then, perhaps a milder manifestation of a long sequence of crustal mobility which has resulted in such varied structures as those we have just reviewed in our Appalachian cross-section.

GEOSYNCLINAL ATTRIBUTES. In the face of such wide diversity of opinion about geosynclines, it is a brave spirit who dares define them explicitly. Perhaps it would be more profitable if I listed a series of "attributes" that I believe are possessed by geosynclines. Some are fairly obvious; others differ more or less from beliefs of various geologists.

(a) Geosynclines formed during sedimentation rather than afterwards, and are more sedimentary than deformational features. Characteristically, they received greater thickness and volume of sediments during their life than non-geosynclinal areas.

(b) Geosynclines are not ordinary synclinal folds or even groups of folds like the Allegheny synclinorium. Synclines and synclinoria were imposed on the strata after they had been deposited, and are not inherent in the deposit.

(c) Thick accumulations of sediment are caused by subsidence of the crust beneath them, but this is a gradual process. Ideally, at the end of a geosynclinal phase, the floor is bowed down in the manner of a syncline, but the last sediments to be deposited are nearly horizontal. Such downbowing is very gentle—the trough is likely to be 200 kilometers or more wide, but maximum depth of depression as expressed by thickness of sediments is merely 10 to 15 kilometers.

(d) Geosynclines commonly occur along the margins of continental platforms, where they form belts that are much longer than wide; they thus resemble ordinary synclines in their linear form. Basins within the continental platform and basins of non-linear form are not properly geosynclines, although they have been so-called by some geologists. Nevertheless, one type of basin grades into the other, so that distinctions are not absolute.

(e) In detail, sediments of geosynclines are varied; no one suite can be set off exclusively as "geosynclinal." Several different sedimentary facies occur in geosynclines, some sufficiently distinct as to warrant separate names (see below). These facies commonly occur in different parts of the geosyncline, where they persist through small to great thicknesses of strata, but sometimes they succeed each other in the same part of the geosyncline in one sequence of rocks.

(f) Sediments of some of these facies were laid down in relatively shallow water, as observed long ago by Hall. Such sediments differ little in kind from those of non-geosynclinal regions, but they did accumulate to greater thickness and with less interruption. In areas of shallow-water sedimentation the geosynclinal trough filled as it subsided; its base was bowed down gradually, but its upper surface at no time had a synclinal form.

(g) Sediments of some other facies were probably laid down in much deeper water. The Los Angeles and Ventura basins of southern California were deep troughs at the beginning of Pliocene time and were filled by sediments that accumulated in progressively shallower water. Although evidence is more elusive in the earlier geosynclines, sediments of parts of them also probably formed in deep water. In those parts of geosynclines where the water was deep, sedimentation did not keep pace with subsidence; thus, subsidence is not a necessary consequence of sedimentation but an independent process.

(h) Subsidence of the crust beneath the geosyncline must have resulted primarily from forces at work within the earth. The floor of the geosyncline was bent down by these forces, and sediments accumulated thickly because a place was made for them. Weight of the sediments themselves depressed the crust still farther, but not as far as the thickness of the strata deposited. Geosynclines, therefore, are sedimentary basins that formed under marked tectonic control.

(i) A geosyncline is a mobile belt, but degree of mobility varies—from one geosyncline to another, between parts of one geosyncline, and with time. Some geosynclines had only low-order mobility throughout their history; others show a steadily mounting crescendo of mobility, so that the geosyncline was finally transformed into a consolidated orogenic belt. Crustal unrest in the belt may become manifest long before the end of the geosynclinal phase itself.

(j) If geosynclines are mobile belts in which sedimentation took place under marked tectonic control, it follows that they are merely the surface expression of more deep-seated crustal structures. What these substructures are has been much debated; considerable fact and much fancy has accumulated regarding them, as we will see in Chapter V.

GEOSYNCLINAL TERMINOLOGY. These "attributes" make clear, I think, that the geosynclinal concept is useful for bracketing larger sedimentary features and structures that have a significant bearing on the evolution of a continent. Nevertheless, the attributes show that geosynclines have many guises not expressed by the word "geosyncline" alone. Many geologists have decided that analysis would be sharpened if names were given to these species of geosynclines, and an extensive terminology has therefore grown up. Unfortunately, attempts to name such parts have resulted merely in a confusion of tongues, as each author has proposed his own set of names. Some thirty-seven names were listed in a compilation made about thirty years ago (Glaessner and Teichert, 1947), and others have probably been created since.

The German geologist, Hans Stille, used the term *geosyncline* not only for the linear troughs along the margins of continental platforms but also for non-linear sedimentary basins within the continental platforms, calling the first "orthogeosynclines" and the second "parageosynclines." The American geologist, Marshall Kay, in turn recognized and named half a dozen or so species of the genus "parageosyncline." But if "parageosynclines" are not truly geosynclines, all this elaborate terminology is unnecessary, and the distinctions can be more effectively indicated by descriptive phrases in the English language. We owe to Stille, however, two names for subdivisions of his "orthogeosynclines"—*miogeosyncline* and *eugeosyncline*—which are the only terms of genuine utility, and which will be used henceforth throughout this book.

Miogeosynclines formed along the margins of the continental platforms on continental crust and are, in essence, sedimentary embankments built from the continents toward the ocean basins. They are composed of sediments much like those laid down on the continental platforms, but with a thicker, more complete sequence. In most of the North American examples (notably the Appalachian and Cordilleran geosynclines), the lower halves of these sequences are carbonate rocks, with some associated quartzose clastics derived from the continental interior. The upper halves of the sequences consist of more varied deposits derived from the interiors of the orogenic belts, reflecting the increasing mobility of the latter. As sedimentary embankments, the floors of miogeosynclines slope away from the continental platforms, ordinarily without an opposing "synclinal" flank. Some geologists have therefore dropped the "syn" and prefer to call them "miogeoclines". While this is perhaps technically justified, I prefer the traditional name "miogeosyncline" and will continue to use it.

Eugeosynclines are composed of a considerably different suite of deposits—graywackes, slates, cherts, tuffs, submarine lavas, and the like—all "off-the-continent" deposits and probably laid down largely on oceanic crust, in moderate to very deep water. Because much of the eugeosynclinal material has subsequently been strongly deformed, metamorphosed, and plutonized, understanding of the nature and history of eugeo-synclines has occurred only within the last few decades. It is now apparent that the genus includes a wide variety of species, formed in different environments—on continental slopes, deep-sea trenches, island arcs, or even the ocean floor itself. Understanding of true eugeosynclinal history can only come from discrimination of these different varieties, yet this is not always easy and is often more subjective than objective, partly because of the subtleties in the rocks themselves, partly because of the complex structures that were superposed on them later. It is therefore desirable to retain the term *eugeosyncline* as an operational but perhaps genetically meaningless expression for an unusual suite of rocks, quite unlike those found in the continental interior, which have been added to the continent through time by a variety of orogenic processes—and the term will be so used throughout the remainder of this book.

5. GROWTH OF THE APPALACHIANS

APPALACHIAN MIOGEOSYNCLINE. With the general character of geosynclines in mind, we can now examine the time relations of the Appalachian structures. We will begin with the miogeosynclinal area, from whose rocks the sedimentary Appalachians and the Valley and Ridge province were created.

The miogeosynclinal area borders the edge of the Interior Lowlands and continental platform; the eugeosynclinal area is farther out, away from the continent. Miogeosynclinal deposits are much like those laid down over the Interior Lowlands—marine carbonates and clastics passing upward into continental beds—and, like them, were laid down in shallow water or on low-lying surfaces. But unlike the interior area, where initial deposits are no older than Late Cambrian, deposition began in the miogeosynclinal area in Early Cambrian time. Besides, the whole sequence from base to top of the Paleozoic column is ten times as thick, amounting to about 8 to 10 kilometers. Throughout the long period during which these deposits accumulated, the miogeosyncline was a region of quiet sedimentation and slow subsidence with little other crustal activity and no volcanism.

Let us now analyze the miogeosynclinal deposits in several dimensions: first in vertical sequence, then along the trend of the miogeosyncline, finally across the trend from eugeosyncline to foreland.

To demonstrate the character of the deposits in vertical sequence and their variations along the trend, three sections in representative areas are generalized in Figure 35: in the Southern Appalachians of Alabama and of Tennessee, and in the Central Appalachians of Pennsylvania. The thickness of each of the three sections totals about 6,500 meters, but note the considerable differences in them, especially in the upper half. (Similar se-

quences occur in the Northern Appalachians, especially in western Vermont and along the west coast of Newfoundland, but they are thinner and less complete at the top.)

Initial Paleozoic deposits in all three sections are Early Cambrian marine clastics—conglomerates, arkoses, and shales that pass upward into cleanly washed quartzites. They vary somewhat in thickness from place to place because of irregularities of the surface of the Precambrian floor and local differences in subsidence.

Then follows a great carbonate sequence with a nearly constant thickness of 3,000 meters. It embraces the remainder of the Lower Cambrian and extends through Middle and Upper Cambrian and Lower Ordovician; in places it includes Middle Ordovician as well. It is a mass of limestones and dolomites with only occasional interbedded layers of shale and sandstone.

These two components, the basal clastics and the mass of carbonates, form the miogeosynclinal sequence proper. They were laid down during a prolonged time of crustal quiescence on a surface that sloped gently seaward from the continental interior. No nearby lands were being strongly eroded. The sediments bear no indication of any lands to the southeast, and their sandy and shaly layers were derived from distant parts of the continental interior.

Southeast of the early Paleozoic carbonates are the very different but partly coeval eugeosynclinal deposits, which we will discuss presently, but the zone of change from one to the other is seldom preserved. Commonly the change takes place across the Blue Ridge uplift, and the related Green Mountains and Long Range uplifts to the north, which raise basement rocks to the surface; in the past, many geologists have speculated that these uplifts or their precursors formed an actual barrier between the miogeosynclinal and eugeosynclinal deposits, so that the miogeosyncline was "synclinal" in fact. Increasing evidence now suggests, instead, that the carbonate deposits ended southeastward in an abrupt shelf break, comparable to the edge of the present continental shelf, beyond which there was an abrupt descent into the deep water of the eugeosyncline. Certain peculiar breccias and block beds on the eugeosynclinal side of the boundary throughout the Northern Appalachians then come into focus as landslips off the steep face of the carbonate embankment into deeper water.

The edge of the carbonate embankment corresponds significantly in trend to the known southeastward extent of the crystalline Precambrian (Grenvillian) basement beneath, which lies only a little farther southeast. Beyond, there appears originally to have been only oceanic crust. The southeastern limit of the Grenvillian basement, and the edge of the carbonate embankment, thus mark the *actual edge of the North American continent during early Paleozoic time.*

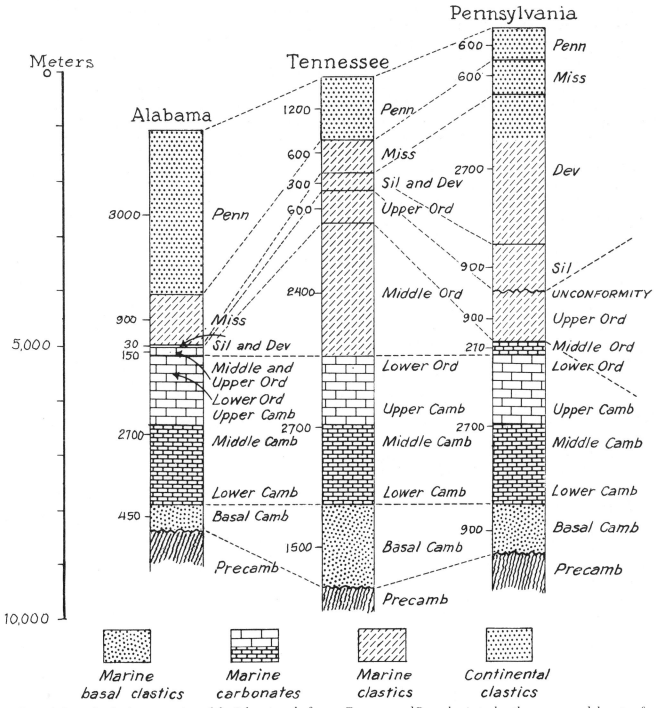

FIG. 35. Generalized columnar sections of the Paleozoic rocks from southwest to northeast in the Valley and Ridge province in Alabama, Tennessee, and Pennsylvania, to show the sequence and character of the deposits along the strike of the Appalachian miogeosyncline.

FLYSCH AND ALLOCHTHONOUS MASSES. The upper half of the sequence in the miogeosynclinal area formed after a radical change in conditions had taken place. The carbonate sequence gives place upward to marine clastic deposits, beginning in many places in the Middle Ordovician, in others in the Upper Ordovician. They were derived from erosion of lands to the southeast, where there had been none before. These deposits will be considered under this and the following heading.

In the Northern Appalachians the first part of the later clastic deposits forms the Middle and Upper Ordovician Normanskill and Martinsburg Formations of New York State and Pennsylvania. They are flysch, or masses of thinly interbedded layers of sandstone and shale—the sandstones with structures characteristic of turbidites, the shales laid down during intervals of pelagic sedimentation between the turbid flows. Flysch is a deep-water deposit, formed in rapidly subsiding linear troughs in orogenic regions, where it accumulates to great thickness; the Normanskill and Martinsburg deposits are 1,500 to 3,000 meters thick.

Lying on or in the flysch of the Northern Appalachians are *allochthonous masses*, of which the most famous are those of the Taconic Range of eastern New York and western New England, but others occur in Pennsylvania and in western Newfoundland. The allochthonous masses are slices of shaly and sandy rocks of Cambrian and Ordovician ages like those in the eugeosyncline to the east but thinner; in the Taconic Range, successive slices are piled one above the other. The rocks of the Taconic Range have been a source of controversy ever since they were first observed by Ebenezer Emmons of the first New York Survey more than a century ago, but their problems are now mainly resolved.

The allochthonous masses of the Taconic Range embrace about the same age span as the miogeosynclinal sequence on which they rest, but are of very different facies (Fig. 36). Clearly, they have been moved from their original area of accumulation, which appears to have been east of the site of the present Green Mountains uplift, at the foot of the shelf break at the edge of the miogeosynclinal carbonate sequence. Individual slices are rather thin, and it is unlikely that they could have been propelled into their present positions by ordinary thrusting from behind. Instead, they moved as great gravity slides onto the sea floor where the Normanskill flysch was accumulating. (The highest slices are more consolidated and coherent, and are thought to have been emplaced last of all by more normal processes of thrusting.)

Similar slide masses of the same facies of Cambrian and Ordovician rocks rest on the flysch at the top of the miogeosynclinal sequence along the west coast of Newfoundland. Here, the highest slices are great tabular masses of *ophiolite or oceanic crust*. The layering exhibits an upward sequence from mantle material (lherzolites and harzburgites), through gabbro cumulates and sheeted dike complexes, to pillow lavas at the top. These displaced outliers furnish conclusive proof of the existence of oceanic crust beneath the eugeosynclinal rocks not far to the east of the Newfoundland miogeosyncline.

Between Newfoundland and New York state, lower Paleozoic rocks like those of the Taconic sequence form all the south shore of the St. Lawrence Estuary in Quebec and adjoin the Precambrian rocks of the Canadian Shield on the opposite shore, with no miogeosynclinal carbonates between. The former existence of such carbonate deposits is attested, nevertheless, by their presence in breccias and block beds in the Taconic-like rocks. Where the structure of these rocks has been worked out in detail near Quebec City, they consist of many thrust sheets or slide masses like those in the Taconic area, which leads to the suspicion that all the rocks on the southeastern shore of the St. Lawrence are part of a gigantic replica of the Taconic allochthon, which has not been breached by erosion.

Accumulation of the flysch and emplacement of the allochthonous masses upon it is an early phase of the *Taconian orogeny*, which deformed much of the northwestern part of the Northern Appalachians during Ordovician time. The terminal effects of this orogeny are evident along the northwestern border of the Normanskill and Martinsburg belts, where the flysch is strongly deformed and is overlain with structural unconformity by Silurian and younger Paleozoic rocks; this unconformity fades out southwestward across Pennsylvania.

CLASTIC WEDGES. The clastic deposits of the Central and Southern Appalachians, mainly younger than those just discussed, are illustrated in the columnar sections of Figure 35. North of central New York these younger deposits are not preserved, and the terrane consists of older rocks; how far they originally extended in this direction is unknown. The clastic deposits in the Tennessee segment begin in the Middle Ordovician, as in the Northern Appalachians, but here and elsewhere they are succeeded by younger Paleozoic clastic deposits, chiefly marine below, but passing upward into continental beds that begin in places in the Devonian or Mississippian, in others in the Pennsylvanian. Those of the middle Paleozoic include persistent units of sandstone that are the chief ridge-makers of the Valley and Ridge province.

These southern clastic deposits, the Ordovician included, have few or none of the flysch-like qualities of

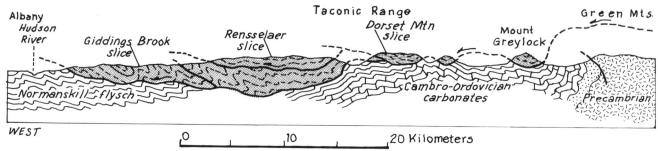

FIG. 36. Sketch section of Taconic allochthonous slices in the latitude of Albany, New York, and Mount Greylock, Massachusetts. Based on Geologic Map of New York State (1970) and Zen (1967).

those of the Northern Appalachians. Instead, they are broad sheets of detritus that spread over the miogeosyncline and far northwestward across the foreland, thinning and tapering in this direction. Such deposits are here termed *clastic wedges*.

First, let us consider these clastic deposits along the strike of the miogeosyncline. In Alabama (Fig. 35), the Middle and Upper Ordovician, the Silurian, and the Devonian are all inconsequential; the thick clastic deposits are in the Mississippian and Pennsylvanian. In Tennessee, the Pennsylvanian is thinner, the Silurian and Devonian are inconsequential, and the thick clastic deposits are in the Middle and Upper Ordovician. But in Pennsylvania, the greatest development of clastics is in the Silurian and Devonian; the Pennsylvanian continental beds that cover the Allegheny Plateau to the west are thin by comparison.

Consider now the form of the clastic deposits across the strike. In most of them, the form in this direction is obscured by deformation and erosion so that only downfolded or downfaulted strips are preserved, extending along the strike rather than across it. Reconstruction of deposits across the strike must be made by correlation between stratigraphic sections that are now separated.

Relations are better shown in the Devonian clastic wedge where it emerges at the northeastern end of the Allegheny synclinorium; we can infer that the principles proven for it apply to the others. The Devonian crops out along a north-facing escarpment that extends eastward across New York state for some 500 kilometers,

from Lake Erie to the Catskill Mountains overlooking the Hudson River. Throughout this distance the Devonian rocks have been little folded or faulted, and beds can be walked out from one end of the wedge to the other, with the results shown in Figure 37.

As shown by the figure, the whole Devonian is only 800 meters thick near the western edge of the state, but is more than 3,000 meters thick in the Catskill Mountains, where its top has been eroded. Observe that much of this thickening is in the Upper Devonian, some in the Middle Devonian, and very little in the Lower Devonian. Note also that red beds and continental deposits of the thick end of the wedge pass westward through marine sandstones into marine shales. Moreover, these rock facies are not bounded by vertical partitions; continental beds, for example, spread farther west as one ascends the section. When work was first done in the area, these westward-spreading facies were thought to be time-stratigraphic units; the thick continental beds in the Catskill Mountains were then thought to be the youngest Devonian deposits of the region, but we now know that they are of early Late Devonian and Middle Devonian ages.

If we combine our cross-section of the Devonian clastic wedge (Fig. 37) with our earlier data (Fig. 35), we can appreciate its dimensions more fully. The wedge is then found to thin, not only westward toward Lake Erie, but southwestward toward Virginia and Tennessee. Its northeastern part, which once must have extended into northern New York state, has now been lost by erosion.

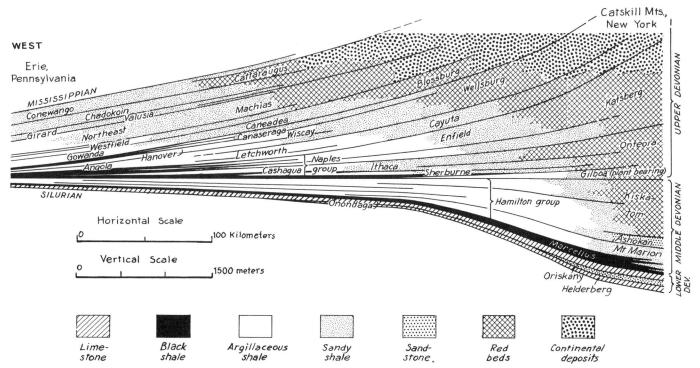

Fig. 37. Stratigraphic diagram from west to east in New York State showing the clastic wedge structure of the Devonian rocks and details of their lithology and thickness. After Moore (1940), based on the work of G. H. Chadwick and G. A. Cooper.

These and other wedges have been likened to fans or deltas, although rather inappropriately, as they are a different sort of sedimentary deposit. Even more fancifully, the whole mass of clastic wedge deposits in the Appalachians can be thought of as a set of gigantic fish scales rooted on the southeast, each wedge thinning not only northwestward across the strike, but northeastward and southwestward along it. Each wedge (or "fish scale") lies at a different level, and each younger one overlaps the older one adjoining it (Fig. 38).

SOURCE OF THE FLYSCH AND CLASTIC WEDGES. We have shown that in the first part of Paleozoic time the carbonate bank of the miogeosyncline ended southeastward in a shelf break, beyond which was deep water; we have shown further that from Middle Ordovician time onward there was a fundamental change in geography, and that erosion of highlands to the southeast gave rise to floods of detritus that were laid down as flysch and clastic wedges in the miogeosyncline. What were these highlands that thus rather abruptly came into being?

A widely held view during the earlier part of the century was that the clastic detritus was derived from the *borderland of Appalachia*, a mysterious kingdom of Precambrian crystalline rocks that included large parts of the crystalline Appalachians and extended thence well out into the present Atlantic Ocean. Unlike the tectonically quiet Precambrian area of the Canadian Shield, this and other borderlands surrounding the continent were supposed to have been highly mobile, rising steadily or spasmodically as geanticlines, while the complementary geosynclines (the miogeosynclines of our terminology) subsided on their inner sides.

In its time the borderland theory was a blurred and somewhat naive means of expressing the known mobility of the continental borders, but with increasing knowledge it has had to give way to more complex and sophisticated explanations. We now believe that some of the features ascribed to the borderlands existed, but that many others did not.

We now know that the crystalline Appalachians are Precambrian only in small part and that a much greater part consists of metamorphic and plutonic rocks of Paleozoic age. Originally these rocks formed in a eugeosynclinal area, and their metamorphism and plutonism was a product of the orogenies to which these rocks were subjected. In the Northern Appalachians two principal disturbances can be documented—the *Taconian orogeny* toward the end of the Ordovician, and the *Acadian orogeny* toward the end of the Devonian. These orogenies raised the lands to the southeast, and gave rise to the flysch and clastic wedges we have already discussed. In the Central and Southern Appalachians the orogenic times in the crystalline area are less clearly documented, but it seems clear that the clastic wedges of that segment originated in the same manner.

APPALACHIAN EUGEOSYNCLINE. We are now ready to explore the area "farther back" in the Appalachian geosyncline, or southeast of the miogeosynclinal area and away from the continent. This is the eugeosynclinal area, from which the rocks of the crystalline Appalachians—the New England Upland and the Piedmont Plateau—were formed.

Let us recall that rocks of the crystalline Appalachians are extensively metamorphosed and full of plutonic rocks today, so that their record is difficult to decipher. Original sedimentary or volcanic structures, fossils, and even whole sequences have been more or less obliterated; much reconstruction is necessary to interpret their original character. Such reconstructions become easier northeastward in the Northern Appalachians, where metamorphism decreases, and can be applied by analogy for considerable distances farther southwestward. But many problems still remain in the crystalline rocks of the Central and Southern Appalachians, parts of which are severely metamorphosed, and where very few fossils have been discovered.

The southeastern border of the crystalline belt, and even the whole of it along the eastern shore of Newfoundland, were rifted away during Mesozoic and Cenozoic time, when the North Atlantic Ocean opened, so that the eastward continuation of the Appalachian structures is now found in the trans-Atlantic continents. This rifting and separation, of which the tensional faulting associated with the Upper Triassic Newark Group is an initial manifestation, is abundantly documented by many lines of evidence. If global tectonics during Mesozoic and later times is a regime of shifting crustal plates, it seems most unlikely that this supplanted a tectonic regime of different kind during the Paleozoic. However, for this earlier time accurate documentation disappears, and the subject is open to the wildest conjecture.

New light was shed on the problem, at least as it pertains to the Appalachians, when in 1966 the Canadian geologist J. Tuzo Wilson asked, "Did the Atlantic Ocean close and then reopen?" Much suggestive evidence for such an interpretation has since accumulated, and most of the modern reconstructions of Appalachian history, and especially of its eugeosyncline, are based on elaborations and improvements of the idea.

In brief, Wilson and his successors suppose that the trans-Atlantic continents were joined together in some manner during later Precambrian time, but that in latest Proterozoic or earliest Paleozoic time they were rifted apart somewhere near the present southeastern edge of the Grenvillian basement, producing an oceanic area similar to the present Atlantic, and perhaps even as wide. During the last two-thirds of the Paleozoic the ocean basin gradually closed again, and the impact of the continental masses on each side contributed to, if it did

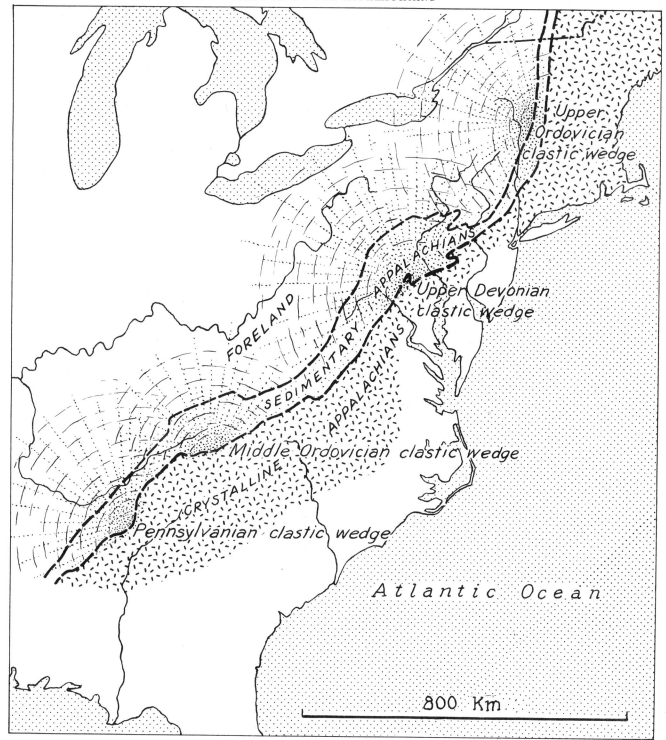

FIG. 38. Sketch map of eastern United States showing extent of the principal clastic wedge deposits of different ages in the sedimentary Appalachians (miogeosynclinal area) and the foreland of the Appalachian system.

not cause, the orogenies in the Appalachian chain. When the continents again rifted apart during the early Mesozoic, the new line of rupture paralleled but did not coincide with the earlier line of rupture, so that parts of the North American plate remained attached to Europe and Africa, and parts of the latter remained attached to North America.

This casts the eugeosynclinal area of the Appalachians in a very different guise from the classical concepts of several decades ago. Instead of being a geosynclinal trough only slightly broader than its present width, it was actually a highly diverse domain of sub-oceanic or even oceanic width, embracing many different elements, now crushed together and parts subducted and lost. Our discussion of the eugeosyncline will now proceed on that basis.

Much of New England, the northern part of the Canadian Appalachians, and the central part of Newfoundland have a typical eugeosynclinal assemblage of Cambrian to Devonian age—slates, graywackes, cherts and volcanics, with remnants of ophiolites, or the oceanic crust on which the deposits accumulated. The areas are divisible into longitudinal belts, each with significant variations in sequence, structure, and history.

In New England and adjacent Canada, for example, the area is divided into the Connecticut Valley-Gaspé synclinorium on the northwest, next to the Precambrian basement uplift of the Green Mountains, followed southeastward by the Bronson Hill anticlinorium and its extensions to the northeast, and then by the Merrimack synclinorium (Fig. 33A). The Cambrian part of the sequence extends across the Green Mountains from the miogeosynclinal area, into the Connecticut Valley-Gaspé synclinorium, where it and the Ordovician thicken dramatically to 9,000 or as much as 15,000 meters; they are followed by 4,500 to 6,000 meters of Silurian and Devonian. In the Bronson Hill anticlinorium the Ordovician, so far as exposed, is 4,500 meters thick, followed by thin Silurian and about 1,500 meters of Devonian. In the Merrimack synclinorium the Silurian and Devonian are more than 10,000 meters thick and the older Paleozoic rocks are only scantily exposed.

Even these thickness figures give some hint of the varied nature and history of the eugeosynclinal area. The Cambrian and Ordovician in the Connecticut Valley-Gaspé synclinorium are a mass of schists and graywackes probably laid down in an oceanic trough, whereas the Ordovician of the Bronson Hill anticlinorium is mainly volcanic and probably formed on an island arc. The Cambrian and Ordovician of these belts, and as far northwest as the St. Lawrence River, were deformed during the Ordovician Taconian orogeny, and at least the northwestern part was not deformed again. The Silurian that follows unconformably is a thin shelf deposit of quartzite and carbonate, marking a pause in the eugeosynclinal regime, but the thick Devonian above is again eugeosynclinal. Southeastward into the Merrimack synclinorium, the Silurian itself thickens and becomes eugeosynclinal. In the southeastern belts, the Taconian deformation fades out or becomes sporadic. In Aroostook County, northeastern Maine, is a conformable sequence of calcareous flysch that includes both Ordovician and Silurian, deposited on a deep ocean floor far from any area of orogenic activity. All the eugeosynclinal rocks southeast of the Taconian belt were deformed by the Acadian orogeny during Middle Devonian time, during and after which they were invaded on a grand scale by granitic plutons, mainly of the New Hampshire Plutonic Series. In eastern Maine, the deformed rocks are overlain by patches of postorogenic red continental deposits of late Middle Devonian and Late Devonian age.

This, in brief, is a very generalized and imperfect account of the rocks and history of the New England part of the eugeosyncline; it would weary the reader to add further details. Similar, or even more complex relations occur in the eugeosynclinal area in Newfoundland. Here again, the Silurian seems to mark a pause in eugeosynclinal development; it includes in places coarse conglomerate and even continental redbeds. All these facts have their implications in a plate tectonics history—of rifting apart of plates and of plate collision. Probably the eugeosyncline was originally very much wider and has been strongly telescoped. Various histories have been proposed for local areas, but the story of the whole remains elusive and will not be attempted here.

The eugeosynclinal belt has a variable width and, in places, is nearly closed off by convergence of the next belts to the southeast, presently to be described (Fig. 39). On the north coast of Newfoundland, it is 200 kilometers broad, but it is nearly cut out on the south coast. It reappears on the mainland, where it reaches a width of 250 kilometers, but on the south shore of New England it is no more than 100 kilometers across, as a result of steepening and attenuation of the component structures. The lower part of the eugeosynclinal sequence persists in the Central Appalachians of Maryland, but it appears to be closed out near the south edge of Virginia, to reappear no more in the Piedmont of the Southern Appalachians. What happens to these fine sequences of Paleozoic eugeosynclinal deposits, so well displayed in parts of the Appalachians? Probably they once extended much farther, but have been subducted and lost during convergence of plates on each side.

SOUTHEASTERN BELTS OF THE APPALACHIANS. Southeast of the eugeosynclinal area in Newfoundland is a narrow belt of basement gneisses overlain by argillaceous sediments that were metamorphosed before Middle Ordovician time (Fig. 40). Because of their polymetamorphic history, no reliable radiometric dates have been obtained from the basement gneisses. Could they be a fragment of the Grenvillian basement that was rifted away from the main area to the northwest? These rocks are faulted against the Avalonian belt, next to the southeast, where the record is plainer.

The *Avalonian belt*, typically displayed in the Avalon Peninsula in the southeast corner of Newfoundland, is a terrane of late Precambrian (Upper Proterozoic) rocks, overlain by a small thickness of the earliest Paleozoic. Its rocks are only broadly deformed and lightly metamorphosed, in contrast to those of central Newfoundland. The lowest exposed rocks are volcanics, intruded by the Holyrood Granite with a date of about 600 million years. The volcanics intergrade with and pass up into tuffaceous marine slates, followed by terrestrial arkoses, conglom-

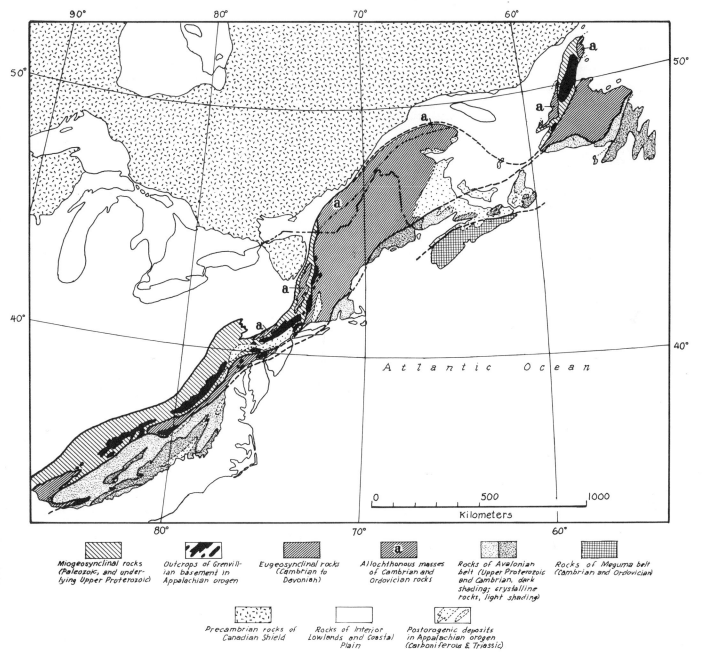

FIG. 39. Map of the Appalachians, showing varying width of different belts in eugeosynclinal area, probably resulting from plate convergence.

Legend:

Miogeosynclinal rocks (Paleozoic, and underlying Upper Proterozoic)

Outcrops of Grenvillian basement in Appalachian orogen

Eugeosynclinal rocks (Cambrian to Devonian)

Allochthonous masses of Cambrian and Ordovician rocks

Rocks of Avalonian belt (Upper Proterozoic and Cambrian, dark shading; crystalline rocks, light shading)

Rocks of Meguma belt (Cambrian and Ordovician)

Precambrian rocks of Canadian Shield

Rocks of Interior Lowlands and Coastal Plain

Postorogenic deposits in Appalachian orogen (Carboniferous & Triassic)

erates, and redbeds, the whole attaining a thickness of at least 12,000 meters. They are topped by a thin quartzite layer, which is followed by fossiliferous Cambrian and Ordovician, with Lower Cambrian at the base—miogeosynclinal but with very different facies and faunas from the miogeosynclinal deposits on the opposite side of the orogen. The faunas match those south of the Caledonian belt in western Europe; Paleozoic rocks with North American faunas occur northwest of the belt, at least in the Northwest Highlands of Scotland. J. Tuzo Wilson made the significant observation that Cambrian faunas of the North American realm to the northwest, with *Olenellus*, lie on Grenvillian basement with ages of

1,000 million years or so, whereas Cambrian faunas of the European realm to the southeast, with *Paradoxides*, lie on basement with ages of about 600 million years.

Although the surface exposures of the Avalonian belt are rather small, diving and drilling beneath the sea to the east indicate that it forms the basement of much of the Grand Banks, so that its area must equal or exceed that of the other Appalachian areas so far considered. It has been suggested that the Avalonian belt originated as an island arc, but rather tenuous evidence from components of its sediments suggests that its basement includes some sialic as well as simatic crust.

The Avalonian belt has many affinities with the trans-

65

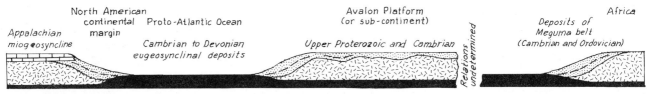

North American
continental   Proto-Atlantic Ocean   Avalon Platform   Africa
Appalachian   margin   (or sub-continent)   Deposits of
miogeosyncline   Cambrian to Devonian   Upper Proterozoic and Cambrian   Meguma belt
                         eugeosynclinal deposits   (Cambrian and Ordovician)

Relations
undetermined

FIG. 40. Restored section of eugeosynclinal part of Appalachians in the latitude of Newfoundland, showing the original positions of the different tectonic elements. Based on Williams (1974).

Atlantic continents, yet still another eugeosynclinal area intervenes. Southeast of the extension of the Avalonian belt onto the mainland in Cape Breton Island and southern New Brunswick, is the *Meguma belt*, preserved only in Nova Scotia—with a 13,000-meter sequence of graywacke and slate containing Ordovician fossils near the top. Sedimentological studies indicate that these deposits were derived from a land mass to the southeast, that has now vanished or has now been rifted away across the Atlantic. The Avalonian belt thus seems to be some sort of independent fragment in the midst of an originally very wide Appalachian orogen.

Another fragment of late Precambrian rocks occurs east of the New England eugeosynclinal area in Rhode Island and southeastern Massachusetts (Fig. 33A). Here, wide areas are formed of the Dedham Granodiorite with an age of about 570 million years, which is overlain unconformably by fossiliferous Lower Cambrian, again with *Paradoxides* and related fossils. The rocks of the region are cut by fresh-looking alkalic granites (the Quincy, Cape Ann, and others) with Ordovician ages of about 450 million years. The region is beyond and east of the belt affected by the mid-Paleozoic Acadian orogeny and plutonism.

The Piedmont province of the Southern Appalachians consists of the *Inner Piedmont belt* on the northwest of gneisses and migmatites, with a profusion of embedded Paleozoic granitic plutons on the southeast (*Charlotte belt*); and southeast of it the *Carolina Slate Belt* (Fig. 33B). The Slate Belt rocks are a sequence of gently deformed, low-grade metamorphic clastic rocks and volcanics as much as 10,000 meters thick. A few Cambrian *Paradoxides* have been found above the middle of the sequence, but radiometric ages in excess of 600 million years have been obtained elsewhere, so that the sequence probably extends from the Cambrian down into the Upper Proterozoic. The Slate Belt rocks are invaded by widely spaced granitic plutons with ages of 520 to 595 million years, which are probably congenerically related to the volcanic activity. The gneisses and migmatites to the northwest, and in anticlinoria within the Slate Belt, may include altered equivalents of the Slate Belt rocks, but are probably mainly older. The Piedmont rocks are thus quite different from the Paleozoic eugeosynclinal sequence of the Northern Appalachians, but closely resemble the Avalonian rocks of Newfoundland, and the basement rocks which border them on the northwest.

In North and South Carolina, these Piedmont rocks are juxtaposed against the Blue Ridge rocks to the northwest along the *Brevard zone*. The contrast between the two terranes is illustrated by the Henderson Gneiss, which lies along its southeastern side for 130 kilometers. The Henderson is a floored body that is a migmatized arkosic sediment or volcanic rock, or else an igneous granite, which has yielded a Middle Cambrian radiometric age of 535 million years—or of the same age as the Cambrian carbonates not far to the northwest in the Blue Ridge. The Brevard in this segment must be a suture between two crustal plates that were originally far apart, between which much material that originally existed has been lost by subduction or otherwise. Paleozoic eugeosynclinal rocks like those of the Northern Appalachians might once have been present in the missing interval and have been lost in this manner. Also, the Grenvillian and overlying rocks of this part of the Blue Ridge province are allochthonous clear back to the Brevard zone, yet no roots for these allochthonous masses now exist. Late in Paleozoic time, after closing of the suture, the Brevard zone underwent further strike-slip displacement.

GRANITIC ROCKS OF THE CRYSTALLINE APPALACHIANS. The granitic plutonic rocks of the crystalline Appalachians have already been mentioned several times. Some of them are closely related to the growth of the eugeosyncline and its orogenies; others are not. Ordovician granitic rocks are extensive in the eugeosynclinal area in Newfoundland and occur more sparingly on the mainland. In New Hampshire small bodies of the Highlandcroft Plutonic Series invade the Ordovician of the Bronson Hill anticlinorium, but are truncated by the overlying Silurian (Fig. 30). The larger bodies of Ordovician alkalic granite in southeastern Massachusetts (Fig. 33A) are east of the eugeosynclinal belt. In the Northern Appalachians the most extensive granitic rocks are Devonian, with ages of 350 to 380 million years, and are related to the Acadian orogeny. Finally, along the south coast of Rhode Island, the Pennsylvanian is invaded by late Paleozoic granites with ages of about 250 million years.

In the Piedmont province of the Southern Appalachians, the older granitic rocks precede the regional metamorphism that occurred 380 to 420 million years ago. The oldest of these, congenerically related to the volcanism in the Slate Belt, have already been noted.

66

Somewhat more extensive are granitic plutons with middle Paleozoic ages of 385 to 415 million years, or approximately equivalent to the Acadian granites of farther north. In contrast to the Northern Appalachians, upper Paleozoic granites occur in many parts of the Piedmont province, especially toward the southeast, and have ages of about 300 million years; the youngest is Permian and has been dated at 270 million years.

In central New England there is a surprising array of Mesozoic granitic rocks—the *White Mountain Plutonic Series*, with ages of 110 to 185 million years, or from early Jurassic to early Cretaceous. The series forms cross-cutting bodies of fresh alkalic granite that are largely responsible for the topographic eminences of the White Mountains, and consists mainly of ring dikes, which coalesce in places into sizable batholiths (Fig. 30). Within some of the rings are sunken blocks of the supracrustal *Moat Volcanics*, which are surface manifestations of the plutonism. Related to the White Mountain granites are the shallower, smaller *Monteregian intrusives*, with Cretaceous ages of 84 to 123 million years, which extend in a chain northwestward from the eugeosynclinal area at the Canadian border, across the Appalachian orogen to its foreland at Montreal.

OROGENY IN EUGEOSYNCLINAL AREA. Our review of the eugeosynclinal area (or crystalline Appalachians) indicates that it was a region of much crustal mobility throughout its history, and that mobility reached an orogenic climax in mid-Paleozoic time, by which time its rocks had been thoroughly deformed, metamorphosed, and plutonized. In terms of modern concepts, this was largely the result of rifting apart of crustal plates, and of subsequent plate collision. The initial rift, somewhat before the beginning of Paleozoic time, defined the edge of the North American continental plate at the southeastern limit of Grenvillian metamorphic basement and opened up a broad oceanic domain to the southeast in the eugeosynclinal area. Subsequent closing of the domain by convergence of opposing continental plates is recorded by the succession of Appalachian orogenies, beginning with the Taconian orogeny in the north, continuing with the Acadian orogeny, and with still later orogenic events farther south. These movements can be matched broadly by the emplacement of successive granitic plutons, which suggest a like deformational history throughout the length of the chain.

Variations in details of orogenic history from one segment to another are probably caused by the variable impingement of the opposing plates. The eugeosynclinal domain was largely closed in Newfoundland by the end of the Ordovician, whereas it continued much longer in New England and Maritime Canada, where there are impressive Silurian and Devonian eugeosynclinal deposits; final closure here was in the middle of the Devonian. The record is more obscure in the Southern Ap-

palachians, where most of the Paleozoic systems are missing, but the existence here of early, middle, and late Paleozoic granites suggests the same movements, and movements that continued later.

The clastic wedges of the miogeosyncline and foreland in both the Northern and Southern Appalachians suggest a like source—deformed lands that were raised in the eugeosynclinal area as a result of plate impingement. This caused a reversal of the topographic relations of early Paleozoic time—from a shallow-water shelf in the miogeosynclinal area breaking off into a deep oceanic area in the eugeosyncline, into a highland area in the latter, which could shed detritus over the former shelf. The clastic wedges of different ages from one part of the chain to another illustrate the variations in plate collision from place to place.

After mid-Paleozoic time, mobility gradually diminished in the former eugeosynclinal area. Postorogenic deposits of later Paleozoic time in the Maritime Provinces are little deformed in places and somewhat affected by deformation in others. The much younger Late Triassic deposits are products of a new regime of plate motion—the initiation of rifting that produced the present Atlantic—with the formation of tensional grabens in which the Triassic continental sediments could accumulate.

Under the scheme just outlined, the Mesozoic plutonic rocks of New England and southeastern Canada (the White Mountain and Monteregian Series) are quite anomalous. They are through-breaking postorogenic intrusives that have no relation to the Appalachian orogenic history. It has been suggested that they formed when the North American plate had moved their site over a "hot spot" in the underlying mantle.

OROGENY IN MIOGEOSYNCLINAL AREA AND FORELAND. What, then, of the deformation of the sedimentary Appalachians with their miogeosynclinal rocks, and of the foreland beyond them? Date of their deformation cannot be proved; it merely can be inferred from ages of the youngest rocks involved.

Rocks of the sedimentary Appalachians and foreland form a nearly unbroken sequence in the Central and Southern Appalachians extending from Cambrian to Pennsylvanian, and to as high as lower Permian in a few places. The sequence contains occasional disconformities indicative of failures of deposition or moderate erosion, but there are no angular unconformities indicative of times of deformation. Even the clastic wedges that are products of deformation elsewhere are conformable with the deposits on which they lie.

Mississippian rocks are preserved in many remnants in the strongly deformed sedimentary Appalachians, some as far southeast as the front of the Blue Ridge. Pennsylvanian rocks are also preserved in places in the strongly deformed belt as near Birmingham, Alabama, and in the Broadtop and Anthracite coal basins of Pennsylvania. Early Permian rocks are more restricted and lie mostly well out in the foreland.

Deformation was thus certainly later than Mississippian, Pennsylvanian, or early Permian time, depending on locality. Much or all of it may, in fact, have been younger than early Permian. But many parts of the sedimentary Appalachians show a succession of superposed structures; for example, thrust sheets have been emplaced, then folded, then offset by transverse faults. Such superposed structures did not develop during any single deformational event but during a considerable span of time—perhaps as long as a geological period or two. Very possibly, structures in the southeastern part of the sedimentary Appalachians began to form earlier than those in the northwestern part.

Be that as it may, this deformation of rocks in the sedimentary Appalachians is the so-called *Appalachian Revolution*. But was it so revolutionary? As we have seen, the whole Appalachian region was not transformed from geosyncline to mountain belt in a single cataclysm. Most of its interior on the southeast had been thoroughly deformed and consolidated by middle Paleozoic time (Fig. 41B). Marginal deformation of the sedimentary Appalachians and foreland was merely a later, and in part a concluding phase (Fig. 41C).

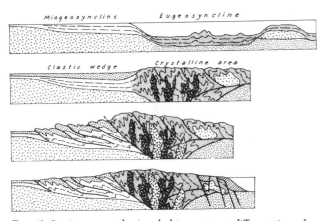

FIG. 41. Sections across the Appalachian system at different times during the Paleozoic and early Mesozoic, showing its inferred orogenic development. (A) Early Paleozoic: geosynclinal phase and plate separation. (B) Middle Paleozoic: early orogenic phase and plate convergence. (C) Late Paleozoic: late orogenic phase and deformation of the miogeosyncline. (D) Early Mesozoic: postorogenic phase, and renewed rifting.

To avoid false implications, it would be best not to refer to these structures as having been formed in *the* Appalachian Revolution; the word "Appalachian" would apply better to the whole prolonged series of movements. It would be more expressive if we spoke of the deformation of the miogeosyncline and foreland as having taken place during an *Allegheny orogeny*, with the implication that this was of the same or less magnitude as the earlier Acadian and Taconian orogenies.

CONCLUSION. We have now carried our story of this great mountain system far enough for our present purposes. What followed was pale aftermath—prolonged erosion of the system with burial or submergence of some of the parts, as set forth in section 1 of this chapter. The lesson of the whole complex story is that the growth of the system occupied much of Paleozoic time.

Possibly it might be felt that I have labored the story too greatly, but I have done so in order to present the modern philosophy of mountain growth, using as an example a mountain system where the features are unusually well laid out. We will encounter similar features and problems again when we take up the Cordilleran system in the west (Chapter VI, et seq.)—the miogeosyncline, the eugeosyncline, the zone of metamorphic and plutonic rocks, and the rest—but these will be overlaid by many more complications, as we shall see.

6. PALEOZOIC STRUCTURES WEST OF THE MISSISSIPPI RIVER

We now leave the Appalachians and all the country east of the Mississippi River. But recall that the Appalachian system is only part of an originally more extensive system of mountain structures that once extended much farther west (Plate I). These emerge again from the cover of younger rocks in small areas beyond the Mississippi River, in Arkansas, Oklahoma, and Texas. Branches of the system also extended even farther into the Cordilleran region, where they greatly influenced the structures formed there later (Chapter VII, section 5).

In Alabama the whole Appalachian deformed belt passes southwestward beneath deposits of the Gulf Coastal Plain. At the place where the belt goes underground, it shows no change in its usual trend or structure nor any diminution in intensity. Clearly, it must continue farther, but where? We will return to this question later; in the meantime let us jump ahead a little.

MARATHON REGION OF TEXAS. I entered my study of Paleozoic structures on the southeast and south sides of the continent through the back door, so to speak. I first encountered these structures in one of their westernmost areas of exposure, the Marathon Region of western Texas. Instead of launching directly into generalizations of the Paleozoic structures west of the Mississippi, it might therefore be more interesting to approach the subject indirectly, as did geologists of my own generation, and see how the puzzles were solved step by step and what problems still remain.

If the reader has traveled by rail on the line of the Southern Pacific from El Paso to New Orleans, or if he has driven over U.S. Highway 90, he has passed through the town of Marathon (Fig. 22). He might recall it as a little ranch settlement, several hundred kilometers southeast of El Paso, set down in a wide plain that is rimmed on the west by the first range of the western mountains and elsewhere by limestone mesas and escarpments.

This plain is the *Marathon Basin*, a topographic feature 55 kilometers across, produced by erosion of the crest of the *Marathon dome*. This dome was formed by arching of the Cretaceous limestones that cover much of the semi-arid, southwest Texas country. Many of the mesas and scarps that surround the basin are carved from these Cretaceous limestones; the basin itself is cut on the Paleozoic rocks which underlie them (Fig. 42).

From the floor of the Marathon Basin project low northeast-trending ridges formed of the more resistant layers in the deformed Paleozoic rocks; they resemble on a somewhat smaller scale those of the Valley and Ridge province in the Appalachians. The folding and faulting that turned up the Paleozoic rocks in the basin are of pre-Cretaceous age, as shown along its edges where a great angular unconformity can be observed between the Paleozoic and the Cretaceous (Fig. 43).

There is, however, an additional structural element in the Marathon dome. The northern side is bordered by the Glass Mountains, which are made up of tilted marine Permian rocks (Fig. 42). Like the earlier Paleozoic rocks, the Permian is truncated by the Cretaceous; but like the Cretaceous it lies unconformably on the earlier Paleozoic. The Permian rocks are part of the southern margin of the West Texas basin (Chapter III, section 6); they are foreland deposits, but they differ from the Appalachian foreland deposits in that they lie unconformably on earlier rocks of the adjacent deformed belt.

The Marathon Region thus consists of three parts: (1) Deformed earlier Paleozoic rocks, which emerge on the crest of the dome; (2) Permian rocks of the Glass Mountains on the north flank, which lie unconformably on the earlier Paleozoic rocks and are tilted northward toward the West Texas basin; (3) Cretaceous rocks, which lie unconformably on the truncated edges of both the Permian and earlier Paleozoic strata, but which were later raised into a broad dome.

Let us now say more about the deformed pre-Permian Paleozoic rocks. Their structure is much like that in the sedimentary Appalachians—a series of northeast-trending folds broken by thrust faults that dip southeast, with some low-angle thrusts that have carried the rocks above them many kilometers northwestward (Fig. 42, section AA'). The date of their deformation is well-defined, unlike the inferred dating of the deformation in the sedimentary Appalachians. Its beginnings can be traced in conglomerates in the Pennsylvanian sequence, and its climax was toward the end of that period, as Pennsylvanian rocks are deformed and Permian rocks lie unconformably on them.

The pre-Permian rocks themselves cover about the same age span as those in the Appalachians, from Cambrian to Pennsylvanian; one difference is that the oldest beds that come to the surface are Upper Cambrian, and it is unknown how much of the earlier Cambrian lies beneath. As in the Appalachians the lower beds are fine-grained deposits and the upper ones are clastic, but there are significant differences between these and those of the Appalachians, which we will find are characteristic of the whole Ouachita chain.

The lower strata above the Cambrian are a rather thin sequence of Ordovician graptolite-bearing shales, thin-bedded limestones, and bedded cherts, topped by a unit of massive white chert or novaculite of Devonian and early Mississippian age. There is no Silurian, but there is no evidence of emergence or erosion in the Ordovician-Devonian interval; more likely, there was simply a long failure of deposition on the sea floor. These strata thus contrast with the thick, lower Paleozoic carbonate sequence in the Appalachian miogeosyncline. In the Marathon area, the thick lower Paleozoic carbonate bank lay north of the orogenic belt beneath the West Texas basin; its southern edge has been penetrated by deep wells in the northern part of the Marathon Basin that have drilled through the thrust sheets of Ouachita rocks. Very likely the carbonate bank ended southward in a shelf break, as in the Appalachians, and the Marathon lower Paleozoic rocks were laid down in deeper water below it, somewhat after the fashion of the Taconic sequence in the Northern Appalachians. Confirmation of this inference is found in the occurrence in all the Ordovician formations of conglomerates and boulder beds formed of clasts of the carbonate facies, which have slid off the bank or its shelf break into the deeper water of the trough.

The upper part of the sequence, from Mississippian into the middle Pennsylvanian, is a much thicker mass of flysch, which appears with dramatic abruptness on top of the novaculite. As with the Ordovician flysch of the northern Appalachians it is a sequence of thinly interbedded sandstones and shales, the sandstones with graded bedding and other indications that they were brought in by turbid flows. A significant variant in the upper part is wildflysch or boulder beds, composed of clasts of many kinds of rocks of all sizes up to gigantic blocks 45 meters across, the latter formed of lower Pennsylvanian shelf limestone which, like the boulders in the Ordovician lower down, have slumped or slid off the shelf break that bounded the depositional basin on the north.

The flysch cycle ended in the middle Pennsylvanian, and the upper Pennsylvanian (Desmoinesian and younger) that succeeds it is a thin shallow-water sequence of conglomerates, shales, and limestones. The conglomerates are composed of older formations of the

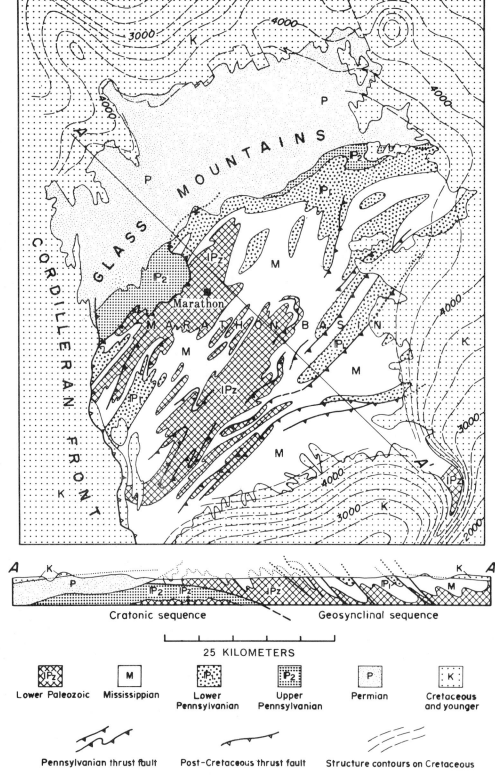

FIG. 42. Geologic map and section of Marathon Region, West Texas, showing the three structural units: the domed Cretaceous, the tilted Permian on the north flank, and the strongly deformed earlier Paleozoic rocks of the Marathon Basin. Generalized from King (1937).

FIG. 43. Angular unconformity between tilted Mississippian sandstones and flat-lying Cretaceous limestones on east rim of Marathon Basin, West Texas. Redrawn from King (1937).

sequence and indicate that the major deformation of the Marathon rocks was in process of completion.

However, this was not the final deformational episode. The whole deformed mass—Pennsylvanian and older—has been driven northwestward on a nearly flat thrust plane for at least 15 kilometers over upper Pennsylvanian, which drilling indicates lies on lower Paleozoic foreland carbonates. This upper Pennsylvanian is of flysch facies like the older Pennsylvanian and Mississippian of the Marathon sequence, and was formed in a new deep trough along the front of the orogenic belt. Drilling north of the Marathon Region indicates that the deposits occur in a longitudinal trough,

the *Val Verde basin*, in which upper Pennsylvanian and lower Permian flysch attains a thickness of 4,500 meters or more.

The backlands of the Marathon structure are little known, because they are largely concealed beneath the Cretaceous cover. About 50 kilometers south of the last Paleozoic exposure in the Marathon Basin, on the opposite side of the Rio Grande in Mexico, is a small exposure of low-grade metamorphic rocks that have yielded late Paleozoic radiometric dates of 260 to 275 million years—probably expressing the time of their metamorphism.

REGIONAL RELATIONS OF OUACHITA SYSTEM. If we take a broader view, the contrast between pre-Permian Paleozoic facies of the Marathon Region and of the foreland areas to the north and northwest turns out to be general through Texas and Oklahoma (Fig. 44).

The carbonate facies is exposed in the Llano uplift of central Texas and the Ozark uplift of Missouri and adjacent states, where the rocks are little deformed. It also appears in the Wichita and Arbuckle Mountains of southwestern Oklahoma, where the rocks are thrown into the folds of the Wichita system that we will discuss below.

But pre-Permian rocks with a facies and structure nearly identical to those of the Marathon Region reap-

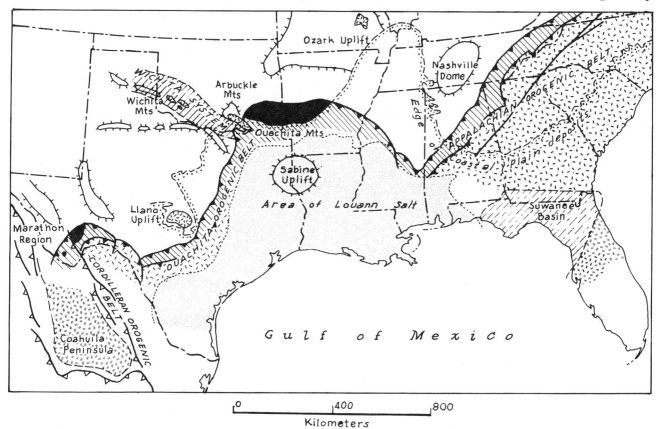

FIG. 44. Map of south-central United States, showing regional relations of Ouachita orogenic belt in surface exposures and in subsurface. Exposures of the Ouachita belt in the Ouachita Mountains and Marathon Region are in black.

71

pear 800 kilometers to the northeast in the Ouachita Mountains of southeastern Oklahoma and southwestern Arkansas (Fig. 45). Here again are folds and faults like those in the sedimentary Appalachians (Fig. 46); here again is a thin sequence of graptolite shales and cherts, topped by novaculite, followed by Mississippian and lower Pennsylvanian flysch—here with an imposing thickness of more than 12,000 meters, and again with wildflysch somewhat above the middle.

We thus have some pieces of a jigsaw puzzle, but with many parts missing due to the wide separation of the pre-Permian outcrops. Great intervening areas are covered by younger deposits, partly Mesozoic, partly later Paleozoic (upper Pennsylvanian and Permian), which conceal much of the earlier structures (Plate I). Little progress on the puzzle could ever have been made without the aid of drilling, which has probed below the younger cover and determined the pattern of the earlier rocks and structures. From drilling we have learned much, although problems yet remain to be solved. Drilling has at least disposed of some of the earlier "wrong guesses," such as Udden's proposed northeastward-trending "Marathon fold" (Chapter III, section 6).

Briefly stated, these data indicate that the deformed rocks exposed in the Marathon and Ouachita areas are parts of a single orogenic belt that may be termed the *Ouachita system*. As noted earlier, the two exposed parts

probably lie on apices of sharply curved salients in the belt; a recess lies in a buried segment between, where it curves around the foreland buttress of the Llano uplift (Plate I). This orogenic belt developed from a geosyncline whose growth was about as prolonged as that of the Appalachian geosyncline, but here, curiously, the carbonate bank remained outside the orogenic belt, and its geosyncline received deep-water, "off-the-shelf" deposits, almost of eugeosynclinal character. The geosyncline was transformed into an orogenic belt by a series of deformations that culminated in the latter part of Pennsylvanian time.

Drilling in the buried segment of the belt southwest of the Ouachita Mountains, in north-central Texas, discloses the existence of an internal belt of low- to medium-grade metamorphic rocks like those exposed in Mexico south of the Marathon Region. But south of the Ouachita Mountains themselves neither the Ouachita rocks nor this internal belt have been penetrated, as there is a thick fill of postorogenic deposits. The area is part of the great embayment of Louann Salt of early Jurassic age, which forms the base of the Mesozoic sequence of the Gulf Coastal Plain, and which lies so deeply and is so thick that it has not been penetrated by drilling, except at its edges. Along its northern edge, near the Ouachita Mountains, drill holes pass beneath it into red Triassic continental deposits (Eagle Mills For-

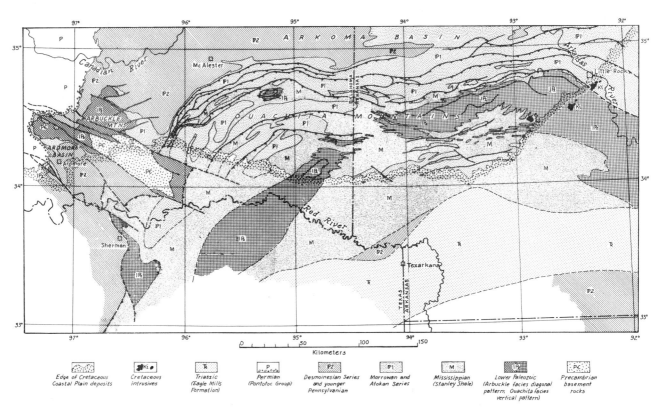

FIG. 45. Geologic map of Ouachita Mountains and Arbuckle Mountains, Arkansas and Oklahoma, and of subcrop features immediately south of them. Compiled from Geologic Map of Oklahoma (1954), Geologic Map of Arkansas (1975), Flawn (in Flawn et al., 1961), Harlton (1966), and Vernon (1971).

mation) which lie in fault troughs like those of the Newark Group of the Appalachian area (Fig. 45). Below and adjacent to the Triassic are little deformed upper Pennsylvanian (Desmoinesian) shelf carbonates and shales, which overlap northward on the deformed Ouachita rocks. In this interior part of the Ouachita system, orogenic deformation had been completed by middle Pennsylvanian time. This same time of deformation is indicated more obscurely by minor conglomerates and unconformities in the middle Pennsylvanian in the exposed foreland north and northwest of the Ouachita Mountains.

RELATIONS BETWEEN THE OUACHITA AND APPALA-CHIAN SYSTEMS. Having gone this far in our reconstruction, we return again to the greatest puzzle: how do the Appalachian rocks and structures relate to those of the Ouachita system? Complete answers are not yet available, although some progress has been made in the last few decades. Oil has long been known in the western part of the Gulf Coastal Plain in Texas, Louisiana, and Arkansas. Later on, exploration proceeded eastward; now Mississippi has become an oil-producing state and Alabama is being prospected. During this exploration some drill holes have passed through the Coastal Plain deposits into the Paleozoic rocks beneath.

The southwestern extension of the Appalachian rocks beneath the Coastal Plain deposits is well defined. Rocks like those in the Valley and Ridge province—belts of lower Paleozoic carbonates and upper Paleozoic clastics—extend southwestward and cross into the state of Mississippi near Meridian, where they bend to the west-northwest. South of these rocks, some wells penetrate more metamorphosed slate, quartzite, and marble, evidently part of the interior belts of the Appalachians. The extension of the Ouachita rocks is less definite, as there is less well control, but a few wells in Mississippi penetrate slate, seemingly a part of the Ouachita belt that extends southeastward toward Meridian. The exact nature of the junction is uncertain, because of wide spac-

ing of well control in the critical places; either the Appalachian rocks simply change facies westward into the Ouachita rocks, or the latter are thrust over the former. The foreland structures are better documented. The two convergent trends of the orogenic belts enclose between them the triangular *Black Warrior basin*, thickly filled by more than 3,000 meters of Pennsylvanian coal measures and shallow-water deposits like those exposed to the east. There must be a shelf break between these and the deep-water flysch of the same age along the front of the Ouachita Mountains, across the Mississippi Embayment to the west.

PROBLEMS OF THE OUACHITA SYSTEM. The Ouachita belt, like the Appalachian belt, formed along the margin of the original North American continent, and was no doubt involved in the same sort of rifting and plate convergence, but the history of this southern side of the continent is much more obscure. Instead of dealing with interaction between trans-Atlantic plates, we are dealing with a complex of smaller shifting plates between the North and South American continental blocks, which eventually evolved into the present Caribbean seas and islands (Chapter V, section 3).

During its early geosynclinal and orogenic history, the Ouachita belt was a deep-water, "off-the-continent" area, beyond the shelf break at the edge of the great lower Paleozoic carbonate bank, probably largely floored by oceanic crust. Later in Paleozoic time, the geosyncline was filled by a great volume of flysch.

Whence came this flysch, and why? The history of the continental interior to the north records no unusual tectonic events in Mississippian and early Pennsylvanian time that could produce such a volume of clastic sediments; they must be a product of mobility in the orogenic belt itself. Sedimentological studies show that the older, largely Mississippian flysch is a "dirty" sediment with a large proportion of metamorphic rock fragments, that was brought in by currents from the southeast, evidently from tectonic ridges made up of the

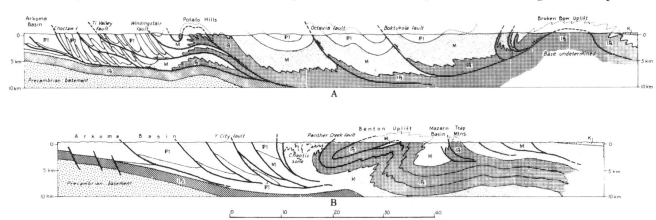

FIG. 46. Sections of Ouachita Mountains: (A) In Oklahoma. (B) In Arkansas. Geologic letter symbols the same as those on Fig. 45. Section A compiled from Berry and Trumbly (1968), Hendricks and others (1947), and Miser (1929). Section B after Viele (1973).

earlier geosynclinal deposits. The younger, largely Pennsylvanian flysch is more quartzose and cleanly washed, and was transported by currents from the east that flowed along the axis of the depositional trough. This source must have been more distant, and at least part of the material may have come from as far away as the Appalachians.

The deep depression south of the Ouachita Mountains, where only postorogenic deposits have been reached, contrasts with the broad massive area of the crystalline Appalachians to the east, and to some extent with what is known of the basement south of the Marathon segment. This internal area seems to have been peculiarly susceptible to collapse after the orogenic phase. Perhaps the original backlands of this segment have been rifted off and pulled away to the south, to Yucatan or some other continental area south of the Gulf of Mexico. The Gulf of Mexico itself is a Mesozoic and Cenozoic feature floored by oceanic crust, which we will consider later (Chapter V, section 2). Its origin is to be sought in the later history of the Ouachita orogenic belt that fringes it on the north; it is, in effect, the "daughter" of the Ouachita orogenic belt.

WICHITA SYSTEM. A final component of the Paleozoic structures west of the Mississippi River remains to be considered—the Wichita system of southwestern Oklahoma. Here, deformed Paleozoic rocks and their crystalline basement of a character quite different from the rocks of the Ouachita Mountains emerge in several small areas—the Arbuckle Mountains and Criner Hills on the east (Fig. 47), and the Wichita Mountains on the west. As with other Paleozoic structures of the region, these are greatly obscured by younger deposits—here redbeds and continental sediments of Permian and later Pennsylvanian age. As elsewhere, much has been learned by drilling through these later deposits.

The Wichita system is a "within-the-continent" rather than an "off-the-continent" structure like the Ouachita system, which we now know had a history as long or longer. The basement of the Arbuckle Mountains on its north side is the Tishomingo Granite with an Elsonian age of 1,320–1,400 million years, but the basement of the Wichita Mountains to the west is granite and gabbro with rather surprising early Cambrian ages of 535–550 million years. They are shallow, floored intrusives; the granite, in fact, is overlain by congeneric effusive rhyolites of about the same age. Drilling indicates that the granite and gabbro overlie a sequence of graywackes at least 5,000 meters thick of Cambrian and Late Proterozoic age that filled an *aulocogen*, or deep transverse rift in the continental block, that extended westward south of the Arbuckle Mountains through the Wichita Mountains, and for an unknown distance eastward.

Both the Tishomingo Granite and the Wichita plutonic rocks are overlain unconformably by the Upper Cambrian Reagan Sandstone, the local representative of the basal Paleozoic deposits that spread widely over the continental platform (Chapter III, section 4). Above it follow other lower Paleozoic deposits like those elsewhere in the Interior Lowlands, but here greatly overthickened; the initial aulocogen had evolved into an intra-cratonic geosyncline. Next above the sandstone is the great mass of Cambrian and Ordovician Arbuckle Limestone, followed by the limestones and sandstones of the Simpson Group (Fig. 47). The sequence is much like that in the Appalachian miogeosyncline, and as thick or thicker.

When orogenic forces affected the region in later Paleozoic time, the original aulocogen and its early Paleozoic geosynclinal successor were peculiarly susceptible to deformation. Beginning in late Mississippian time and continuing through the Pennsylvanian it was broken into a series of west-northwest-trending mountain ridges and intervening troughs. Their history was complex; as the uplifts rose, troughs subsided between them in which great thicknesses of Pennsylvanian deposits accumulated (Fig. 48). These were themselves deformed during progress of the orogeny, so that sequences in the troughs are broken by many unconformities.

One of the largest troughs is the *Anadarko basin*, which flanks the north side of the Wichita Mountains (Fig. 49), where Pennsylvanian and Permian sediments were piled to a thickness of more than 6,000 meters. The basin is asymmetrical with the deepest part close to the Wichita chain on the south and its floor rising gradually northward toward the Interior Region in Kansas. Farther southeast is the similar but narrower and smaller *Ardmore basin* crowded between the uplifts of the Arbuckle Mountains and Criner Hills (Fig. 47).

The foreland basins of the Appalachians, which we have considered previously (Chapter III, section 5), were covered by clastic wedge deposits derived from erosion of the inner parts of the mountain belt, but lying conformably over the earlier deposits. By contrast, sources of the clastic deposits in the basins of the Wichita system are in the uplifts immediately adjacent, and the deposits themselves are broken by successive unconformities; uplifts and deposits are thus parts of the same structural complex.

After the deformations of Mississippian and Pennsylvanian time, the Wichita structures were nearly or wholly buried by Permian deposits. These spread indiscriminately over older rocks of every age, although they thicken somewhat into the earlier basins. Unlike the Pennsylvanian deposits, which are nearly all marine, all the Permian deposits surrounding the Wichita system are continental—conglomeratic near the uplifted earlier sediments, arkosic near granitic basement rocks, and passing into redbeds away from the uplifts.

EXTENSIONS OF WICHITA SYSTEM TO THE EAST. In

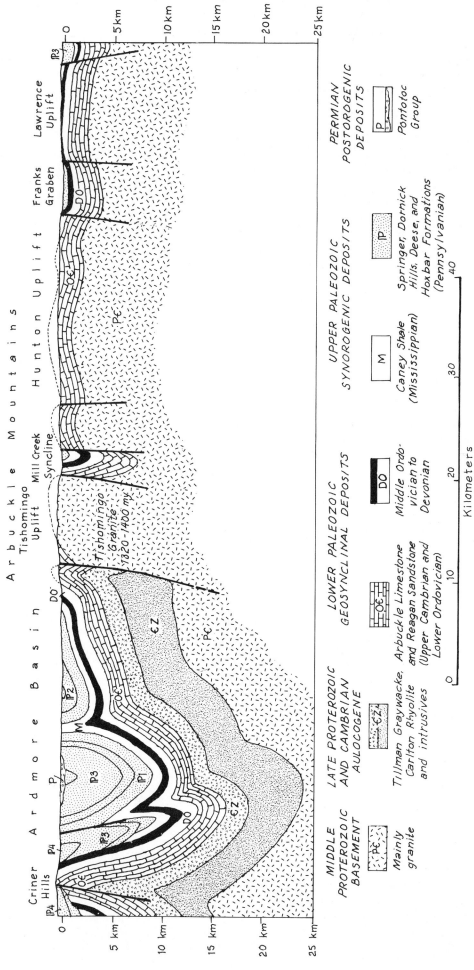

FIG. 47. Section of Arbuckle Mountains, Ardmore Basin, and Criner Hills. In the Ardmore Basin the lowest supracrustal rocks are aulacogen deposits of Late Proterozoic and Early Cambrian age. They are followed by a nearly conformable sequence of Paleozoic deposits extending from Upper Cambrian to Pennsylvanian.

In the Criner Hills and Arbuckle Mountains are unconformities in the Pennsylvanian that express times of orogeny, but the greatest unconformity is at the base of the Pontotoc Group at the top. Compiled from Tomlinson (1929), Ham and McKinley (1955), and Ham and others (1964).

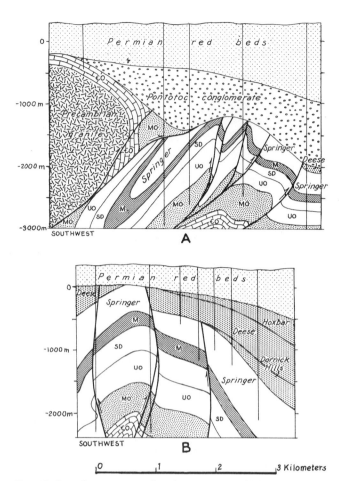

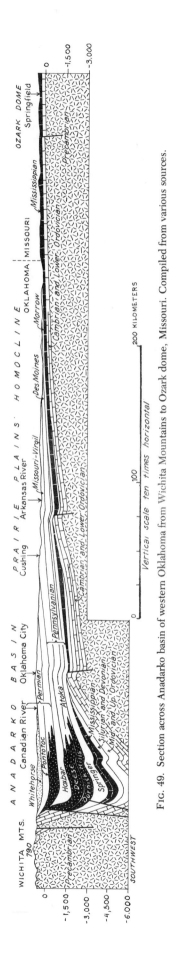

FIG. 48. Complex structures of Wichita system in Oklahoma revealed by drilling. (A) Eola pool, Garvin County, immediately west of Arbuckle Mountains. (B) Velma pool, Stephens County, about 19 kilometers west-southwest of the preceding. Drill holes are indicated by vertical lines. The same unconformities shown in Fig. 47 are present here—one beneath the Pontotoc Conglomerate and Permian redbeds indicating a late Pennsylvanian orogeny; another beneath the Dornick Hills and Deese indicating an early Pennsylvanian orogeny. After Swesnik and Green (1950), and Selk (1951).

Explanation of symbols: CO–Upper Cambrian and Lower Ordovician (Arbuckle Limestone, with Reagan Sandstone at base). MO–Middle Ordovician (Simpson Group). UO–Upper Ordovician (Viola Limestone and Sylvan Shale). SD–Silurian and Devonian (Hunton Group and Woodford Chert). M–Mississippian (Sycamore Limestone and Caney Shale).

FIG. 49. Section across Anadarko basin of western Oklahoma from Wichita Mountains to Ozark dome, Missouri. Compiled from various sources.

south-central Oklahoma the Ouachita structures strike southwest beneath the Coastal Plain cover, and the Arbuckle and Wichita structures, no more than 25 kilometers to the west, strike southeast beneath the Coastal Plain cover. We thus have here in miniature a replica of the problematical relations between the Ouachita and Appalachian systems, but in this case the Coastal Plain cover is no more than a few hundred meters thick, and well penetrations are closely spaced, providing unusually reliable data on the buried Paleozoic geology. The Arbuckle uplift with its core of Tishomingo Granite extends 55 kilometers southeastward beyond its outcrop and creates a deep re-entrant in the Ouachita front, bordered north and south by major high-angle faults, probably with components of both dip-slip and strike-slip displacement (Fig. 45). The frontal Ouachita thrusts of the outcrop are truncated southward by the high-angle faults; other frontal thrusts of the Ouachita structure are known from drilling to occur south of the transverse zone.

Clearly, there was a complex interaction between the Ouachita structures and the Arbuckle-Wichita structures, as both were in process of deformation during the Pennsylvanian, but details of what happened are not entirely obvious. The Ouachita rocks were deformed and thrust northward and northwestward during mid-Pennsylvanian time, and uplift of the Arbuckle horst extended into late Pennsylvanian time, faulting and offsetting the Ouachita thrust sheets. How far the Arbuckle and Wichita structures extend under the allochthonous Ouachita rocks, no man can say; as an extreme possibility, the whole exposed area of the Ouachita system in southeastern Oklahoma and southwestern Arkansas was transported northward over the eastern extensions of the Wichita belt.

EXTENSIONS OF WICHITA SYSTEM TO THE WEST. Drilling has greatly expanded our knowledge of the Wichita structures and has shown that many more mountain ridges were formed than one would suspect from the small areas that happen to project to the surface.

One set of uplifts (the Red River uplift) that nowhere comes to the surface lies south of the exposed ridges in Oklahoma and extends westward across northern Texas under the Great Plains, finally dying out in eastern New Mexico.

The main Wichita chain passes beneath the surface at the west end of the Wichita Mountains but continues beyond into the Amarillo district of the Texas Panhandle, where its structures have been referred to as the *Amarillo Mountains*. These are, of course, mountains in a geological sense only; they are completely buried by Permian, Mesozoic, and Tertiary deposits, and the surface of the Amarillo district is flat as only the Great Plains can be flat. Permian deposits that were spread from the old mountain ridges form wedges of arkosic detritus—the so-called granite wash. In them, great quantities of natural gas have accumulated, and the district has been one of the great natural gas fields of the world. Drilling has not been sufficient to indicate whether or not the Upper Proterozoic-Early Cambrian aulocogen extends as far west as the Amarillo district.

The Wichita chain continues beyond the Amarillo district through various other disconnected or in echelon buried uplifts but comes to the surface once more in the Southern Rocky Mountains of Colorado (Plate I), where its structures have been greatly obscured by those imposed on the region during Late Cretaceous and Tertiary time. It is probably no accident that the Rocky Mountains of southern Colorado contain half a dozen small intrusives that have yielded Cambrian dates of 520–580 million years, which are probably extensions of the Wichita plutonic province. These Paleozoic structures form the *Colorado system*, which we will explore later (Chapter VII, section 2).

We have now arrived in the Cordilleran system of the west, but before we discuss it, let us retrace our steps for a while and search for modern analogues of geosynclines.

REFERENCES

2. *Geological investigations*

Rodgers, John, 1949, Evolution of thought on structure of middle and southern Appalachians: *Am. Assoc. Petrol. Geol. Bull.*, v. 33, no. 10, pp. 1643-1654.

3. *Appalachian cross-section*

Butts, Charles, 1940, *Geology of the Appalachian Valley of Virginia*: Virginia Geol. Survey Bull. 52, pt. 1.

Cloos, Ernst, 1947, Oolite deformation in the South Mountain fold, Maryland: *Geol. Soc. America Bull.*, v. 58, pp. 918-943.

Emery, K. O., and Uchupi, Elazar, 1972, Western North Atlantic Ocean; topography, rocks, structure, water, life, and sediments: *Am. Assoc. Petrol. Geol. Mem.*, 17, pp. 160-226.

Gwinn, V. E., 1970, Kinematic patterns and estimates of lateral shortening, Valley and Ridge and Great Valley provinces, Central Appalachians, southcentral Pennsylvania, in Fisher, G. W., Pettijohn, F. J., Reed, J. C., and Weaver, K. N., eds., *Studies of Appalachian geology; Central and Southern*: Interscience Publishers, New York, pp. 127-146.

Keith, Arthur, 1923, Outlines of Appalachian structure: *Geol. Soc. America Bull.*, v. 34, pp. 309-380.

Rich, J. L., 1934, Mechanics of low-angle low-angle overthrust faulting as illustrated by the Cumberland Mountain thrust block, Virginia, Kentucky, and Tennessee: *Am. Assoc. Petrol. Geol. Bull.*, v. 18, pp. 1584-1596.

Rodgers, John, 1970, *The tectonics of the Appalachians*: Wiley-Interscience, New York.

Thompson, J. B., Jr., Robinson, Peter, Clifford, T. N., and Trask, N.

J., Jr., 1968, Nappes and gneiss domes in west-central New England, in Zen, E-an, White, W. S., Hadley, J. B., and Thompson, J. B., Jr., *Studies of Appalachian geology; Northern and Maritime*: Interscience Publishers, New York, pp. 203-218.

Zen, E-an, 1967, *Time and space relationships of the Taconic allochthon and autochthon*: Geol. Soc. America Spec. Paper 97.

4. *Geosynclines*

Coney, P. J., 1970, The geotectonic cycle and the new global tectonics: *Geol. Soc. America Bull.*, v. 81, no. 3, pp. 739-748.

Glaessner, M. F., and Teichert, Curt, 1947, Geosynclines, a fundamental concept in geology: *Am. Jour. Sci.*, v. 245, pp. 465-482, 571-591.

Kay, Marshall, 1951, North American geosyncline: *Geol. Soc. America Mem.*, 48, 143 p.

Schuchert, Charles, 1923, Sites and nature of the North American geosynclines: *Geol. Soc. America Bull.*, v. 34, pp. 151-229.

5. *Growth of the Appalachians*

Bird, J. M., and Dewey, J. F., 1970, Lithosphere plate: continental margin tectonics and the evolution of the Appalachian orogen: *Geol. Soc. America Bull.*, v. 81, no. 4, pp. 1031-1060.

Odom, A. L., and Fullagar, P. D., 1973, Geochronologic relationships between the Inner Piedmont, Brevard Zone, and Blue Ridge belts, North Carolina: *Am. Jour. Sci.*, v. 273-A, Cooper volume, pp. 133-149.

Rodgers, John, 1971, The Taconic orogeny: *Geol. Soc. America Bull.*, v. 82, no. 5, pp. 1141-1178.

Williams, Harold, Kennedy, M. J., and Neale, E.R.W., 1972, The

Appalachian structural province, *in* Price, R. A., and Douglas, R.J.W., eds., *Variations in tectonic styles in Canada*: Geol. Assoc. Canada Spec. Paper 11, pp. 182-261.

Wilson, J. Tuzo, 1966, Did the Atlantic close and then reopen?: *Nature*, v. 211, August 13, p. 676-681.

6. *Paleozoic structures west of the Mississippi River*

Flawn, P. T., Goldstein, August, Jr., King, P. B., and Weaver, C. E., 1961, *The Ouachita system*: Texas Univ. Bur. Economic Geol. Publ. 6120.

Ham, W. E., Denison, R. E., and Merritt, C. A., 1964, *Basement rocks and structural evolution of southern Oklahoma*: Oklahoma Geol. Survey Bull. 95.

King, P. B., 1937, *Geology of the Marathon Region, Texas*: U.S. Geol. Survey Prof. Paper 187.

————, 1975, The Ouachita and Appalachian orogenic belts, *in* Nairn, A.E.M., and Stehli, F. G., *The ocean basins and margins*, v. 3, *The Gulf of Mexico and Caribbean*: Plenum Press, New York, p. 201-241.

Miser, H. D., 1929, *Structure of the Ouachita Mountains in Oklahoma and Arkansas*: Oklahoma Geol. Survey Bull. 50.

————, 1943, Quartz veins in the Ouachita Mountains of Arkansas and Oklahoma; their relation to structure, metamorphism, and metalliferous deposits: *Econ. Geology*, v. 38, p. 91-113.

Morris, R. C., 1974, Sedimentary and tectonic history of the Ouachita Mountains, *in* Dickinson, W. R., ed., *Tectonics and sedimentation*: Soc. Econ. Paleontologists and Mineralogists Spec. Publ. 22, p. 120-142.

Thomas, W. A., 1973, Southwestern Appalachian structural system beneath the Gulf Coastal Plain: *Am. Jour. Sci.*, v. 273-A (Cooper volume), pp. 372-390.

Tomlinson, C. W., 1927, *The Pennsylvanian System in the Ardmore basin*: Oklahoma Geol. Survey Bull. 46.

Van der Gracht, W.A.J.M., 1931, *The Permo-Carboniferous orogeny in the south-central United States*: K. Akad. Wetensch, Amsterdam Verh. Afd. Natuurk., Deel 27, no. 3.

Viele, G. W., 1973, Structure and tectonic history of the Ouachita Mountains, Arkansas, *in* De Jong, K. A., and Scholten, Robert, eds., *Gravity and tectonics*: John Wiley & Sons, New York, p. 361-377.

CHAPTER V

LANDS AND SEAS SOUTH OF THE CONTINENT: MODERN ANALOGUES OF GEOSYNCLINES

1. GEOSYNCLINES AND UNIFORMITARIANISM

We have described Paleozoic structures along the southeast and south sides of North America and how they grew from a geosyncline into a deformed belt whose mountainous character was afterwards greatly modified by erosion and burial. Before we take up the similar Cordilleran structures along the west side of the continent, it will be profitable to study the lands and seas to the south along the Gulf Coast and in the West Indies.

Much of the human history, scenery, geography, geology, and geologic history of these regions is of interest, but our treatment of such matters will be incidental to another theme: Are geosynclines forming today, and do these regions furnish us with possible modern analogues of geosynclines?

One of the basic tenets of geology is that of *uniformitarianism*—the present supplies the key to the past. We thus believe that various earth processes—rock weathering, erosion, sedimentation, glaciation, volcanism, crustal movements, and the rest—have been of the same kind, varying only in degree, whether we observe them at work today or read their records in rocks that formed in earlier times. Hence, ancient features such as geosynclines should have modern counterparts, and if we could observe a geosyncline undergoing formation, it would give us greater understanding of geosynclines that formed earlier.

But the problem of identifying a modern analogue of a geosyncline is complicated. We see the ancient ones after they have gone through the full cycle from sedimentary trough to deformed mountain belt. Their strata have been turned up, and we are thereby able to study their sequence and facies from base to top; yet the very upturning and erosion has produced enough gaps across the feature so that it is not always easy to deduce

the geography amidst which the geosyncline formed. If geosynclines were now in process of formation, we could see their geography and their surfaces of sedimentation, but we would not be able to observe directly the masses of sediment that had already accumulated, nor the floor beneath the geosyncline. Even if we were able to probe the substructure of a modern geosyncline by drilling or geophysical means, we would still be unable to look into the future and predict whether this particular sedimentary body is of the sort that inevitably would be deformed and built into mountains at some future time.

Our inquiry will thus not provide us with certain answers. Nevertheless, some thought-provoking comparisons are possible between ancient geosynclines and areas where sedimentation is in active progress today, or was active recently, and where the crust is unstable and undergoing rapid subsidence.

2. GULF COAST AREA

MODERN SEDIMENTATION ALONG GULF COAST. Some of the conditions set forth above exist along the Gulf Coast of the United States.

The map reveals the extensive areas underlain by Tertiary and Quaternary rocks and the many large rivers that flow into the Gulf of Mexico from the interior region. The largest of these rivers is the Mississippi, which, with its many tributaries, drains most of the Interior Lowlands of the United States and enters the Gulf in Louisiana at about mid-length along the coast. But to the west are the Sabine, the Trinity, the Brazos, the Colorado, and the Rio Grande, and to the east are the Tombigbee and the Chattahoochee, as well as many other rivers which drain smaller areas than the Mississippi, all of which are bringing to the coast sediments that were derived from erosion of the land.

The Mississippi is estimated to deliver to its mouth 750 billion metric tons of solid and dissolved material each year. The solid material is laid down as sediments off the mouth of the river; it is estimated that these amount to 0.28 cubic kilometers per year, or that more than two cubic kilometers of sediments are added about every ten years. The projection of land into the Gulf in Louisiana was built by sediment brought down by the river and is the *Mississippi Delta*. If the river were not there, the coast would have been much farther inland, more nearly in line with the coast farther east and west. Deposits of the Mississippi form a low embankment, which has been built across the continental shelf nearly to its edge.

One complication makes modern sedimentation on all continental shelves different from that in the past. At several times during the immediately preceding Pleistocene ice age, sea level was lowered a hundred meters or more when ocean water was withdrawn to form the continental icecaps. Through parts of Pleistocene time, therefore, the continental shelves were above water and were being eroded. Sediments that accumulate on the continental shelves today are thus being laid over this eroded surface, or surface of unconformity (Fig. 50).

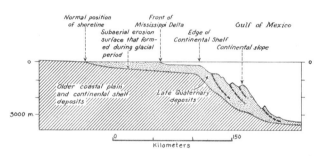

FIG. 50. Generalized section across the Mississippi Delta from the land to the continental shelf and slope, showing the different environments in which sediments are now accumulating. Vertical scale greatly exaggerated. Compiled from Fisk and McFarlan (1955) and other sources.

Modern sedimentary processes around the Mississippi Delta are thus building up the surface to sea level from the Pleistocene erosion surface. Louisiana geologists assure us, however, that the Pleistocene erosion surface has been downwarped beneath the delta area so that actual volume of post-Pleistocene sediments is much greater than would have resulted from upbuilding alone. This raises again the oft-debated question as to whether or not a surface of sedimentation can subside because it is loaded, but we will not pursue this further here.

Even though a large volume of the sediment discharged by the Mississippi and other rivers has been laid down on the delta and continental shelf, an even greater volume is lost to the delta and shelf. Waves and currents gradually shift the sediments out to sea, carrying them beyond the forward edge of the shelf and down the continental slope into the deeper waters of the Gulf. Surveys of the Gulf bottom show that there is, in fact, a second Mississippi Delta, or abyssal fan on the Gulf floor below and in front of the surface delta.

Oceanographic work shows that the continental shelf off the Mississippi River has a complex, hummocky topography scoured by peculiar channels and many little scarps (Fig. 50). These submarine topographic forms seem to have been produced by slumping and landsliding of the unconsolidated, freshly deposited sediments. The hummocky topography is probably the result of landslides; the channels were formed where the sediments moved as turbid flows, and the scarps were produced where the sediments faulted as they slipped and settled. Near the outer edge of the continental slope is a longer, higher, steeper scarp, the *Sigsbee Escarpment*, and geophysical surveys demonstrate that it, too, is confined to the body of sediments and resulted from processes in the deposits older than the Quaternary, which we will examine presently.

In short, modern sedimentation is continually building forward the continental shelf and slope into the deeper water and is thereby extending the continental margin.

Beyond the continental slope is the deeper water of the main basin of the Gulf of Mexico lying between Texas and Yucatan, which reaches a depth of more than 3,600 meters in the Sigsbee Deep toward its south side (Fig. 56). Beyond this, sea bottom rises again into another continental shelf off the coast of Yucatan, where few rivers enter, and where the surface is receiving mainly limestone deposits. Apparently the deepest part of the main basin of the Gulf is placed away from the Texas-Louisiana side and toward the Yucatan side because of an imbalance in the amount of sedimentation from north to south.

SURFACE FEATURES OF THE GULF COASTAL PLAIN. So much for modern conditions. Now let us extend our inquiry into the past, and discover what went on along the Gulf Coast during Tertiary and later Mesozoic time.

The reader will recall the *Mississippi Embayment*, which we mentioned earlier (Chapter III, section 4), the sag containing Cretaceous and Tertiary deposits that extends inland from the coast as far as southern Illinois. This began to form during the Cretaceous Period, since when it has constituted a sort of funnel toward which all drainage of the interior region has been drawn. From well back in Tertiary time, anyway, rivers ancestral to the Mississippi have flowed into and down the sag, carrying much of the erosional waste of the interior region to the Gulf Coast. Sedimentation like that going on along the coast today must therefore have gone on in much the same manner for the last 60 million years or more of geologic time.

Turning to the geologic map, we can view the Gulf Coastal Plain as a whole (Plate I). Note that it has a width from its inland edge to the coast of 240 to 480 kilometers.

But beyond the coast, the same structure extends beneath the surface of the continental shelf, which is only a few kilometers wide where the Mississippi has built its delta nearly across it, and as much as 240 kilometers wide in other places.

On the geologic map note the belted outcrops of the formations of the Coastal Plain, with the Cretaceous farthest inland followed successively by the Paleocene, Eocene, Oligocene, and Miocene, and by Pliocene and Pleistocene along the coast. All the strata of these ages dip gently seaward, probably at angles no steeper than inclinations of the Paleozoic strata of the Interior Lowlands, which we discussed earlier. Let us make a rough calculation. If we assume an average width of the Coastal Plain of 480 kilometers and an average dip of 10 meters per kilometer, the thickness of the Coastal Plain sediments at the coast line from Cretaceous to Recent should be about 5 kilometers (Fig. 51A). We will see presently that, for various reasons, they are actually very much thicker.

SUBSURFACE FEATURES OF GULF COASTAL PLAIN. The Gulf Coastal Plain, as we know, is one of the great oil provinces of the United States. In the search for its oil resources, it has been penetrated by many closely

spaced wells to depths of 5 kilometers or more. Stratigraphy and structure of the Coastal Plain are thus known far beneath its relatively featureless surface. Geophysical work has extended our knowledge even farther, beyond depths reached by the drill.

Considering first the Mesozoic rocks, which are all Cretaceous at the surface, we know from drilling that the Cretaceous of the outcrop thickens greatly down dip and seaward and that down dip and beneath the surface still older rocks wedge in which are nowhere exposed (Fig. 52). Some of them are of early Cretaceous age, but others have been proved by fossils (recovered from drill cores) to be of later Jurassic age.

Beneath the fossiliferous Jurassic, an older Jurassic sequence wedges in—the Louann Salt, as much as 4,500 meters thick, with the Werner Anhydrite at the base in updip sections. The actual salt layer has been penetrated by the drill only in the updip areas, but the salt, which is mobile and of lower density than the other sediments, has flowed upward into salt domes (Fig. 53), which dot

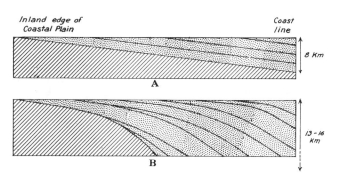

FIG. 51. Sketch sections across the Gulf Coastal Plain showing: (A) Structure that would be inferred from surface features alone, on the assumption of a uniform seaward dip of all the units. (B) The actual structure as known from subsurface data.

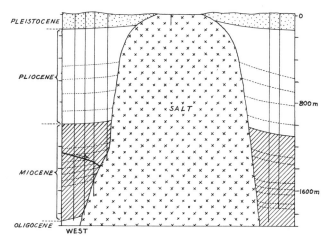

FIG. 53. Cross-section of a typical salt dome that has been outlined by deep drilling; Avery Island, south-central Louisiana. Drill holes shown by vertical lines; horizontal scale same as vertical. After Carsey (1950).

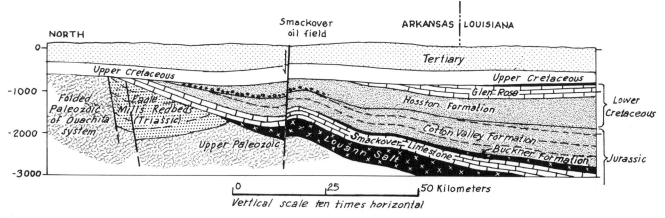

FIG. 52. Section in southern Arkansas and northern Louisiana to show manner in which earlier Mesozoic strata, not exposed at the surface, wedge in down the dip. The Upper Cretaceous lies on the older

Mesozoic rocks with a major unconformity. A minor unconformity separates the Lower Cretaceous (Hosston Formation) from the Jurassic. Based on Imlay (1940) and other sources.

81

the Coastal Plain down to the shore and extend thence across the continental shelf to the continental slope. The Sigsbee Escarpment on the continental slope is, in fact, a salt wall at the front of the mass of salt that is flowing from the Gulf Coast down into the deeper basin of the Gulf of Mexico (Fig. 55).

The lesson of the Mesozoic rocks is that their thickness in their seaward parts is much greater than we would have inferred from their surface outcrops alone, the greater thickness resulting in part from thickening of each layer down the dip and in part from wedging-in of formations down the dip that never extend to the surface (Fig. 51B).

Many of the same relations hold for the Tertiary deposits. On the outcrop and toward the land, these are sands and clays, in part containing beds of coal and various plant remains, which indicate a continental origin, in part containing oysters and other shells indicating that they were laid down in salt water along the shore (Fig. 54). But if one follows any layer down its dip and beneath the surface, it is found to change into marine clays and shales whose contained Foraminifera indicate that they were deposited in progressively deeper water the farther they are from the outcrop and toward the Gulf.

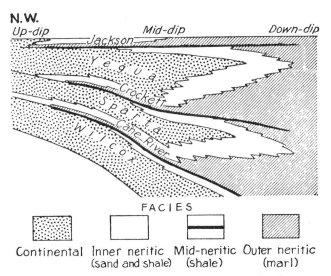

FACIES

Continental | Inner neritic (sand and shale) | Mid-neritic (shale) | Outer neritic (marl)

FIG. 54. Diagram illustrating typical arrangement of sedimentary facies in the Eocene deposits of the Gulf Coastal Plain, east Texas and Louisiana. After Lowman (1949).

Moreover, when any layer in the Tertiary is traced down dip toward the coast, it thickens and steepens. At a certain point in each layer, thickening and steepening become so great that it plunges so rapidly Gulfward that it can no longer be reached by drilling. Obviously the deposits will not thicken and steepen indefinitely—otherwise they would "go right on to China." Further changes in the deposits must take place at depth and farther out.

Compare these relations with those in the modern

sediments. In the modern sediments, the same changes take place toward the Gulf—continental deposits, shore deposits, marine deposits of the continental shelf laid down in deepening water outward, and continental slope deposits that thicken and steepen abruptly (Fig. 50). Could not the abruptly thickened and steepened Tertiary likewise be continental slope deposits? The zones of maximum steepening and thickening of the various Tertiary deposits each lie farther inland the older they are. If they represent former positions of the continental slope, the slope has moved progressively toward the Gulf through Tertiary time by a distance of many hundred kilometers.

Let us now consider the whole mass of sediments laid down in the Gulf Coastal Plain (Fig. 55). We can determine this partly from surface dips, although, as we have seen, these give a much smaller total than the true figure. We can supplement surface information from drill data and from geophysical data on the still deeper layers. The deepest well near the Louisiana coast, and one of the deepest producing wells in the world, reached a total depth of 6,883 meters without passing out of the Miocene; Miocene, Pliocene, and later deposits in this vicinity are at least 7,500 to 9,000 meters thick. When we add the older Tertiary and Mesozoic deposits that undoubtedly underlie them, total thickness of sediments near the Louisiana coast must amount to 12 to 15 kilometers. The mass of deposits has therefore appropriately been called the *Gulf Coast geosyncline*.

THE GULF OF MEXICO. Before going further, we should consider the whole basin of the Gulf of Mexico, into which the Gulf Coast sediments have been built. The Gulf is a nearly landlocked water body, bordered by the United States on the north and east, by Mexico on the west and south, and by Cuba on the southeast, with only narrow passageways on the south and east to connect it with the other oceans, but having a depth in its central abyssal plain of more than 3,600 meters. Geologists formerly assumed that it was a depressed sag in the continental plate, but later geophysical surveys demonstrate that it is floored by oceanic crust of about the same density and thickness as the crust beneath the oceans elsewhere, although with a thicker cover of more than 4 kilometers of sediments (Fig. 56). The Gulf is, in fact, a small ocean basin.

The origin of this basin has been much debated. A puzzling feature is the great salt bed at the base of the sedimentary sequence, which we have seen is extensive on its northern side. The same salt bed occurs in Mexico on the west and south, and even in part of Cuba. Even more curiously, the Sigsbee Knolls near the center of the abyssal plain have also been proved to be salt diapirs. The Gulf, then, seems to have been a gigantic evaporating pan during the early part of Jurassic time. It is not clear whether the salt in the Sigsbee Knolls formed *in*

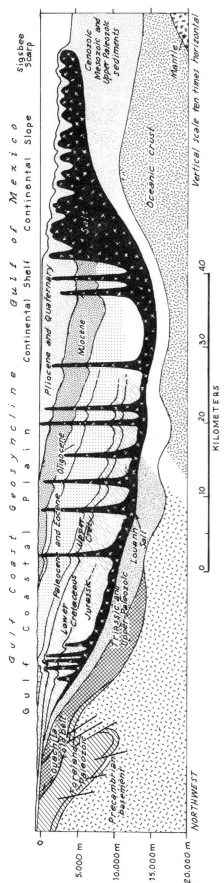

FIG. 55. Generalized section of the Gulf Coast Geosyncline, from central Texas into the Gulf of Mexico. Compiled from Lehner (1969), Emery and Uchupi (1972), Martin and Case (1975), and other sources.

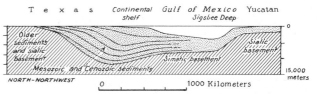

FIG. 56. Sketch section across Gulf of Mexico from Texas to Yucatan, showing inferred variations in thickness of Mesozoic and Cenozoic sediments and their zone of maximum accumulation near the Texas coast.

situ, or whether it flowed in from higher-standing areas roundabout; if the former, it is even less clear whether its site was originally shallow water, or was always as deep as it is now.

Be that as it may, the Gulf may have begun to open during the early Mesozoic, the continental crust that now forms southern Mexico moving away from the continental crust in the United States, including the now-consolidated Ouachita orogenic belt. During initial stages of the opening, when free access to the other oceans was restricted, the early Jurassic evaporites were laid down. Later on, when the Gulf had widened, younger Mesozoic and Cenozoic sedimentary embankments were built into it from the sides—clastics along the north coast, carbonates to the east and south. We have already observed a similar sequence of deposits in the Atlantic Coastal Plain, along the widening rift of the Atlantic Ocean (Chapter IV, section 3). In both cases, sedimentation along the coasts causes the continental area to be expanded progressively over the oceanic area.

COMPARISONS WITH OLDER GEOSYNCLINES. We have gone far enough to see that there are many resemblances between the Gulf Coastal Plain and its continental shelf, with its Mesozoic, Tertiary, and Quaternary sediments and the Appalachian geosyncline discussed in the preceding chapter:

(a) Thickness of sediments amounts to as much as 12,000 to 15,000 meters, or close to the maximum thickness of sediments observed in any part of the Appalachian geosyncline.

(b) Floors of the troughs in which the Gulf Coast and Appalachian sediments accumulated were both downwarped into a synclinal form.

(c) The landward half of the sediments was laid down in relatively shallow water like that of the Appalachian miogeosyncline; the depths to which this half of these sediments have been depressed was accompanied by gradual subsidence.

(d) The seaward half of the sediments of the Gulf Coastal Plain was built forward from the sialic continental crust over the simatic oceanic crust, thus extending the continental area in the same manner as we have suggested for the eugeosynclinal deposits of the Appalachians.

83

But we can also observe differences between deposits of the Gulf Coastal area and those of the Appalachians:

(a) There is no clearly defined miogeosyncline or eugeosyncline. Deposits on the landward side to the north, at least from Tertiary time onward, include very little limestone and there are no volcanic or tectonic lands farther out.

(b) Limestone is being deposited on other parts of the continental shelves around the Gulf of Mexico but not according to any miogeosynclinal pattern. Most extensive areas of limestone are in those parts where few rivers enter the Gulf, notably off Yucatan and Florida.

(c) Some volcanism occurred in the Gulf Coastal area during Cretaceous and early Tertiary time, but not according to the eugeosynclinal pattern. It was along the inner side near a hinge line probably related to downwarping of the trough along the coast, rather than near the edge of the continental shelf.

(d) Main source of sediments is from the landward side, not from tectonic lands offshore; this condition is related to the existence of numerous rivers that are bringing sediments down from the land. This has prevented an accumulation of limestone along the northern shore. These relations are nearly the opposite from those in the Appalachian geosyncline.

(e) The Gulf Coastal Plain is not especially mobile, the only crustal activity being a slow subsidence. It is not a seismic area and there are no significant earthquakes.

(f) No mountains have developed from the geosyncline—if it is one. Possibly mountains will form here during later stages of the geosynclinal cycle, but no present evidence affirms that they ever will.

Whether these differences are so fundamental that they debar the Gulf Coastal area from comparison with the Appalachian or other geosynclines is a subject much debated among geologists.

I myself am inclined to believe that the differences between the Gulf Coastal deposits and those of the Appalachian geosyncline are not very fundamental and that they are mainly the result of differences between internal geography of the continent in Paleozoic and Cenozoic time. In the first half of Paleozoic time the interior of the continent was low; streams that drained it brought to the coast mainly fine clastics or material in solution. During Cenozoic time the interior of the continent had a much greater relief, so that a much larger volume of clastic material was delivered to the shore by streams.

It is true that crustal unrest and volcanic activity in the Appalachian geosyncline was much greater than along the Gulf Coast, but this is a matter of degree and reflects variations in mobility from one geosyncline to another, as we noted in our list of "geosynclinal attributes" (Chapter IV, section 4). Next we will consider another possible

analogue of geosynclines in which there was much more crustal mobility.

WHERE ARE THE ANCIENT COASTAL PLAIN DEPOSITS? Before leaving the subject of the Gulf Coastal Plain, we should consider a broader question that once troubled the minds of geologists: What has become of the coastal plains of earlier geologic times?

The Atlantic and Gulf Coastal Plains of southeastern North America are perhaps better developed than the rest, yet there are many narrower and shorter coastal plains in other continents—in parts of Europe, Africa, and South America—but all known coastal plain deposits of the world are relatively young, mainly of Quaternary, Tertiary, and Cretaceous age. In a few, as in the Gulf Coastal Plain, the initial deposits are Jurassic, but none is Triassic or earlier.

The continents obviously must have had edges before Cretaceous or Jurassic time. We would suppose, by comparing present conditions with the past, that before Jurassic time these edges would have received deposits brought down from the land by rivers, and that these would have been built up as coastal plains. Nevertheless, nothing that can certainly be identified as such has been recognized.

One of the difficulties geologists have had in thinking about earlier coastal plain deposits was too great a preoccupation with the belief that "borderlands" such as Appalachia once lay along the present continental margins. As indicated in Chapter V, section 5, no compelling reason exists for believing that the Appalachian geosyncline or the others did not extend directly to the edges of the ocean basins, just as deposits of the Gulf Coastal Plain extend directly to the edge of the Gulf of Mexico today. For example, we now believe that the Appalachian miogeosyncline was not bounded on the southeast by a structural barrier, but that it ended in a shelf break, beyond which the eugeosyncline was forming at oceanic depths. Moreover, many of the present coasts of the continents were once adjoined directly by other continents, from which they were separated during a general breakup early in the Mesozoic—a time that marks the inception of most of the modern coastal plains.

Our earlier questions of "where are the modern geosynclines?" and "where are the ancient coastal plains?" thus turn out to be opposite sides of the same coin. At least the miogeosynclinal parts of the ancient geosynclines were also the ancient coastal plains. These ancient coastal plains have since been made unrecognizable by conversion of their deposits into mountain belts, which are now incorporated into the continents.

3. THE WEST INDIES

In our search for modern analogues of geosynclines, we have examined one possibility—a deep sedimentary trough that formed along the edge of a continent in a coastal plain area by slow subsidence but with little other crustal activity. Let us take up another and somewhat different example.

ISLAND ARCS AND DEEP-SEA TRENCHES. In discussing the eugeosyncline of the Appalachians we mentioned that its troughs and intervening tectonic lands and volcanic islands might be comparable to modern island arcs and deep-sea trenches. This comparison we will now pursue further.

A map of the world indicates around the edges of the Pacific Ocean remarkable festoons of islands that form a series of arcs convex toward the ocean. In the northwest Pacific some of these, such as the Aleutian, Japanese, and Indonesian islands, lie close to the continents. When the Aleutian arc is traced eastward, in fact, it passes from a chain of islands onto the mainland of Alaska, where it merges with the Cordilleran mountains along the western border of North America (Plate I). The latter continue thence along the Pacific to the south tip of South America and no island chains lie offshore; perhaps the Cordillera is the equivalent on the land of the island arcs at sea. But when the island arcs are traced in the opposite direction from Japan into the southwestern Pacific, they run far out into the ocean, forming such chains as the Marianas, New Zealand, and the Tonga Islands.

Alongside the island arcs on their oceanward sides are equally remarkable trenches—long and narrow like the rows of islands, with steeply sloping sides that descend far below any normal level of the ocean bottom (Fig. 57). The trenches contain some of the greatest deeps of the world; the deepest extend to 11,000 meters below the surface of the ocean, or farther below sea level than Mount Everest rises above it. They are, in fact, mountain ranges in reverse. Such deep trenches lie next to the island arcs that are close to the continents in the northern Pacific, next to the Cordilleras of North and South America in the eastern Pacific, and next to island arcs at sea in the southwestern Pacific. Obviously, island arcs and deep-sea trenches are parts of the same earth struc-

ture; we can designate the whole as an island arc-trench system.

The features so far set forth are merely topographic; origin of the island arc-trench systems must be sought in their geological and geophysical features. They coincide with some of the most seismic and volcanic belts of the world; the latter has been called the "Pacific Circle of Fire." When bedded rocks are present in the islands, they are mainly of later Tertiary age, yet are strongly deformed. On some of the islands, as well, coral reefs have been uplifted many scores of meters above the present shores. These features and others indicate that something very unusual must have happened and may still be happening to the crust of the earth in the island arc-trench systems; they must have been shaped by strong movements late in geologic time.

THE WEST INDIES AS AN EXAMPLE. Fortunately, we have a sample of an island arc-trench system at the back door of North America—not in the Pacific, which has no island arcs on the American side, but in the West Indies and Caribbean Sea southeast of the Gulf of Mexico. We are doubly fortunate, moreover, because the structures of this region are the southeastward continuation of the North American Cordillera, with which we will soon deal.

In the West Indies, as in the Pacific island arc-trench systems, we find the same arcuate island chains—chains of volcanoes, deep trenches, earthquake belts, and indications of deformation in later geologic time. Unfortunately for the example, some features are not as well displayed as in the systems of the Pacific, but these deficiencies appear to be of degree rather than kind, so we can fit the example into the general class with which our inquiry is concerned. Let us, then, review the geographic and geologic features of the area.

CENTRAL AMERICA. The land connection between North and South America, as we can see from the map, is through the isthmus of Central America. From the map alone one would be tempted to connect the Cordillera of North America with the Cordillera of South America (or Andes Mountains) through this land bridge, but examination of the geologic features indicates that the linkage is more complex.

The middle part of Central America centering in Nicaragua is primarily a chain of volcanoes that was built up rather recently to join deformed Tertiary rocks on the south with older structures on the north. Where the basement of the volcanics is exposed, it includes ultramafic rocks and deformed Mesozoic clastics that were probably deposited on oceanic crust. The volcanic chain follows a line of weakness parallel to the Middle America Trench offshore in the Pacific, which apparently formed rather recently in geologic time.

By contrast, northern Central America, in Guatemala and Honduras, consists of folded and partly metamor-

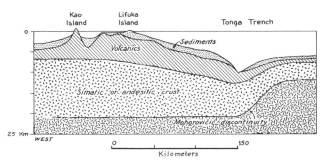

FIG. 57. Section across Tonga Trench, southwestern Pacific Ocean, to illustrate island arc-trench structure. Positions of different crustal layers are derived from geophysical observations. Note exaggerated vertical scale. Modified from Raitt and others (1955).

phosed rocks of Mesozoic, Paleozoic, and possible Precambrian ages. Northwestward in Mexico the folded rocks are continuous with the North American Cordillera and are thus the southeastern extensions of our own mountains of the western states. But instead of trending down the Central American isthmus, they trend across it in an eastward direction and run out beneath the Caribbean Sea (Plate I).

GREATER ANTILLES. The structural zone of northern Central America is not lost in the Caribbean, however; submarine ridges such as the Nicaraguan Rise and the Cayman Ridge extend eastward to the Greater Antilles or northern massive islands of the West Indies—Cuba, Jamaica, Hispaniola (Haiti and Dominican Republic), and Puerto Rico. Structures of their southern part in Jamaica and southern Hispaniola are in direct line with those of northern Central America; structures of their northern part in northern Hispaniola and Cuba are north of the Central American structures and adjoin the flat-lying rocks of Yucatan at their western end, but they curve southward at sea toward Central America along its eastern coast.

Rocks and structures of the Greater Antilles are much like those of such mature mountain belts as the Appalachians and the western Cordillera. Their rocks formed in a geosyncline of considerable mobility. Their Cretaceous rocks include large volcanic components, as do the Paleozoic rocks of the eugeosynclinal belt of the Appalachians. They were strongly deformed near the end of Mesozoic time, as well as several times earlier and later. Some of the older rocks have been metamorphosed and plutonized; they contain bodies of ultramafic, mafic, and intermediate intrusives. Apparently the oldest of these rocks are Mesozoic, and none earlier has been proved; probably the Greater Antilles were built up during Mesozoic time and later on an original oceanic crust, by the addition of magmas from the mantle. However, there are very few young volcanic fields and only shallow seismic activity.

The Greater Antilles are thus the emerged parts of a mountain system that has gone through the full cycle of orogenic deformation and has now attained relative stability.

FORELAND OF THE BAHAMAS AND FLORIDA. Northeast of the Greater Antilles are the broad, partly submerged platforms of Florida and the Bahama Islands. They are thickly covered by flat-lying Tertiary and Cretaceous deposits—largely limestones. Deep wells in southern Florida and on Andros Island in the Bahamas have penetrated 3,000 to 4,000 meters of Tertiary and Cretaceous carbonates with Jurassic beneath. At least their western part was laid down on a sialic continental plate, which is an extension of the North American continent. The limestone deposits are comparable to those of the miogeosyncline and foreland in the Appalachians,

and they in fact form a miogeosynclinal belt in front of the Antillean eugeosyncline along the north coast of Cuba.

LESSER ANTILLES. Beyond Puerto Rico, much more of the structural belt is submerged, but parts project above water in the islands of the Lesser Antilles. These extend southward in a great arc that again joins the continent in Trinidad and Venezuela.

The arc of the Lesser Antilles is double, the islands forming two concentric chains of unlike topographic and geologic character. The inner chain of the arc is a line of volcanoes, some dormant, some active, in part violently so. The outer chain is covered by limestones and other sediments of later Tertiary age that lie on a basement of older volcanics, mainly of earlier Tertiary age. Its islands are spaced more widely than those of the inner chain and extend around only the north half of the arc. In the south half farther out are the islands of Barbados and Tobago, which are emerged parts of other structures we will consider later. Although the crustal forces that produced the Greater Antilles have now largely come to rest, those of the Lesser Antilles are still active, as shown by the modern volcanic and seismic activity in the area.

TRINIDAD AND VENEZUELA. South of the arc of the Lesser Antilles, the structural belt that we have been tracing is again mainly emergent. Its northern border, it is true, appears only in a chain of islands off the coast of Venezuela, but the main body forms the island of Trinidad and continues into the ranges of northern Venezuela, which curve westward to join the main Cordillera of the Andes along the Pacific side of South America (Plate I). From Trinidad westward these ranges are again a mature mountain structure like those of the Greater Antilles and northern Central America.

FAULT ZONES NORTH AND SOUTH OF THE ANTILLEAN ARC. Another item must be added to complete the picture of the surface geologic structure—great zones of transcurrent faults on each side of the Antillean arc, trending generally eastward through Trinidad and Venezuela on the south and the Greater Antilles on the north.

Thus, the North Range of Trinidad and the Cordillera de la Costa in Venezuela together form a line of narrow ridges along the Caribbean Sea, composed of metamorphic Mesozoic rocks unlike the unmetamorphosed Mesozoic and Tertiary rocks south of them. The metamorphic rocks have reached their present position by movements along a fault zone on the south side of the narrow ridge—a sideward shift to the east relative to the rocks on the south—that is, a right-lateral strike-slip displacement. Other faults with the same sense of displacement occur farther west in Venezuela (Plate I).

On the opposite side of the Caribbean Sea the Cayman Trench extends diagonally through the Greater Antilles between Cuba and Jamaica. Its north and south sides descend in steep submarine escarpments to a nearly level floor 95 kilometers broad, with depths as great as 7,000 meters. Land features on the south coast of Cuba and submarine features elsewhere indicate that the trench has been produced by faulting, but it is not an ordinary graben; instead, the floor is formed of thinner, denser, more oceanic crust than that of the escarpments on either side—in other words, it is a "pull-apart" of the crust of the earth. The pattern of the adjacent islands and their structure also suggests a sideward shift by an undetermined amount of the southern side toward the east relative to the side on the north—a left-lateral strike-slip displacement, or movement in the opposite sense from that on the faults in Venezuela and Trinidad.

The two zones of faulting—in Venezuela and Trinidad and in the Cayman Trench—apparently separate stable parts of the crust north and south of the Caribbean Sea, with mature mountain structure, from a more mobile intervening block of the crust, which is shifting eastward toward the arc of the Lesser Antilles, an immature mountain structure.

CARIBBEAN SEA FLOOR. So much for the geology of the land areas of the West Indies. But, as we have seen, West Indies structures are only partly emergent; the remainder lie beneath the sea. To complete the picture, submarine features must be added.

The Caribbean Sea, lying between the Greater Antilles and Venezuela and inside the arc of the Lesser Antilles, is floored by a fairly level plain 3,600 to 5,200 meters deep. This is diversified only by ridges concentric to the arc of the Lesser Antilles—the Aves Ridge on the east and the Beata Ridge farther west—which seem to be folds or volcanic belts related to the same deformation. Many geologists once believed that the Caribbean is a foundered continental area, but recent geophysical work demonstrates that the floor is oceanic—somewhat less dense than normal oceanic crust and with a composition more like andesite than basalt.

This special andesitic crust occurs only in association with island arc-trench systems. In the western Pacific, as in the West Indies, it floors the seas behind the island arcs—for example, the Philippine Sea between the Mariana Islands and Asia. In the Pacific the boundary between the island arcs and the central simatic floor is termed the andesite line. Some geologists have speculated that the areas of andesitic sea floor behind the island arcs are foundered edges of the continental plates. Modern knowledge suggests, however, that they were originally areas of oceanic crust, which are being converted by magmatic and sedimentary processes into less dense crustal material.

PUERTO RICO TRENCH. On the opposite side of the Antillean arc from the Caribbean Sea along the edge of the Atlantic Ocean basin is the Puerto Rico Trench. This originates on the west between Hispaniola and the Bahama Islands, passes north of Puerto Rico, and curves southeast concentric to the island arc, fading out at about mid-length in the arc, beyond which the Barbados Ridge seems to lie on the same trend (Plate I). Its deepest part north of Puerto Rico lies 8,200 meters beneath the surface of the sea, and is the deepest part of the Atlantic Ocean.

The Puerto Rico Trench seems to be a different kind of structure from the Cayman Trench. Instead of cutting through the islands and across the structural grain, it extends concentrically with the arc and outside it on the oceanward side. It is, moreover, marked by a strong negative gravity anomaly, whereas the Cayman Trench exhibits a positive anomaly. The Puerto Rico Trench is of the same structural class as the deep-sea trenches that border the island arcs of the Pacific on their oceanward sides.

The Puerto Rico Trench has a flat floor some kilometers wide, which geophysical work indicates is underlain by a thick body of sediments. The rock floor beneath the sediments must have a more nearly V-shaped cross-section, which was probably shaped by downwarping and downfaulting. In initial stages of trench formation the rock surface was probably nearly bare; sediments were brought to it later by turbid flows derived from the adjacent lands or from shallower parts of the ocean bottom. Various stages of this sequence are illustrated in the trenches of the Pacific, some of which are V-shaped and rock-floored to their bottoms (as in Fig. 57), whereas others are flat-floored and sediment-filled like the Puerto Rico Trench.

THE ISLAND OF BARBADOS. Processes of trench formation and destruction are illustrated on the island of Barbados, which lies on the Barbados Ridge southeast of and outside the Lesser Antilles arc, on the structural prolongation of the Puerto Rico Trench. Here, the following stratigraphic sequence is exposed.

STRATIGRAPHIC SEQUENCE ON ISLAND OF BARBADOS

Coral Rock (Pleistocene). Forms a thin mantle over wide areas of the island. Deposited after the island had been uplifted nearly to its present form.

UNCONFORMITY

Bissex Hill Marl (upper Oligocene-lower Miocene). Globogerina marl and foraminiferal limestone. A marine deposit seemingly laid down at moderate depth .... 30 meters

UNCONFORMITY

Oceanic Series (upper Eocene-lower Oligocene). Radiolarian earth, Globogerina marl, and red clay. A deep-sea marine deposit
500–1,500 meters

GRADATION IN MOST PLACES

Joes River Beds (upper Eocene). Silts of chaotic structure containing small to large fragments of clay, sandstone, and other rocks from the Scotland Formation. A mudflow formed by submarine gravity slides while deformation was in progress .. 0–400 meters

ANGULAR UNCONFORMITY

Scotland Formation (middle Eocene). Silty and sandy shale, grit, and fine conglomerate, strongly and chaotically folded and faulted. The sediments show many structures characteristic of shallow-water origin. Base not exposed; exposed thickness as much as .... 1,500 meters

The Scotland deposits contain many indications of shallow-water deposition, but their chaotic structure indicates that they have been moved from their original site, probably as a great gravity slide from the west into a deepening submarine trench (Fig. 58B). The Joes River Beds may be largely a gravity tectonic feature. After these gravity slides, the trench attained prolonged stability, and the Oceanic Series accumulated in a deep-sea environment. The succeeding strata indicate gradual uplift of the floor of the trench, probably by renewed crustal compression, to form Barbados Ridge and the island that emerges on its crest. The structure of Barbados is thus in a more advanced stage of development than the Puerto Rico Trench, which lies along its continuation to the north.

NEGATIVE GRAVITY ANOMALIES. We mentioned briefly a remarkable feature of the Puerto Rico Trench and others like it—their relation to belts of strong negative gravity anomaly. We will now consider this further.

Geophysicists have found that over the earth the value of gravity varies by slight amounts. The famous apple that struck Sir Isaac Newton would not strike with the same force everywhere. Neither we nor Sir Isaac would have been able to detect these variations with our own senses; they must be measured by delicate instruments.

Most of these variations can be accounted for by well-known physical laws and result from latitude, altitude, and topographic irregularities. One would expect that, when observed readings were corrected for these fac-tors, the value of gravity at all points would be equal. Nevertheless, variations still remain called gravity anomalies,* which result from interposition of geological factors, such as differences in density of rocks of the crust from place to place.

Thus, land areas chiefly yield negative anomalies, and oceanic areas chiefly positive anomalies. These are caused by contrasting densities of the sialic continental plates and the simatic ocean floors. Negative anomalies are largest in the mountain areas, showing that a greater volume of lighter rocks is there present. The crust is thus in isostatic balance; high areas stand high because they are underlain by rocks less dense than those of lower areas.

These principles were established mainly by study of gravity on the land; up to 50 years ago little could be determined about gravity conditions at sea. Observations of gravity have been measured by means of the rate of swing of a pendulum. The instrument is set on a solid base, and a series of measurements is made, sometimes consuming many days. Such observations could not be made on shipboard because of the tossing of the vessel. However, the Dutch geophysicist F. A. Vening Meinesz devised a method of making gravity measurements at sea in a submarine submerged far enough below the surface to be free of oscillation of the water. With the help of the Dutch Navy, he made a series of such observations in the region of island arcs and trenches in Indonesia, which at that time was Dutch territory.

*In this account I have not distinguished between free-air anomalies, Bouguer anomalies, and isostatic anomalies, all of which are used by marine geophysicists. They are based on different mathematical treatment of the same sets of data, but while the results differ considerably in detail, the general results are enough alike for our purpose.

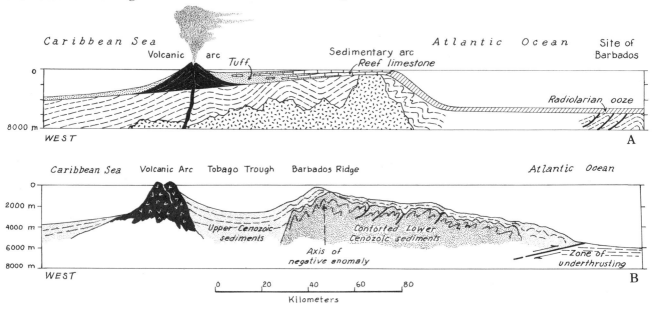

FIG. 58. Sections from the Caribbean Sea to the Atlantic Ocean through the Antillean arc and the island of Barbados. (A) Inferred structure during early Tertiary time (after Senn, 1940). (B) Modern conditions, based on oceanographic surveys (after Daviss, 1971).

These observations yielded startling results. Near the trenches it was found that there was a narrow belt of strong negative gravity anomalies. Trench and anomaly clearly had a close relation, although the axes of the two did not necessarily coincide; sometimes the axis of the anomaly lay on one side of the trench, sometimes on another; in places it crossed an island that lay in its course.

Work done afterwards in other island arc-trench systems has shown that most of them have similar gravity properties. Thus, in the West Indies a belt of negative gravity anomalies lies near the axis of the Puerto Rico Trench on the convex side of the Antillean arc. It swings southward in front of the arc, continues where the trench fades out, and passes through the islands of Barbados, Tobago, and Trinidad. Other less continuous negative anomaly belts lie in the Caribbean Sea north of the coast of Venezuela.

These negative anomalies cannot be accounted for by ordinary geological factors such as isostatic compensation. Oceanic areas generally yield positive anomalies, and one would expect these to be greatest in the trench areas. In fact, the Cayman Trench, apparently with a different structure from the other trenches, does show a positive anomaly. The negative anomaly belts near the trenches are caused by underlying masses of light rocks that are being held down by crustal forces, out of isostatic balance. The belts of negative anomalies associated with the island arc-trench systems prove that structures even more profound than the remarkable surface features lie in the earth beneath them. They show that the trenches are the primary surface features and the island arcs are merely accessory.

DEEP-FOCUS EARTHQUAKES. Another item confirms the great depth of disturbance beneath the island arc-trench systems—the distribution of earthquake foci. By modern methods not only can the geographic position of an earthquake epicenter be located but also the depth at which the shock took place. It has thus been observed that shallow earthquake foci occur along the deep-sea trenches, and that successively deeper foci extend under the adjacent island arcs and for several hundred kilometers inside them. These foci define a plane that descends into the earth, dipping from the trench beneath the island arc at an angle of about 35° to a depth of 300 kilometers, and beyond that at an angle of about 60°. Deepest recorded earthquakes have their foci at the astonishing depth of 700 kilometers. These zones of earthquake foci have been called *Benioff zones*, after Hugo Benioff, a seismologist of the California Institute of Technology, whose study of earthquakes first defined their geometry.

Recall that the Mohorovičić discontinuity, mentioned earlier as forming the base of the crust of the earth, lies at a depth of only 6 to 40 kilometers. We thus see that the disturbances that create the earthquakes near the is-

land arc-trench systems extend into the earth a score or more times as far as the mere crust with which we are mainly dealing.

The Antillean arc, like the island arc-trench systems of the Pacific, is followed by a zone of earthquake epicenters, with the deeper foci extending inward under the islands. However, so far as known, these extend only to relatively modest depths of about 250 kilometers; excessively deep foci like those found in the Pacific have not been recorded. The Caribbean Sea, inside the arc, is nearly aseismic by contrast—indicating the stability and cohesiveness of this segment of the earth's crust.

EXPLANATIONS OF ISLAND ARC-TRENCH STRUCTURE. So much is fact or reasonable inference; now we enter the realm of speculation. What is the origin of the island arc-trench structures?

Vening Meinesz and his associates, in order to explain the negative gravity anomaly belts they had discovered, proposed that the deficiency of mass implied by it was caused by a great downbuckle of sialic rocks of the crust termed a *tectogene*. The downbuckle in its early stages formed a deep-sea trench; later, sediments deposited in the trench were crushed and folded; finally, isostatic compensation asserted itself and the deformed mass of light rocks was raised into a mountain chain. But various geological and geophysical objections to the tectogene theory developed later; for example, the deep-sea trenches mostly lie in areas of simatic crust, so that not enough light crustal material would be available to form such a downbuckle and its anomaly.

Nevertheless, it was apparent that the anomaly was a product of structural forces in the crust. Its meaning, that of the Benioff zones, and of the island arc-trench systems, became clearer when the concept of plate tectonics was appreciated. The oceanic crust of the Pacific is moving outward toward its edges from spreading centers. At its edges the lithospheric slabs of the Pacific plate are being underthrust, or *subducted*, beneath the bordering plates, some of which are of continental crust, others themselves of oceanic crust (Fig. 59). The descending slabs extend downward beneath the bordering plates far below the level of any normal crust, until they are finally consumed and reincorporated into the earth's

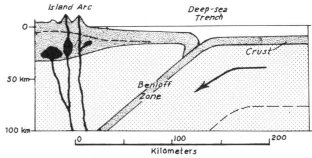

FIG. 59. Diagram of a subduction zone, showing its relation to a deep-sea trench, an island arc, and a Benioff zone.

mantle. Trenches, negative anomalies, and Benioff zones are manifestations of the subduction.

In the case of the West Indies, the crust of the Caribbean is a part of the Pacific plate, which is being carried eastward between the North American and South American plates and is impinging against the plate of the Atlantic sea floor, which it is overriding, creating the arc of the Lesser Antilles and the trench structure in front of it (Fig. 60). To the north, this structure still remains as the Puerto Rico Trench; farther south, where compression has been more advanced, it has been folded up in the Barbados Ridge.

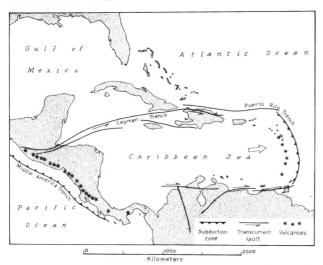

FIG. 60. Sketch map of the West Indies and Caribbean Sea, showing their present situation in terms of plate tectonics (the situation differed somewhat earlier). Compiled from King and Edmonston (1972), Molnar and Sykes (1969), and Marfait and Dinkelman (1972).

COMPARISONS OF WEST INDIES WITH NORTH AMERICAN GEOSYNCLINES. We have now carried our story far enough to hazard some judgments on our original question: Are the West Indies a modern analogue of a geosyncline?

In the West Indies there is a mountain belt still in a state of growth—parts emergent, parts still beneath the sea. The two ends show a mature mountain structure comparable to that in the Appalachian and Cordilleran systems of North America; the middle part is still mobile and immature. These structures are traceable northward and southward into the Cordilleras of North and South America, so that all are members of the same system of deformation, caused by impingement of the American plates against the Pacific plates.

The West Indies are an island arc-trench system comparable to systems that border the Pacific Ocean. Island arc-trench systems are the most active tectonic, seismic, and volcanic belts of the world today, yet they seem to lie on continuations of more mature mountain belts on the land. It is unlikely that their structural features are wholly novel and unrelated to the more mature mountain belts; rather, they are made up of the same sorts of structures, but now in process of growth.

In the ancient examples, eugeosynclinal rocks and structures that developed from them lay in the most mobile parts of the geosynclinal belts. The record of the rocks indicates that growth of the eugeosynclinal areas was attended by tectonic lands formed of uplifted earlier sediments and by chains of volcanic islands; these are analogous to the various concentric chains of modern island arcs. The record indicates that such tectonic and volcanic lands were separated by rapidly subsiding depositional troughs. In the modern examples deep-sea trenches alongside the island arcs are the fundamental structures and lie near the axis of the negative gravity anomaly. In the ancient examples, the anomalies have probably been obliterated by the great deformation and metamorphism to which the rocks have been subjected, and by restoration of isostatic equilibrium.

The miogeosynclinal areas, or those parts of the ancient geosynclines with which we are most familiar, might correspond to depositional basins on the concave sides of modern island arcs. In the modern as well as the ancient examples these are areas of slow subsidence covered by waters of shallow to intermediate depth, whose sediments were derived principally from the mobile central parts of the system. In the modern examples as well as the ancient we would expect that these sediments would be deformed only after the central part of the system had been consolidated.

Be that as it may, perhaps the principal lesson we can draw from our comparison between ancient geosynclines and mountain belts, and modern island arc-trench systems, is that neither are mere superficial features produced by processes of sedimentation and erosion or of loading and unloading of the crust. Instead, they appear to be products of an activity within the crust of the earth, or even far beneath the crust. The geosynclinal and mountain structures we can observe do not express the whole feature, but are merely surface manifestations of more deep-seated earth structures.

REFERENCES

2. *Gulf Coast area*

Fisk, H. N., and McFarlan, E. Jr., 1955, Late Quaternary deltaic deposits of the Mississippi River, *in* Poldervaart, Arie, ed., *The crust of the earth*: Geol. Soc. America Spec. Paper 62, pp. 279-302.

Lehner, Peter, 1969, Salt tectonics and Pleistocene stratigraphy on continental slope of northern Gulf of Mexico: *Am. Assoc. Petroleum Geologists Bull.*, v. 53, no. 12, pp. 2431-2479.

Martin, R. G., and Case, J. E., 1975, Geophysical studies in the Gulf of Mexico, *in* Nairn, A.E.M., and Stehli, F. G., *The ocean basins and margins*, Vol. 3, *Gulf of Mexico and Caribbean Sea*: Plenum Press, New York, pp. 65-106.

Murray, G. E., ed., 1952, Sedimentary volumes in Gulf Coastal Plain of United States and Mexico: *Geol. Soc. America Bull.*, v. 63, no. 12, pp. 1157-1228.

Uchupi, Elazar, and Emery, K. O., 1968, Structure of continental margin of Gulf Coast of United States: *Am. Assoc. Petroleum Geologists Bull.*, v. 52, no. 7, pp. 1162-1193.

Weaver, Paul, 1955, Gulf of Mexico, *in* Poldervaart, Arie, ed., *The crust of the earth*: Geol. Soc. America Spec. Paper 62, pp. 269-278.

Wilhelm, Oscar, and Ewing, Maurice, 1972, Geology and history of the Gulf of Mexico: *Geol. Soc. America Bull.*, v. 83, no. 3, pp. 575-600.

3. *West Indies*

Benioff, Hugo, 1954, Orogenesis and deep crustal structure; additional evidence from seismology: *Geol. Soc. America Bull.*, v. 65, no. 4, pp. 385-400.

Bucher, W. H., 1952, *Geologic structure and orogenic history of Venezuela*: Geol. Soc. America Mem. 49.

Bunce, E. T., Phillips, J. D., and Chase, R. L., 1974, Geophysical study of Antilles outer ridge, Puerto Rico Trench, and northeast margin of Caribbean Sea: *Am. Assoc. Petroleum Geologists Bull.*, v. 58, no. 1, pp. 106-123.

Case, J. E., 1975, Geophysical studies in the Caribbean Sea, *in* Nairn, A.E.M. and Stehli, F.G., eds., *The ocean basins and margins*, Vol. 3, *Gulf of Mexico and Caribbean Sea*: Plenum Press, New York, pp. 107-180.

Daviss, S. N., 1971, Barbados; a major submarine gravity slide: *Geol. Soc. America Bull.*, v. 82, no. 3, pp. 2593-2602.

Donnelly, T. W., ed., 1971, *Caribbean geophysical, tectonic, and petrologic studies*: Geol. Soc. America Mem. 130.

Ewing, Maurice, and Heezen, B. C., 1955, Puerto Rico Trench; topographic and geophysical data, *in* Poldervaart, Arie, ed., *The crust of the earth*: Geol. Soc. America Spec. Paper 62, p. 255-268.

Fisher, R. L., and Revelle, Roger, 1955, The trenches of the Pacific: *Scientific American*, v. 193, no. 5, pp. 36-41.

Hess, H. H., 1938, Gravity anomalies and island arc structure with particular reference to the West Indies: *Am. Philos. Soc. Proc.*, v. 79, pp. 71-96.

Khudoley, J. M., and Meyerhoff, A. A., 1971, *Paleogeography and geological history of Greater Antilles*: Geol. Soc. America Mem. 129.

Malfait, B. T., and Dinkelman, M. G., 1971, Circum-Caribbean tectonic and igneous activity and the evolution of the Caribbean plate: *Geol. Soc. American Bull.*, v. 83, no. 2, pp. 251-272.

Molnar, Peter, and Sykes, L. R., 1969, Tectonics of the Caribbean and Middle America regions from focal mechanisms and seismicity: *Geol. Soc. America Bull.*, v. 80, no. 9, pp. 1639-1684.

Roberts, R. J., and Irving, E. M., 1957, *Mineral deposits of Central America*: U.S. Geol. Survey Bull. 1034.

Schuchert, Charles, 1935, *Historical geology of the Antillean-Caribbean Region*: John Wiley & Sons, New York.

Senn, Alfred, 1940, Paleogene of Barbados and its bearing on history and structure of Antillean region: *Am. Assoc. Petroleum Geologists Bull.*, v. 24, pp. 1548-1610.

Toksöv, M. N., 1975, The subduction of the lithosphere: *Scientific American*, v. 233, no. 5, pp. 89-93.

Weeks, L. A., Lattimore, R. K., Harrison, R. B., Bassinger, B. G., and Merrill, G. F., 1971, Structural relations among Lesser Antilles, Venezuela, and Trinidad-Tobago: *Am. Assoc. Petroleum Geologists Bull.*, v. 55, no. 10, pp. 1741-1752.

Woodring, W. P., 1954, Caribbean land and sea through the ages: *Geol. Soc. America Bull.*, v. 65, no. 4, pp. 719-732.

CHAPTER VI

THE MOUNTAIN BELT OF WESTERN NORTH AMERICA; INTRODUCTION TO THE CORDILLERAN SYSTEM

1. GEOGRAPHIC FEATURES AND THE PROCESSES THAT SHAPED THEM

We take up now the mountain system of western North America, to which we will devote the remainder of this book. It is a belt of ranges, in part massive and continuous, in part disconnected and isolated, and of intermontane valleys, basins, and plateaus, which extends 800 to 1,600 kilometers inland from the Pacific Coast along the entire length of North America (Plate I).

Many of the varied features of the mountain system will be treated in this book, yet it will not be possible to do justice to all of them in view of the size and complexity of the system. Emphasis will therefore be given to the central segment lying mainly in the United States. It is thought that exposition of one segment of the Cordillera will explain much of the remainder in Canada, Alaska, and Mexico, although some different and novel features do occur in these regions.

THE NAME CORDILLERA. The western mountains are commonly termed the *North American Cordillera* or *Cordilleran system.* Why use this rather odd name? Some general term is needed, and none of the more familiar names such as Rocky Mountains, Sierra Nevada, Coast Ranges, or Sierra Madre adequately covers the whole.

The name Cordillera is derived from the Spanish word for "cord" or "rope," and is used in that language as we in English would use "chain" in the sense of a mountain chain. In Spanish the name is pronounced Cor-di-*yerra,* but in North America it is frequently Anglicized to Cor-*dill*-era.

In the Western Hemisphere, the term Cordillera was first applied to the Cordillera de los Andes or Andes Mountains, which form a compact and continuous bundle of ranges along the western side of South America. Later, the term was extended by the German geographer Alexander von Humboldt to the more complex and less compact system of ranges in the western part of the continent to the north.

BROADER RELIEF FEATURES. As with the mountain belt southeast of the Interior Lowlands, we can introduce the one on the west by examining the maps—first physiographic maps, next geologic maps—and then pass on to features not evident from maps alone.

If we recall the Appalachian Mountains southeast of the Interior Lowlands (Chapter IV, section 1), it is at once evident that the mountains of the Cordillera on the west are both wider and higher. In mid-section in the United States between San Francisco and Denver the mountain belt is about 1,600 kilometers wide and includes the highest points of the forty-eight states— Mount Whitney of California projecting to 4,418 meters, and Mount Elbert in the Rocky Mountains of Colorado projecting to 4,389 meters. Northward and southward from this mid-section, the Cordilleran ranges are relatively lower and narrower, but even compared with these parts the Appalachian Mountains are insignificant.

PHYSIOGRAPHIC SUBDIVISIONS. In the segment between San Francisco and Denver we cross a number of contrasting regions (Plate I). Along the Pacific Coast on either side of San Francisco Bay are the *Coast Ranges.* Inland follows the *Great Valley* of California drained by the Sacramento and San Joaquin Rivers, beyond which rise the lofty *Sierra Nevada.* East of the Sierra is the lower and much more broken country of the *Great Basin,* whose surface does not drain to the sea but into interior basins. Beyond the Great Basin is the high tableland of the *Colorado Plateau* at whose farther edge stand the *Rocky Mountains*. Passing through the defiles of these ranges we come abruptly to the *Great Plains* on the edge of the Interior Lowlands, which, by contrast with the broken country we have left behind, appear as level and featureless as the ocean.

But these units are not constant along the strike of the Cordillera. Northward in Oregon, Washington, and Idaho the extension of part of the features just mentioned is masked by a great sheet of volcanic rocks, expressed partly by the *Cascade Range*, with its line of high, young volcanic cones, and partly by the *Columbia Plateaus* to the east, mantled by gently dipping lavas.

Still farther north in Canada, the Cordillera draws together into a narrower, more continuous bundle of ranges that intervene between the Pacific border and the Interior Lowlands. These continue into Alaska, where they partly run out to sea in the Aleutian Islands and partly cross Bering Strait into Asia.

Southward, also, the high Sierra Nevada, Colorado Plateau, and Rocky Mountains die away, so that near the Mexican border the Cordillera is merely a succession of little mountains separated by desert basins, a fact utilized in laying out the line of one of the transcontinental railroads—the Southern Pacific between Texas and Los Angeles.

In Mexico beyond, the mountains rise again to form two groups of ranges: the *Sierra Madre Occidental* and the *Sierra Madre Oriental*. Here, relations of the Cordillera differ significantly from those farther north; instead of fronting eastward on the Interior Lowlands and Central Stable Region, it now faces directly on the Gulf Coastal Plain and Gulf of Mexico. Still farther south in northern Central America (Guatemala and Honduras) the continuation of the Cordillera turns eastward and passes thence into the Greater Antilles of the West Indies (Chapter V, section 3).

GEOGRAPHICAL VERSUS GEOLOGICAL "MOUNTAINS." We have made an unflattering comparison between the Appalachians and the Cordillera with respect to the breadth and height of their present mountains; certainly all the surface features of the Appalachians are much less impressive. But we should recall the distinction we made earlier between geographical and geological mountains (Chapter I, section 2).

The Appalachians were not always so low and unimpressive. During the last half of Paleozoic time when their construction was in process of completion, the Appalachians and kindred ranges must have been a high, massive mountain system along the eastern and southeastern sides of the North American continent—raised partly by deformation of the rocks themselves, partly by processes following the deformation. Subsequently,

crustal forces became quiescent so that the system was worn down and partly buried or submerged. The present ranges are erosion remnants lying well inland from the former southeastern edge of the highland.

The Cordilleran system is wider and higher than the Appalachians mainly because it is younger. Main orogeny took place in the last half of Mesozoic time and early in Tertiary time. As in the Appalachians, the initial features shaped by this orogeny have been deeply eroded and partly buried, but height and width have been maintained by a continuation of crustal mobility through much of Tertiary and Quaternary time. The eastern half of the Cordillera is now largely stable, but modern earthquake shocks indicate that in the western half from Nevada to the Pacific Coast crustal processes are still at work.

Thus, even though the Cordilleran system began to grow later than the Appalachians, their present form is not caused directly by folding, thrust faulting, metamorphism, and plutonism—the combination of orogenic processes we have described in the Appalachians. Such structures occur in the Cordillera as well, but they were formed mainly during an early chapter in its history. As in the Appalachians, other events took place later which had a greater effect in shaping the present surface. These later events and structures were more extensive than in the Appalachians and have greatly confused the initial pattern, as may be seen on both the physiographic and geologic maps.

PROCESSES THAT MODIFIED THE FUNDAMENTAL CORDILLERAN STRUCTURE. Among the processes that operated during Tertiary and Quaternary time to modify the original orogenic structure of the Cordillera were the following:

(a) Volcanic activity and accompanying shallow intrusions. Such volcanism occurred during Tertiary and Quaternary time at one place or another over nearly the whole Cordilleran area, although there were several conspicuous volcanic centers, including those in the Cascade Range and Columbia Plateau of the northwestern United States and the Sierra Madre Occidental of western Mexico.

(b) Formation of basins between the mountain uplifts soon after the main orogeny in which Tertiary and especially Eocene sediments were deposited. Such basins are extensive in the Central and Southern Rocky Mountains of Wyoming, Colorado, and adjacent states.

(c) Breakup of the deformed terrane by block faulting resulting from crustal tension or other causes to produce a succession of block mountains and intervening basins. Block-faulting has largely shaped the surface forms of the Great Basin between the Colorado Plateau and Sierra Nevada, and the Sierra is itself a tilted mountain block larger than the rest. Block-faulting also took place along the Rio Grande in New Mexico and at many other places.

(d) Regional uplift of broad areas without much folding or faulting in later Tertiary and Quaternary time. Such uplifts late in the history of a mountain system have also taken place in the Appalachians and other mountain belts, probably because of isostatic and other crustal adjustments. Regional uplift is thus responsible for much of the present height of the Central and Southern Rocky Mountains and Colorado Plateau. Streams invigorated by the uplift have etched out the mountain ranges of the first two areas and have carved the myriad canyons in the third.

(e) Continuing sedimentation, deformation, and orogeny along the Pacific Coast, notably in the Coast Ranges of California, where the Tertiary and even parts of the Quaternary strata have been greatly folded and faulted, and where seismic records indicate that the crust is still active.

(f) In the Coast Ranges of California and elsewhere, development of great faults such as the San Andreas, along which movements were not upward and downward but sidewise—that is, transcurrent faults with strike-slip displacement.

Significance of geographic units. Most of the present landscape of the Cordillera has resulted from the processes that operated in Tertiary and Quaternary time. Present geographic units thus have only indirect meaning in terms of fundamental orogenic structure.

This is most evident in the volcanic fields of the northwestern United States, where lavas and other eruptive products effectively bury the underlying structure.

Also, the Sierra Nevada is made up of rocks with a complex fundamental structure, yet its present shape has little relation to that structure. The fundamental structures are much more extensive than the present range, and the Sierra is a block that was raised within them by later faulting and tilting.

The most confusing geographic name used for any part of the Cordillera is "Rocky Mountains." It came into use by explorers, trappers, and pioneers a century and a half ago to denote the first mountain chain encountered after crossing the Great Plains. This might mean any of the diverse frontal structures of the Cordillera—the uplifted masses of basement rock in Colorado, or the folded and faulted geosynclinal strata of Montana and Alberta; outlying peaks of intrusive igneous rock in the Great Plains of Montana have been called the "Little Rocky Mountains." Geographers have perpetuated the name because high summits of these diverse rocks and structures extend from Canada southeastward into Colorado and New Mexico as though they were parts of a single system. But in order to give the term any geological meaning it will be necessary in this account to break the "Rocky Mountains" into several parts—the *Northern, Central,* and *Southern Rocky Mountains*.

2. THE FUNDAMENTAL OROGENIC STRUCTURE

Where, in the midst of all this confusion of surface features are features like those of the Appalachians, which we had come to believe were characteristic of mountaiin belts in general—the continental platform, miogeosyncline, and eugeosyncline of the formative stage, and the foreland, sedimentary belt, and crystalline belt of the orogenic stage?

In the Cordillera, as in the Appalachians, our problem is to clear away the battering and modification that the system has undergone after the climactic orogeny. Here, however, we must not only restore what has been worn down, buried, and submerged but also unravel those features that were imposed on the fundamental structures later—the uplifts and downwarps, folds and faults, and igneous features that have been responsible for most of the surface forms.

Orogenic features in Canada. Our analysis will be simplest if we begin with the Cordillera in Canada, where resemblances are strongest between the mountains on the west and those southeast of the Central Stable Region.

In Canada the "Rocky Mountains" of local terminology front the Great Plains eastward and are made up of miogeosynclinal strata, mainly Paleozoic but with Triassic and Jurassic above, topped by clastic wedges of Cretaceous age. These have been thrown into long folds and thrust blocks like those in the Valley and Ridge province of the Appalachians. The interior ranges west of the Rocky Mountains consist of eugeosynclinal rocks, likewise of Paleozoic, Triassic, and Jurassic age, which have been heavily deformed, metamorphosed, and plutonized.

Here, as in the Appalachians, climactic orogeny was mainly earlier on the side toward the ocean, in the eugeosynclinal area, than it was on the side toward the continent in the miogeosynclinal area. Much of the eugeosynclinal area was deformed and plutonized during the latter half of the Mesozoic time, whereas the miogeosynclinal area was not deformed until near the end of the Mesozoic or a little later. According to the terminology used in the United States, the western part was deformed during the *Nevadan orogeny* and the eastern part during the *Laramide orogeny*.

Geologists formerly pictured these two orogenies as having produced two mountain systems: an earlier one to the west and a later one formed alongside it to the east. Concepts we have developed in studying the Appalachians suggest, on the contrary, that the whole Cordillera is a unit that was formed by a continuing process of deformation.

EASTERN RANGES AND PLATEAUS OF THE UNITED STATES. When we proceed southward from Canada into the United States, relations become more complex, and additional structural elements appear.

If we define the eastern edge of the miogeosyncline as a line along which Paleozoic rocks thicken abruptly, with Lower Cambrian wedging in at their base, that line would not be at the eastern edge of the Rocky Mountains near Denver, but at the western edge of the Colorado Plateau in Utah. At least a third of the Cordilleran system in mid-section in the United States—comprising the Southern Rocky Mountains and Colorado Plateau—thus lies outside the miogeosynclinal belt and consists of structural elements unlike any in the Appalachians. For want of a better name, we will call this part of the Cordillera the *Eastern Ranges and Plateaus*.

The Colorado Plateau is an old stable block, a part of the continental platform when this was outlined in Cambrian time (Chapter III, section 4), which later was detached from the main platform by development of structures in the Rocky Mountains to the east. Its strata still lie nearly flat over wide areas, but elsewhere they have been thrown into broad folds or depressed into basins that were filled with Tertiary sediments or covered by lavas.

The Southern Rocky Mountains on the east were likewise originally part of the continental platform, but during later Paleozoic time they grew into a mountain belt that was the northwestern extension of the Wichita system. Its folds were rejuvenated and accentuated during the *Laramide orogeny* toward the end of Mesozoic time. The region is now a succession of great anticlinal uplifts, many raised so high that their cores of basement rock are brought to the surface, with deep intervening downfolds containing sediments that are much deformed.

MIOGEOSYNCLINAL AND EUGEOSYNCLINAL BELTS IN THE UNITED STATES. We can now return to the main belt of the Cordillera, which passes southward from Canada behind and to the west of the Eastern Ranges and Plateaus.

Miogeosynclinal rocks appear west of the edge of the Colorado Plateau and continue thence across western Utah into Nevada. Here is a great thickness of Paleozoic carbonate rocks with Triassic and Jurassic strata at the top. Orogenic deformation of the miogeosynclinal rocks must have occurred before the end of Mesozoic time, or before the climax of Laramide orogeny in the Rocky Mountains to the east (the Sevier orogeny). Clastic wedges in the Cretaceous rocks thicken westward toward the Great Basin, along the edges of which they contain coarse conglomerates that lie unconformably on earlier deformed strata.

Farther west in the Great Basin, in the western half of Nevada, Paleozoic and earlier Mesozoic miogeosynclinal rocks give place to eugeosynclinal rocks of the same ages, which continue with greater development into the Sierra Nevada and Klamath Mountains beyond. In the Sierra Nevada and Klamath Mountains they have not only been deformed but have been metamorphosed and invaded by felsic plutonic rocks. As in Canada, orogeny reached its climax earlier in the eugeosynclinal area than in areas to the east. Important Paleozoic movements took place in the eastern part of the eugeosyncline in Nevada, but the main deformation here and westward took place during the *Nevadan orogeny*, which extended, from one place to another, from early in the Jurassic until well into Cretaceous time. On the west sides of the Sierra Nevada and Klamath Mountains, Cretaceous sediments dip gently off the heavily deformed earlier rocks; neither the Cretaceous nor the later Jurassic of the Coast Ranges to the west are regionally metamorphosed.

In this segment of the Cordillera, as farther north, its structures were formerly interpreted as consisting of two systems of different ages; one in the Rocky Mountains formed during the Laramide orogeny, another in the Sierra Nevada formed during the Nevadan orogeny. In this segment contrast between the two has been heightened because the two mountain ranges are now separated by a wide tract of diverse country—the Colorado Plateau and Great Basin, whose place in the Cordilleran pattern had not been well understood.

We now know, however, that Nevadan orogeny was itself prolonged and that deformation at times intermediate between the Nevadan and Laramide orogenies took place in the Great Basin. The Cretaceous conglomerates and clastic wedges along its eastern edge are products of the *Sevier orogeny*, which overlaps in time both the Nevadan and Laramide orogenies. Crustal activity progressed eastward across the Cordillera through the latter half of Mesozoic time, and it is best to consider the whole mountain belt as a single system formed by a continuing process.

OROGENIC FEATURES IN MEXICO. South of the complex segment in the United States the Cordilleran system narrows again, mainly by the ending of the Eastern Ranges and Plateaus. In Mexico Paleozoic rocks are only scantily exposed, so that little is known of the earlier history of the system. The available record is mainly of Mesozoic and later time.

To the east is a broad Mesozoic miogeosyncline in which great thicknesses of Jurassic and Cretaceous limestones accumulated; these are now thrown into the series of parallel folds of the Sierra Madre Oriental, which face the Gulf Coastal Plain and in places the Gulf of Mexico itself.

Fundamental structures farther west are much obscured by a thick pile of Tertiary lavas that forms the great dissected plateaus of the Sierra Madre Occidental in western Mexico; the boundary between the miogeosynclinal and eugeosynclinal rocks is thus not plain. However, the basement of the peninsula of Baja California along the Pacific Ocean is much like that of the Sierra Nevada farther north—a body of metamorphosed Mesozoic and earlier rocks. The basement rocks of Baja California probably originated in the eugeosynclinal part of the Cordilleran system.

3. GEOLOGICAL EXPLORATION OF THE CORDILLERAN SYSTEM

Before we describe details of the Cordilleran rocks and structures, it will be well to set forth how some of our knowledge of them was acquired. Our knowledge was not "handed to us on a silver platter," nor was it delivered in one package. It was gained through the labor of many geologists working over a wide region, mostly within the last hundred years.

WESTERN HISTORY IN GENERAL. The reader is doubtless familiar with the broader facts of the opening of the West:

Of acquisition by the United States of the northwestern part of its domain by division of the Oregon Country with Great Britain along the 49th parallel into Oregon Territory (later to become the states of Oregon, Washington, and Idaho) on the south, and into British Columbia on the north. Of acquisition of the southwestern part by cession from Mexico as an aftermath of the Mexican War of 1846 and 1847.

Of the discoveries of mineral riches in the new domain: discovery of gold at Sutter's Mill at Coloma in the foothills of the Sierra Nevada, and the great Gold Rush to California, which followed in 1849; the discovery of silver in the Comstock Lode of Nevada a decade later, in time to provide an economic boost to San Francisco when prosperity of Gold Rush days was declining; and other discoveries a little later, such as those in the Rocky Mountains of Colorado, which for many years made Denver a mining capital.

Of the filling up of the region by settlers from the East: the great trek to the Oregon Country, beginning even before United States sovereignty had been established; the migration of the Mormons to Utah, with Brigham Young going ahead of the main party to find "the place," which was to become Salt Lake City; the rapid settlement of California, first in the north, later in the south; and many others.

Exploration occurred simultaneously with the rest of the human drama. First exploration was by fur trappers and "mountain men," who ranged over the whole country as early as the 1820s. But although they found out much about the land, they did little accurate surveying and left few written records. First scientific exploration was largely geographical. Early scientific explorers such as John Charles Frémont devoted their efforts to finding routes of travel and location of mountains, rivers, deserts, and spots favorable for agriculture.

Later it became evident that something more must be learned about what this new land was made of—as a guide to mineral development and to aid the settlement of people who were arriving from the East in increasing numbers.

PACIFIC RAILROAD SURVEYS (1853–1854). The first serious geological exploration of the West came in the 1850s immediately before the Civil War, when there was set up a series of "explorations and surveys to ascertain the most practicable and economical route for a railroad from the Mississippi River to the Pacific Ocean," so that the west could be joined with the settled eastern part of the country by communications better than the Prairie Schooner or Pony Express.

These explorations were made by Army Engineers under the direction of the Secretary of War, Jefferson Davis, who was later to attain greater fame as President of the Confederate States of America. In reports of these explorations one sees the names of many men who came more into public eye during the Civil War. One of the surveys, for example, was under Captain John Pope, later to become the General Pope who led the Union forces to their great defeat at the Second Battle of Bull Run in Virginia in 1862. Pope must have been a better engineer than he was a leader of men, or at least a leader of great armies into battle.

All these exploring parties were accompanied by geologists, whose observations provide the first idea of the geology of many parts of the West. Or perhaps we can call them "geologists," for geological observations were only part of their assigned duties. Many of them had been educated in medicine and did double duty as physicians for the party and as scientific explorers.

GEOLOGICAL SURVEYS AFTER THE CIVIL WAR. Geological study of the West, rather than mere exploration, did not begin until after the Civil War had ended. Opening the West now began apace. Many young men who were mustered out of service found ordinary civilian existence dull and searched for new fields and new careers. Some of these young men found an outlet for their energies in scientific exploration of the West.

It seems sad that today these men remain merely names in musty books, to be memorized by students, when once they were full of life, enthusiasm, and a spirit of adventure. They thought and felt much as young men of our own day who have been mustered out of service after our later wars, but at that time the great West was still open before them.

Some of these young men with more vision and genius for organization than the rest worked up and presented to Congress proposals for geological explorations and surveys of the western country.

U. S. GEOLOGICAL AND GEOGRAPHICAL SURVEY OF

THE TERRITORIES (HAYDEN SURVEY). Among these men was Ferdinand Vandiveer Hayden, who had served as a physician in the Medical Corps during the Civil War. He first received a grant from Congress of a few thousand dollars a year for geological and geographical surveys of the country immediately west of the Missouri River. Appropriations were gradually expanded until they reached the munificent sum (for those days) of $75,000 a year. Hayden's field of inquiry was also expanded, and between 1870 and 1880 large crews of his geologists and surveyors were sent each year for surveys and studies in Colorado, Wyoming, and adjacent territories. Geologists of the Hayden Survey were among the first white men to see the geysers and other wonders at the head of the Yellowstone River, and their reports were influential in setting aside this area as the first National Park.

GEOLOGICAL EXPLORATION OF THE FORTIETH PARALLEL (KING SURVEY). Another of the young men was Clarence Rivers King, who proposed to Congress that the resources along the line of the new transcontinental railroad (the Union Pacific and Central Pacific) should be explored and studied. This survey was intended to cover a belt of country on each side of the railroad, approximately along the Fortieth Parallel from Wyoming to California.

King's organization was the aristocrat of the surveys. It was staffed largely by men trained at Yale or Harvard, many of whom had taken advanced study in German universities. It is related that, later on when all the surveys had been combined into a single U.S. Geological Survey, the men of the former King Survey would not speak to those of the former Hayden and Powell Surveys if they met them on the street—these were too plebeian to be noticed.

King himself, in his day, must have been a very dynamic and charming man. His enthusiasm for geology and his way of presenting the facts of science to laymen made him the friend of important people in Washington—senators, congressmen, and many others.

King's most spectacular achievement was really a side issue of the Fortieth Parallel Survey itself, and had to do with the "great diamond swindle." In 1872 two weather-beaten prospectors, Philip Arnold and John Slack, came out of the mountains and presented themselves to William Ralston, president of the Bank of California in San Francisco. They showed him a bag of diamonds that they had collected at some remote spot in the West. They came at a favorable psychological time, for a speculative madness had taken over San Francisco after the opening of the Comstock Lode. Every day brought disclosures of new mineral deposits in the West—of gold, silver, and the baser metals. The Kimberley diamond fields had been opened in South Africa only a few years before. Could there not be similar deposits in western North America? Ralston, a great plunger and speculator who

had made a fortune in the Comstock mines, was greatly excited, and made up his mind to gain control of the new diamond deposit.

After some persuasion the prospectors consented to have their find examined on the spot, provided the inspectors were brought in blindfolded. The inspectors came back even more impressed than Ralston—diamonds were all over the place, as well as rubies, sapphires, and emeralds—on the surface of the ground, in ant hills, in crevices in the rocks. A sample of the stones collected by them was submitted to Tiffany's in New York and Mr. Tiffany personally valued the sample alone as worth $150,000. The prospectors reluctantly sold their claim for $360,000 with a stock interest that they sold in turn for $300,000, a return of $660,000 in all.

The San Francisco group then organized the San Francisco & New York Mining & Commercial Co. to develop the deposit, capitalized at $10,000,000. All the stock could easily have been sold to the avid public in San Francisco, but instead it was offered to twenty-five of the outstanding business and financial leaders of the city.

It was at this point that Clarence King entered the picture. Returning from a field season in Nevada in the fall of 1872, he learned of the new discovery, which rumor placed at such widely separated points as Arizona, New Mexico, and Utah. He wondered whether the deposit lay within the area covered by his Fortieth Parallel Survey, and whether it had been somehow overlooked during investigations of the survey.

"Feeling that so marvelous a deposit as the diamond fields must not exist within the official limits of the Fortieth Parallel Survey, unknown and unstudied, I availed myself the intimate knowledge possessed by the gentlemen of my corps, not only of Colorado and Wyoming, but of the trail of every party traveled there, and was enabled to find the spot without difficulty."

This turned out to be in the northern foothills of the Uinta Mountains, only a short distance south of the Union Pacific Railroad. Going to the place in bitter November weather, King and his trusted subordinates observed that it lay in a region of tilted sedimentary rocks without any evidence of igneous intrusion or mineralization. In addition, the association of diamonds, rubies, sapphires, and emeralds seemed incongruous. They found that most of the stones had lain on the surface; none was embedded in the rocks themselves, and some even bore marks of the work of jewelers! Tiffany's appraisal to the contrary, the stones were very inferior—mere jeweler's waste that had been bought up and planted for purpose of fraud. Bit by bit, contrary to their expectations, King and his men were forced to conclude that Ralston and his friends had fallen into a trap.

Having made up his mind that the find was a fraud, King traveled night and day to San Francisco and demanded of Ralston and the Bank of California that sales of stock be stopped at once, announcing that he intended to publish his findings. All hell must have broken loose over the head of this young government geologist, for he was facing up to some of the richest and most powerful men in California. But he stood his ground and the company collapsed.

That was the beginning of the end for poor Ralston, whose bank failed in the panic of 1875, and he ended as a suicide in the waters of the Golden Gate. The prospectors disappeared, but Arnold was eventually traced to Kentucky where, on threat of lawsuit, he surrendered $150,000 of his ill-gotten gains.

But I have strayed too far into this side-issue. Let us return to the geological story.

U.S. Geographical and Geological Survey of the Rocky Mountain Region (Powell Survey). Another survey was led by John Wesley Powell—Major Powell who served under Grant in the Civil War and lost an arm at the Battle of Shiloh, who was afterwards a teacher of science at a little college in Illinois. Like the other men of whom I have spoken, he had the urge to get into the West, and organized summer expeditions to the Rocky Mountains under the auspices of the Illinois Academy of Science. Once in the West, the country cast its spell, and Illinois saw little more of him.

As Powell explored beyond the Rocky Mountains he became aware of the great remaining challenge of western exploration. The head streams of the Colorado River, the Green and the Grand, were known to enter the Colorado Plateau on the northeast; the Colorado was known to issue from the plateau on the southwest. Almost nothing was known of the river between. Why not find out? Why not descend the river by boat through the whole plateau country?

To carry out this daring design, he enlisted the aid of the Smithsonian Institution, the first Federal support he had received. On May 24, 1869, his four little boats cast off into the Green River at Green River Station, Wyoming, on the line of the newly built Union Pacific Railroad.

What followed was one of the great adventures of western exploration. We do not need to dwell on the perils and excitements of the trip; they are wonderfully set forth in Powell's own account of his "Exploration of the Colorado River of the West." On August 30 the expedition came out of the lower end of the canyon, and were welcomed by Mormon settlers of the Virgin River valley in Nevada.

But of the nine men who began the trip, three were missing. In the last discouraging week, with provisions nearly gone and formidable rapids still ahead, some of the party concluded that there was no hope of completing the river journey, and they begged Powell to give up and scale the canyon walls on foot. After much debate the party divided, six continuing by boat, three setting

off to climb their way out. Unfortunately, the three on foot were waylaid and killed by Indians before they reached the settlements.

But Powell was more than an adventurer. He was a scientist at heart, something of a crusader for his beliefs, and probably also an ambitious man. His thrilling adventure was designed to "put him on the map" in western geological studies. On the strength of his exploration still another organization was set up by Congress, the U.S. Geographical and Geological Survey of the Rocky Mountain Region (part of the time also called U.S. Geological and Geographical Survey of the Territories, Second Division). The name was a misnomer, as the work of the survey was largely in the Colorado Plateau rather than the Rocky Mountains. It was never as large as the other surveys, did not receive as much money from Congress, and mapped less country. But its contributions were as significant, or more so, than the rest for the theories of the West and the theories of geology.

Powell had a strong social conscience and strong convictions about the needs of the West. He was concerned over the fate of the Indians and the fate of the white settlers too, and was one of the first to realize that western resources were exhaustible—that the timber, soil, water, and mineral resources had limits of exploitation, and must be *conserved* if permanent, prosperous communities were to arise in the region. Although these aspects of Powell's career are important in the history of the West at large, we are more concerned with his geological achievements and those of his men.

The Colorado Plateau was a wonderful place to develop new principles of geology—much of it a bare desert region in which the rocks are well exposed and laid out on a vast scale with great simplicity of form. Over wide tracts the strata dip gently, but here and there they are bent abruptly into great arches or flexures, all exposed in cross-section on the walls of the myriad canyons. These structures could be observed and analyzed in a manner seldom possible elsewhere.

Then, too, there were problems of river work and erosion. What made the Grand Canyon—or any other canyon or valley? It is well to remember that only twenty or thirty years before, Charles Darwin, the great British naturalist, in his account of "The Voyage of the Beagle" around the world, ascribed every great canyon or chasm he saw to "some great cataclysm of nature," and every great escarpment to erosion by the sea at some former time and level—not to erosion by streams on the land. Darwin was a young man at the time of his voyage, but his ideas were not mere youthful fancies. He was well trained in science, and his conclusions represented the prevailing scientific thinking of his day.

Powell did not invent the theory of stream erosion; an unfashionable minority of geologists had realized its importance long before. But his work and that of his men in the Colorado Plateau did much to establish the theory against opposing views. Although the Colorado Plateau is dry and bare, it was proved that the gigantic chasm of the Grand Canyon was cut by the stream now flowing in it. Moreover, this was not the whole story; there was an additional great denudation of the surface of the plateau, mainly during a time before the canyon cutting. The rim of the Grand Canyon is formed by the Kaibab Limestone of the Permian age. Off to the north, the Kaibab is succeeded by younger Triassic, Jurassic, and Cretaceous formations, all of which once overlay the Grand Canyon region and have now been stripped away by processes of denudation.

Also, many of the rivers showed a curious disregard for the folds in the plateau. The Green River, for example, flows directly across the great fold of the Uinta Mountains (Fig. 72), whereas by only a slight detour it could have passed around the end of the mountains. Why? For this Powell developed the principle of antecedent streams—streams that were flowing across the country before the uplifts began, and were able to continue cutting down as the uplifts were raised across their courses. Some of Powell's supposed antecedent streams are now believed to have originated in other ways, but the principle remains valid.

Powell's co-workers also made important contributions:

Major Clarence Edward Dutton worked for Powell from 1875 to 1891 while on leave from the Ordinance Department of the U.S. Army. Among his other tasks Dutton filled in many of the geological details of the Grand Canyon that had been so boldly sketched by Powell himself. Dutton's publications are notable for containing some of the most vivid writing in American geological reports.

Grove Karl Gilbert studied the laccoliths of the Henry Mountains near the center of the Colorado Plateau, which he found had been formed by blister-like masses of igneous rock that had domed the strata above them. In explorations farther west before he joined Powell, he concluded that the peculiar mountain ranges of the Great Basin had been shaped by block-faulting, the blocks being uplifted on faults along their edges, the faults now largely concealed by outwash from the ranges themselves. Gilbert went on later to study the great vanished lakes of the Great Basin, especially *Lake Bonneville* of which Great Salt Lake is the shrunken remnant.

(In this account I have purposely ignored the fourth western survey, the *U.S. Geographical Surveys West of the One-hundredth Meridian*, under the direction of Lieut. George Montague Wheeler, but its objectives were primarily topographic mapping for military purposes. It is true that geologists, including Gilbert, had accompanied some of its expeditions, but they usually

transferred at the first opportunity to one of the more geologically oriented surveys.)

CONSOLIDATION OF THE SURVEYS. As these different surveys progressed they inevitably came into conflict, for the areas they covered began to overlap, with much duplication of effort and much rivalry between men and organizations.

A phase of this duplication was that of the vertebrate paleontologists, Othneil Charles Marsh and Edward Drinker Cope. Marsh was located at Yale and served with the King and Powell Surveys, whereas Cope was located in Philadelphia and served with the Hayden Survey. They competed for fossil finds. At times one of the men, when he discovered a new bone in the field, would dash off a description on the spot and send it to a scientific journal by telegram from the nearest railroad station so as to obtain publication before his rival. All this was a side issue to the main conflict between the surveys and seems only amusing now, but it was bitterly felt at the time. The rivalry is significant because both Marsh and Cope were wealthy, influential men, each of whom had a strong following and many friends in Congress.

The real difficulties were deeper and were not merely a struggle between intellectuals and theorists. They were as serious as any duplication between government agencies today, and much of the future of the development of the West depended on how the problem would be resolved.

After congressional investigations through several years and the consideration of various alternative plans, the warring surveys were consolidated in 1879 into a single United States Geological Survey. The consolidation owed much to the negotiation and scheming of Powell, although he remained behind the scenes and had retired to the Smithsonian Institution to direct his Bureau of American Ethnology. Clarence King was named first director of the united bureau.

But some spark seemed to have gone out of King since the bold adventure of the Fortieth Parallel Survey. He was puzzled as to how to organize the functions of the new organization and was more interested in mining promotion for himself. After a year he resigned, and Powell took his place as director, a post he held for nearly fifteen years. In those years he did much to organize the Geological Survey on its present footing, and also to carry out his ideas on conservation in the West.

AFTERMATH. After Powell's day the Geological Survey became the "mother" of many other government bureaus, for its functions expanded until they had to be split from the parent organization—the Bureau of Mines to deal with mining technology, the Bureau of Reclamation to deal with use of water for irrigation, the Forest Service to deal with timber resources, and others. The Geological Survey has retained its essential core—a study and mapping of geological features in the west and elsewhere, and appraisal of the mineral resources that the rocks contain.

There are many sequels to the story—the geologists who continued to investigate the Cordilleran region for the U.S. Geological Survey, the Geological Survey of Canada, and other organizations public and private; the things they discovered, the conclusions they drew, and the controversies in which they became involved, and how this resulted in our present knowledge of the region. But all these sequels are too long to set down here; we will mention some of them at appropriate places in later chapters.

REFERENCES

1. *Geographic features*
    King, P. B., 1958, Evolution of modern surface features of western North America, *in* Hubbs, C. L., ed., *Zoogeography*: Am. Assoc. Advancement of Science Publ. 51, pp. 3-60.
    Thornbury, W. D., 1965, *Regional geomorphology of the United States*: John Wiley & Sons, New York, pp. 322-552.
2. *Fundamental orogenic structure*
    Burchfiel, B. C., and Davis, G. A., 1972, Structural framework and evolution of the southern part of the Cordilleran orogen in the United States: *Am. Jour. Sci.*, v. 272, no. 2, pp. 97-118.
    Douglas, R.J.W., and others, 1970, Geology of western Canada, *in Geology and economic minerals of Canada*: Canada Geol. Survey Econ. Geol. Rept. 1 (5th ed.), pp. 366-488.
    Gilluly, James, 1963, The tectonic evolution of the western United States: *Geol. Soc. London Quart. Jour.*, v. 119, pp. 133-174.
    Hamilton, Warren, and Myers, W. B., 1966, Cenozoic tectonics of the western United States: *Reviews of Geophysics*, v. 4, no. 4, pp. 509-549.
    Mallory, W. W., ed., 1972, *Geologic atlas of the Rocky Mountain Region*: Rocky Mountain Assoc. Geologists, Denver.
    Maxwell, J. C., 1974, Early western margin of the United States, *in* Burk, Creighton, and Drake, Charles, *Geology of continental margins*: Springer-Verlag, Berlin, pp. 831-852.

    Stille, Hans, 1936, Die entwicklung des Amerikanschen Kordilleransystems in zeit und raum: *Prussischen Akad. Wiss. Sitzungberichten*, Phys. Math. Kl., v. 15, p. 134-155.
3. *Geological exploration of the Cordilleran system*
    Bartlett, R. A., 1962, *Great surveys of the American West*: Univ. of Oklahoma Press, Norman.
    Darrah, W. C., 1951, *Powell of the Colorado*: Princeton Univ. Press.
    Merrill, G. P., 1924, *The first hundred years of American geology*: Yale Univ. Press, New Haven, chap. 8, pp. 500-552.
    Powell, J. W., 1875, *Exploration of the Colorado River of the West and its tributaries*: Washington. (Reprinted as *The exploration of Colorado River*: Univ. Chicago Press, 1957.)
    Rickard, T. A., 1932, *A history of American mining*: Am. Inst. Min. Eng. series (especially "The great diamond hoax," pp. 380-396).
    Stegner, Wallace, 1954, *Beyond the Hundredth Meridian*: Houghton-Mifflin Co., Boston.
    Stone, Irving, 1956, *Men to match my mountains; the opening of the far west, 1840-1900*: Doubleday & Co., Garden City, New York.
    Wilkins, Thurman, 1958, *Clarence King; a biography*: Macmillan Co., New York.

CHAPTER VII

THE EASTERN RANGES AND PLATEAUS;
A NOVEL STRUCTURAL ELEMENT

1. A NOVEL FEATURE OF AMERICAN GEOLOGY

The first unit of the Cordillera that we will consider will be the Central and Southern Rocky Mountains, the ranges of New Mexico, and the Colorado Plateau—that is, the ranges extending from central Montana through Wyoming and Colorado into New Mexico and the plateaus behind them on the west, which extend into Utah and Arizona. These, for want of a better title, we have referred to as the *Eastern Ranges and Plateaus.*

It is interesting to recall that Major Powell early recognized these great geographic and structural divisions, and that he termed the Southern Rocky Mountains the "Park province," the Colorado Plateau the "Plateau province," and the Great Basin (or "Basin Ranges" of Gilbert) the "Basin province." The term "Park province" is somewhat curious, as it emphasizes the high mountain valleys or "parks" that are enclosed within the Rocky Mountains, rather than the mountains themselves.

Powell also emphasized the differences between these western mountains and plateaus and the more familiar eastern mountains such as the Appalachians with which most of the geologists of his generation had grown up. He realized that this was more than a matter of scenery and climate, and that there were fundamental differences in the geology—in the strata, the structure, and the geologic history—that here was something truly novel in American geology, which had no counterpart in the Eastern States.

Powell did not fully realize why this was, but our later knowledge has given us appreciation of its meaning. As we have seen in Chapter VI, the Eastern Ranges and Plateaus lie inland from the true miogeosyncline of the

Cordillera, and were originally part of the continental platform; it was only later that they became mobile so that their rocks were disordered in the manner we now see.

As with the Appalachians, we will deal with this region in both space and time—of what its forms and structures are and how they developed. Here, however, we will follow an order the reverse of the other one. We will first describe the rocks and events that preceded the great deformation of later Mesozoic time, then the structures produced by this deformation. Finally, we will treat the events that followed the great deformation and how the region was modified between then and the present.

2. ROCKS AND EVENTS BEFORE THE GREAT DEFORMATION

THE PRECAMBRIAN. Our first concern will be with the Precambrian, or the rocks that form the basement on which all the succeeding rocks and structures have been built.

Here, in contrast to the Interior Lowlands and the Appalachians, we can learn much about the Precambrian because it projects to the surface in many more places and over much wider areas. Its manner of exposure, it is true, is not like that in the Canadian Shield; it does not form the whole surface over vast areas. Rather, it emerges in the cores of the great uplifts in the mountains and is revealed in the canyon bottoms in the plateau (Fig. 61), forming perhaps only 5 or 10 percent of the surface in all. The remaining 90 or 95 percent of the surface is covered by younger rocks downfolded between the ranges in the mountain areas or spread across the country between the canyons in the plateau areas.

101

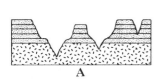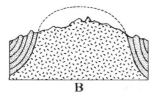

A　　　　　　**B**

Fig. 61. Sketch sections illustrating the manner in which the Precambrian rocks are exposed in the Eastern Ranges and Plateaus. (A) In plateau area. (B) In the mountain uplifts.

EARLIER PRECAMBRIAN ROCKS (ARCHEAN AND LOWER PROTEROZOIC). Much of the exposed Precambrian of the Eastern Ranges and Plateaus, as in the Canadian Shield, consists of heavily metamorphosed, steeply tilted rocks, originally of supracrustal origin, in which small to large masses of felsic plutonic rocks are embedded. Such rocks form most of the cores of the ranges in Colorado and Wyoming, and also come to the surface in the outlying Black Hills of South Dakota (Fig. 62).

As a result of much patient fieldwork, coupled with radiometric dating, we now know much about these metamorphic and plutonic rocks. Most of the Precambrian of the ranges in Wyoming is Archean and is a complex of paragneiss and orthogneiss, which has yielded ages in many places of 2,570 million years, and in the Beartooth Mountains on the Wyoming-Montana border ages in excess of 3,100 million years. Along the southern edge of the Archean area in the Medicine Bow Mountains, the ancient rocks are succeeded by a 10,000-meter sequence of Lower Proterozoic quartzite, slate, and limestone.

These Archean and Lower Proterozoic rocks are truncated on the south by a northeast-trending shear zone, south of which is a metamorphic complex that forms most of the basement of the Southern Rocky Mountains. It is a body of felsic paragneiss with some interbedded mafic paragneiss, which has yielded radiometric ages of 1,750 million years—in other words, Lower Proterozoic like the Lower Proterozoic north of the shear zone, but of eugeosynclinal rather than of miogeosynclinal facies. Structural trends in the complex are northwest or southwest, transverse to the northerly trends of the Rocky Mountain uplifts in which they lie.

Embedded in the metamorphic complex, and forming more than half of the exposed Precambrian area in the Southern Rocky Mountains, is an array of granitic plutonic rocks. The oldest (Boulder Creek type) has ages of about 1,700 million years, nearly contemporaneous with the Lower Proterozoic metamorphic complex itself. Much more extensive is a set of granitic rocks with ages of 1,390 to 1,470 million years, which includes the Sherman Granite that forms most of the southern part of the Laramie Range, or northward extension of the Front Range in Wyoming. North of it, and between it and the Archean of the north part of the range, is a large body of

anorthosite, which recalls the anorthosites of the Grenville province of the Canadian Shield and apparently is of about the same age. Youngest of all the plutonic rocks is the Pikes Peak Granite, which covers an area of 3,100 square kilometers at the south end of the Front Range in Colorado, which has a Grenvillian radiometric age of 1,040 million years.

LATER PRECAMBRIAN ROCKS (MIDDLE PROTEROZOIC). More revealing of historical record than these highly altered and plutonized rocks, but of less extent and occurring mainly toward the west, are little deformed rocks that are comparable to the last class of supracrustal rocks that we have listed in the Canadian Shield—"tilted or flat-lying sediments and lavas, unaltered or little metamorphosed."

As with rocks of this class in the Canadian Shield, they are not necessarily young in absolute terms; some are actually rather ancient. They are at least younger than other Precambrian rocks in their immediate neighborhoods; they have had a much less complex history and they lie unconformably on them. They appear so fresh, in fact, that they are not unlike Paleozoic strata, yet they are overlain more or less unconformably by fossiliferous Cambrian rocks—although in most places these are not the earliest Cambrian. When geologists first encountered them, they supposed that they were of Early Cambrian age, or only a little older at most. Nevertheless, the Belt Series or extensive representative of the later Precambrian in northwestern Montana, is now known from radiometric dating to have been deposited between 900 and 1,300 million years ago, and the other sequences farther south appear to be of similar age.

The little altered, mainly Middle Proterozoic rocks differ from most of those of the same general class in the Canadian Shield. Unlike the Keweenawan Series, for example, they are not volcanic and red clastic rocks that were laid down in a continental environment. Most of them are fine-grained, well-bedded sediments such as argillites and cleanly washed sandstones, with considerable thicknesses of limestone in places and only occasional lavas. Clearly, they were deposited under water and very probably in a marine environment. During later Precambrian time when local basins in the Canadian Shield were receiving continental deposits, marine deposits were accumulating in a geogeosyncline along the western edge of the continent, thus foreshadowing the growth of the marginal geosynclines in Cambrian and later times.

The similarity in distribution of these little altered Precambrian deposits to those of the Cambrian is illustrated by their occurrence only along the western edge of the Eastern Ranges and Plateaus—that is, at about the place where the thicker and earliest Cambrian deposits set in westward. They also come to the surface in many

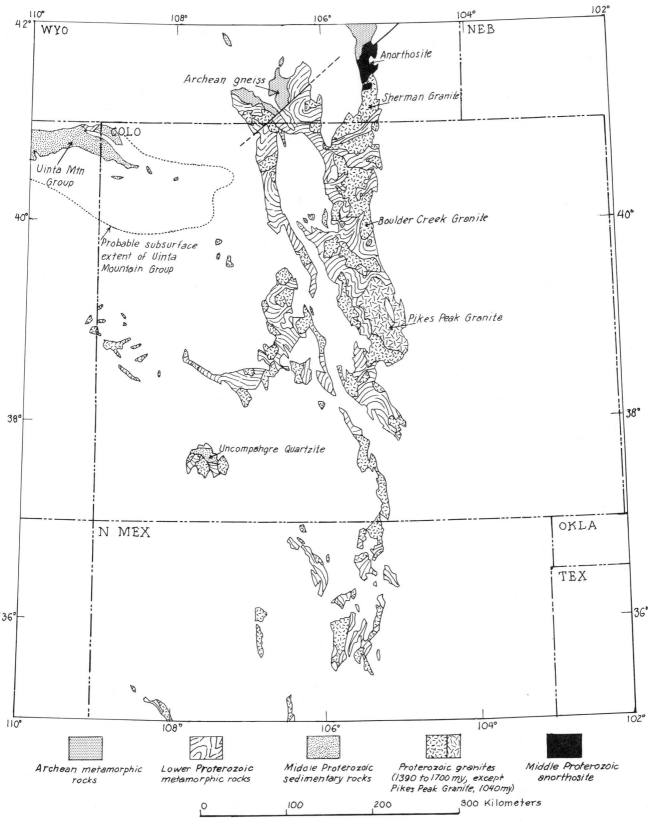

FIG. 62. Part I of a series showing structural development of Southern Rocky Mountains. Map shows exposed areas of Precambrian rocks and their lithology and structure. After Geologic Map of United States (1974) and other sources.

parts of the miogeosynclinal area, west of the region we are now considering.

In the far north these little altered Precambrian rocks are the *Belt Series*, named for the Big Belt and Little Belt Mountains of west-central Montana, which are part of our "Eastern Ranges." But the main development of the Belt is in the miogeosynclinal area of the Northern Rocky Mountains farther west and northwest, which we will consider later. It seems best to reserve discussion of the Belt Series until that time (Chapter VII, section 2).

Farther south in northeastern Utah is the *Uinta Mountain Group*, which is raised in the core of the Uinta Mountains (Fig. 72). It is a mass of sandstone and quartzite as much as 7,600 meters thick, whose base, lying unconformably on older metamorphic rocks, is exposed at Red Creek on the north flank of the range. Like the Uinta Mountains themselves, the Uinta Mountain Group extends eastward, and it probably accumulated in an aulocogen, or rift in the continental platform, like the late Precambrian-early Cambrian of the Wichita system in Oklahoma. Like the Belt Series, the group extends westward into the miogeosynclinal area, and its equivalents occur in the Wasatch Mountains at the edge of the Great Basin.

But one of the finest displays of these later Precambrian rocks is in northwestern Arizona, where the *Grand Canyon Series* is laid bare in the depths of the Grand Canyon.

ROCK SEQUENCE IN THE GRAND CANYON. Here it is appropriate to digress and to anticipate some of the later parts of our story by describing the Grand Canyon and all its rocks at one place along with the geologic history they imply.

The plateau country of northern Arizona is about what one would expect in a high region of little rain—a topography of moderate relief whose lower parts are bare desert; higher parts are clad in groves of juniper and pinyon, and the highest covered by spruce forests. Among the highest parts of the region are the Coconino and Kaibab Plateaus, which rise to altitudes of 2,100 and 2,500 meters, respectively; here, in an area about 160 kilometers long and 40 kilometers wide, the rocks of the plateau have been raised higher than elsewhere. According to Powell, Kaibab is an Indian word meaning "mountain lying on its side"—an appropriate description of this great swell in the plateau surface.

The plateaus of northern Arizona are capped partly by highest Paleozoic limestones, partly by lowest Mesozoic redbeds, which dip so gently over wide areas that only small thicknesses of strata come to the surface. Little in the plateaus gives much hint of the underlying rocks or structures. In Texas, our recourse would have been the records of deep drill holes. Here there are few drill holes as yet. Actually we have something better, for the Colorado River has cut across the highest part of the region,

laying bare in the Grand Canyon a great cross-section of the lower rocks two kilometers in depth. All the Paleozoic and later Precambrian rocks are revealed, as well as the basement of earlier Precambrian rocks on which they lie.

More than half the upper slope of the canyon is formed of Paleozoic sedimentary rocks which descend in a series of giant steps (Fig. 63).

Rimrock of the canyon is the *Kaibab Limestone** of middle Permian age, which is underlain in turn by the *Coconino Sandstone*, *Hermit Shale*, and *Supai Redbeds*, of earlier Permian age. The Kaibab and Coconino make great lines of cliffs, but the Hermit and Supai form slopes and minor steps, the lower part spreading out in a broad bench called the Esplanade.

Below the Supai is another great line of cliffs formed of the *Redwall Limestone* of Mississippian age. The Redwall is not actually red as its name implies, but an ordinary gray marine limestone; its surface has been colored by red silt washed down from the Supai above it.

Beneath the Redwall cliffs is another set of steps formed by the *Tonto Group* of Cambrian age, which leads out onto a broad bench well down in the canyon, the Tonto Platform, whose surface is maintained by the basal layer of the group, or *Tapeats Sandstone*.

The whole span of Paleozoic time from Cambrian to Permian is thus represented in this 1,200-meter Grand Canyon sequence. Observe, however, that we have failed to mention the presence of deposits of many of the Paleozoic systems—the Pennsylvanian, which should occur between the Supai and Redwall, and the Devonian, Silurian, and Ordovician, which should occur between the Redwall and Tonto. All the Paleozoic strata in the canyon lie parallel and are seemingly conformable, yet there are breaks in the sequence, each representing a hiatus, or interval of time for which no deposits are preserved; the sedimentary record is thus incomplete. Contacts between the Supai and Redwall, and between the Redwall and Tonto, where the breaks in the record occur, are disconformities (Fig. 63).

In some parts of the canyon country the record is partly filled. In places Devonian deposits (*Temple Butte Limestone*) lie in pockets and channels on the surface of the Tonto Group, and in the western part of the canyon Pennsylvanian limestones wedge in between the Redwall and Supai. But any record in the region of Ordovician and Silurian time, if ever one were present, is now lost.

The Tapeats Sandstone of the Tonto Group, or initial Cambrian deposit, has another relation to the rocks be-

---

*It is now recognized that the upper limestones of the canyon represent two distinct cycles of sedimentation, to the higher of which the name Kaibab has been restricted, the lower unit being termed the Toroweap Limestone (see Figs. 63 and 64). The two units are not far apart in age, both being middle Permian (Leonardian). For our purposes the earlier and broader definition of Kaibab is still useful.

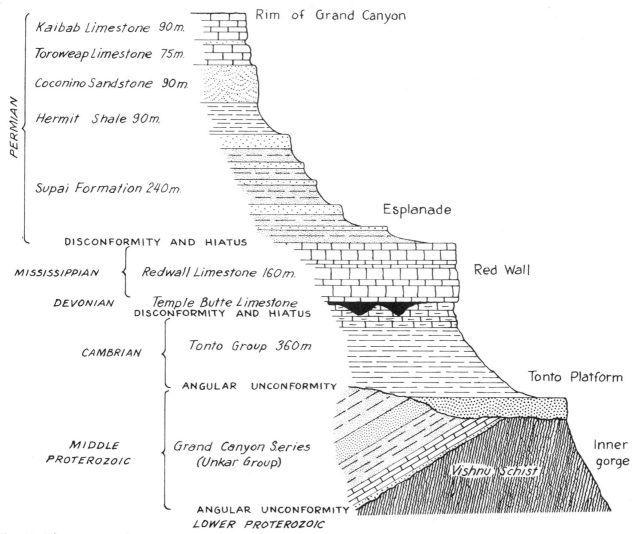

FIG. 63. Columnar section showing sequence of Paleozoic and Precambrian formations in the Grand Canyon and their topographic expression. Compiled from McKee (1931) and other sources.

neath. In much of the canyon it lies with *angular unconformity* on the eroded edges of steeply tilted, dark, old-looking metamorphic rocks of the *Vishnu Schist*—a basement of Lower Proterozoic age upon which all the superstructure of the plateau region has been built (Fig. 64). Intrusives which invade it have been dated at about 1,775 million years.

But in other parts of the canyon the Tapeats lies on other rocks—the strata of the *Grand Canyon Series*. As with the Vishnu, the Tapeats lies on the Grand Canyon Series with angular unconformity, but here one sedimentary series lies on another sedimentary series that had previously been tilted, faulted, and then truncated (Fig. 64). The Grand Canyon Series, like the Tapeats, lies with angular unconformity on the eroded surface of the Vishnu Schist. No doubt the tilting and faulting of the Grand Canyon Series produced block mountains like those of later times in the Cordilleran region, but these mountains were planed off by erosion at

some time before the Cambrian so that the initial Cambrian deposits lie indiscriminately on either Vishnu or Grand Canyon.

If we recall our example in Iowa of *layer-cake geology* discussed in Chapter III, section 5, we will recognize in the Grand Canyon another fine example of the same structure—the highest layer made of the Paleozoic formations, the next of the later Precambrian Grand Canyon Series, and the lowest of the highly altered earlier Precambrian Vishnu Schist. Here, in contrast to Iowa and elsewhere in the Interior Region, one need not search over a wide area or have recourse to drill data to prove the relation; it is all exposed in cross-section at the surface in the walls of the Grand Canyon.

The Grand Canyon Series consists of two parts; the Unkar and Chuar Groups. The lower or *Unkar Group*, which is the part seen by most visitors to the canyon, is a sequence of limestone, sandstone, and red shale, with lavas at the top. The upper or *Chuar Group* is preserved

105

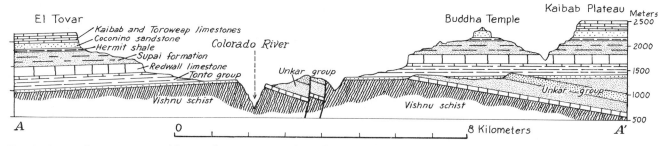

FIG. 64. Section showing structure of the Grand Canyon. Section from El Tovar northward to Kaibab Plateau along line A–A' of Fig. 67. After Darton (1925).

above the Unkar only in remote alcoves in the eastern part of the canyon and is dominantly shaly. When these different parts are added together, the whole has a thickness of 3,600 meters, or about three times the thickness of the Paleozoic rocks that lie above it. The lavas at the top of the Unkar have a radiometric age of about 1,100 million years, which suggests that the group is broadly equivalent to the Middle Proterozoic Belt Series farther north; the Chuar Group is younger, and might even extend into the Upper Proterozoic.

EARLIER PALEOZOIC ROCKS AND EVENTS. As already noted, the site of the Eastern Ranges and Plateaus was like the remainder of the continental platform during earlier Paleozoic time; its deposits of that time thus have much the same character as those of the Interior Lowlands.

As elsewhere, Cambrian deposits overlapped the continental platform, so that through much of the Eastern Ranges and Plateaus the Upper Cambrian, where present, lies directly on the Precambrian, with the earlier Cambrian missing. Some exceptions seem to invalidate the rule; the Tonto Group of the Grand Canyon belongs to the Middle rather than the Upper part of the system, and Lower Cambrian beds wedge in near the lower end of the canyon. But although these Cambrian deposits are earlier than most of those that lie on the continental platform, they are much like the later ones and are the edges of deposits that attain a much greater thickness in the miogeosyncline farther west.

In many parts of the Eastern Ranges and Plateaus, the Cambrian is missing entirely either because it was never deposited or because it was laid down thinly and afterwards eroded. One such area is that near Albuquerque, New Mexico, where, as we have seen (Chapter III, section 4), the Pennsylvanian lies directly on the Precambrian (Fig. 12A). This area is part of the continental backbone or belt of country extending southwestward from Minnesota across the Interior Lowlands, where relatively young rocks lie directly on the basement, and where earlier rocks either were never deposited or have since been eroded.

Of the remaining earlier Paleozoic deposits through the Mississippian we need say little. They are relatively thin and consist mostly of limestone; there are many hiatuses between the units—for example, those below and above the Redwall Limestone in the Grand Canyon. Different systems are present in different places recording the extent of successive ephemeral seas, but some of the systems are notable only for their poor representation; no Silurian occurs in Colorado or Wyoming, or in any areas east of the miogeosyncline from Montana to southern New Mexico for that matter, and these areas were probably land throughout most of the period.

COLORADO SYSTEM OF LATER PALEOZOIC TIME. A marked change took place in later Paleozoic time in part of the Eastern Ranges and Plateaus, and its character as a continental platform began to break down. Beginning in late Mississippian time and continuing through Pennsylvanian into Permian time structures of the Colorado system or "Ancestral Rockies" were formed in the Southern Rocky Mountains at the same time and along the same trend as in the Wichita system in Oklahoma.

Because of deformation that took place in the Southern Rocky Mountains later on during the Laramide orogeny, these later Paleozoic structures are obscure and hard to identify specifically. The main record of their former existence and history is in the sediments that were eroded from the uplifted areas and deposited along their flanks. These sediments indicate the following structural pattern and history:

During later Paleozoic time two main uplifts or geanticlines were raised in Colorado and adjacent states (Fig. 65). The Front Range geanticline lay to the northeast on the site of the present Front Range and the ranges immediately west of it. The Uncompahgre geanticline lay to the southwest in southwestern Colorado and is less clearly expressed in surface features. Its Precambrian rocks still emerge in places, as in the Uncompahgre Plateau and Needle Mountains, but most of the geanticline in the Paleozoic and earlier rocks has been concealed by Mesozoic sediments and by the great pile of Tertiary volcanics in the San Juan Mountains. Extending across Colorado between the two geanticlines was the long Colorado trough, similar to the Anadarko basin of Oklahoma, which received sediments derived from the geanticlines on each side. Pennsylvanian and Permian deposits in the trough are more than 3,000 meters thick.

The two geanticlines were formed at somewhat differ-

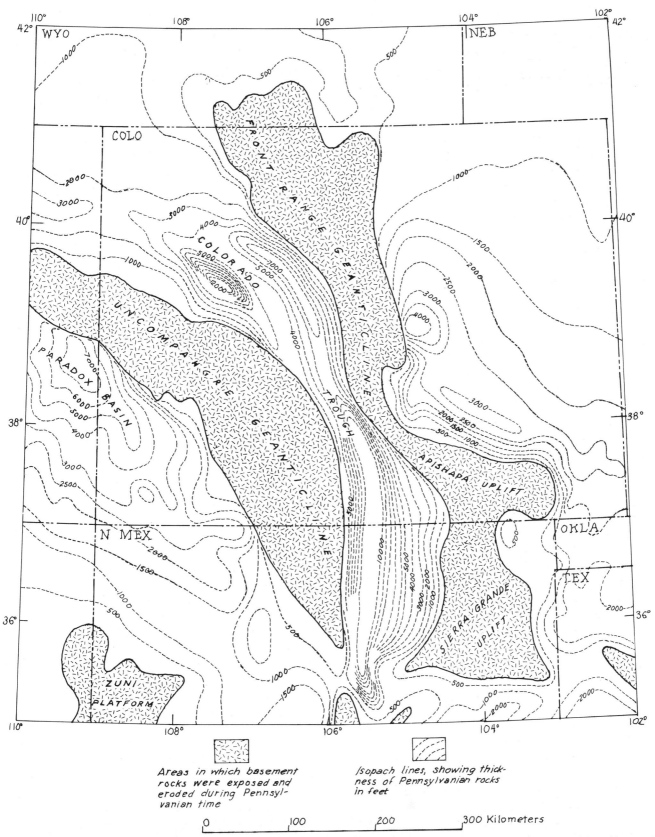

FIG. 65. Part II of a series showing structural development of Southern Rocky Mountains. Map shows positions of late Paleozoic uplifts and basins of the Colorado system. Based on Geologic Atlas of Rocky Mountain Region (1972).

ent times, as shown by the record of sediments derived from them. The Front Range geanticline was raised in late Mississippian and early Pennsylvanian time. Its existence is indicated by the thick mass of coarse arkose and sandstone of the Fountain Formation of Pennsylvanian age, whose strata are turned up in hogbacks along the eastern edge of the present Front Range, where they form such picturesque localities as the Garden of the Gods near Colorado Springs (Fig. 66). Similar deposits of about the same age occur west of the Front Range. The overlying red clastic deposits of Permian age along the edge of the Front Range are finer grained, indicating that by then the geanticline was quiescent and had been worn down to low relief.

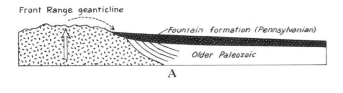

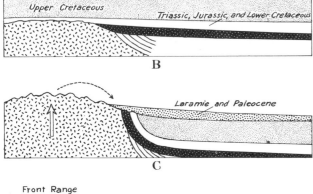

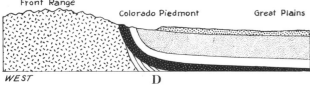

FIG. 66. Sketch sections illustrating structural evolution of the Front Range of Colorado. (A) In late Paleozoic time during formation of Colorado system. (B) In late Mesozoic time when the range was quiescent and buried. (C) In early Tertiary time immediately following Laramide orogeny. (D) Present relations following later Tertiary regional uplift and dissection.

The Uncompahgre geanticline was raised in late Pennsylvanian and Permian time. This is suggested toward the northwest end of the present Uncompahgre Plateau, where Triassic rocks lie directly on basement rocks along the crest of the uplift, whereas Permian and Pennsylvanian rocks that had been truncated before Triassic time wedge in along its flanks (Fig. 77). The age of the geanticline is shown more definitely in the Sangre de Cristo Mountains east of its southeast end, where there is a great thickness of coarse bouldery sediments of late Pennsylvanian and Permian age. These sediments

were deposited in the Colorado trough that lay between the two geanticlines, and were derived from the Uncompahgre geanticline, which then stood not far to the west but is now buried beneath Tertiary sediments and volcanics of the San Luis Valley and San Juan Mountains.

OTHER LATER PALEOZOIC ROCKS. Away from the uplifts of the Colorado system the later Paleozoic deposits are thinner and finer grained. Some of them are still sandstones and redbeds, but they were derived from distant rather than nearby uplifts, and there are some rather widespread marine units. Two of the latter are worth recording—the middle Permian *Kaibab Limestone* (including the Toroweap Limestone), which forms the rim of the Grand Canyon and extends over most of the southern part of the Colorado Plateau, and the upper Permian *Phosphoria Formation* of shale, chert, phosphate rock, and limestone, which covers a broad area in southeastern Idaho, western Wyoming, and adjacent states.

At least one large evaporite basin formed in the region, represented by the *Paradox Formation* of Pennsylvanian age, which underlies an area in the northeastern part of the Colorado Plateau along the southwest edge of the Uncompahgre geanticline. The Paradox consists of salt, gypsum, and other evaporites, which accumulated to a thickness of 2,100 meters in a basin that probably became landlocked by uplift of ridges of the Colorado system. The Paradox comes to the surface mostly in a remarkable series of anticlines that were produced by plastic flow of the salt beds, beginning shortly after deposition, but accentuated during the orogenies of Mesozoic time; we will have more to say about them later in this chapter (section 6).

By early Mesozoic time, crustal activity had largely ceased in the Colorado system. Its ridges had been worn down to low relief and were finally buried by Triassic and Jurassic deposits. Nevertheless, the scar in the continental platform thus created remained a zone of weakness, ready to express itself in new forms when the region was again subjected to crustal forces. Although the area of the Eastern Ranges and Plateaus had returned to quiescence in latest Paleozoic and earliest Mesozoic time, this was merely an interlude between orogenies. Once Mesozoic time was under way, crustal forces again came into play, and the great Cordilleran deformation had begun.

3. ROCKS AND EVENTS DURING THE GREAT DEFORMATION

MESOZOIC SEQUENCE NORTH OF THE GRAND CANYON. It will be appropriate to introduce the Mesozoic rocks of the Eastern Ranges and Plateaus by returning to the Grand Canyon (Fig. 67).

The Kaibab Limestone of Permian and latest Paleozoic

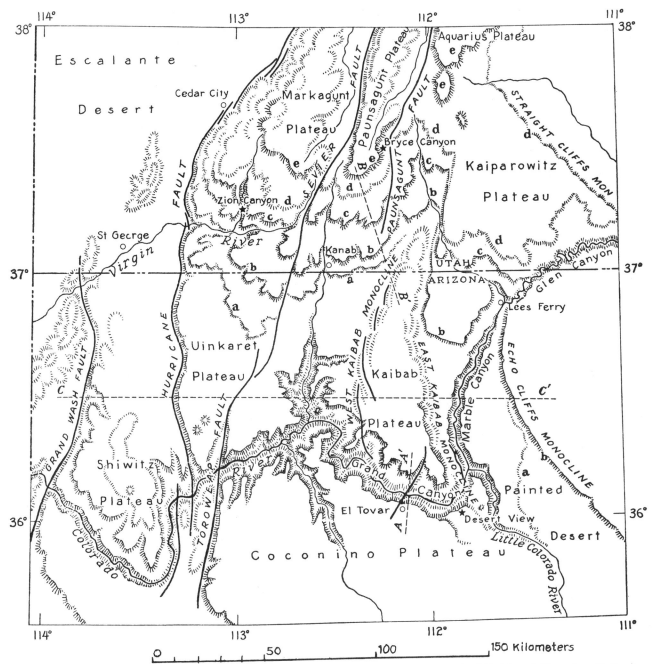

FIG. 67. Map of western part of Colorado Plateau in Arizona and Utah, showing cliff lines produced by erosion of formations, and fault lines. Letters indicate the following: (a) Chocolate Cliffs (Shinarump Conglomerate, Triassic). (b) Vermillion Cliffs (Wingate Sandstone Triassic). (c) White Cliffs (Navajo Sandstone, Jurassic). (d) Gray Cliffs (Cretaceous rocks). (e) Pink Cliffs (Wasatch Formation, Tertiary). Lines A–A′, B–B′, and C–C′ indicate locations of sections on Figs. 64, 69, and 82. Compiled from geologic maps of Arizona and Utah and other sources.

age forms the rim of the Grand Canyon. Away from the canyon it also forms the surface over wide areas, as though it was the last stratum to have been deposited in the region. Nevertheless, from Desert View at the eastern end of the canyon (Fig. 67) one can see the little knob of Cedar Mountain, which is formed by a unit overlying the Kaibab—the redbeds of the Moenkopi Formation. These redbeds, easily subject to erosion, have been removed except in scattered remnants, such as this one.

More than canyon cutting is thus involved in the shaping of the plateau country. There was also a great denudation by which the weaker, higher formations were stripped from the resistant surface of the Kaibab Limestone, not only along the canyon rim, but also over wide areas of the Kaibab and Coconino Plateaus.

Record of these higher formations can best be seen by passing northward from the canyon rim across the Kaibab Plateau toward the High Plateaus of Utah (Fig.

69). The strata dip gently in this direction, and the land surface increases in altitude to heights of 3,000 meters or more. Successively higher Mesozoic formations come in above the Kaibab, some poorly resistant, others strong and cliff-making. One thus ascends the sequence in a series of giant steps. This Mesozoic sequence is quite as wonderful in its way as the Paleozoic sequence that underlies it in the Grand Canyon; but instead of being exposed in one canyon wall it is spread out over a distance of 40 or 50 kilometers. The lines of cliffs are among the most striking scenic features of the plateau country and reappear in many places across its extent wherever the appropriate formations happen to be present.

In southern Utah these cliffs have been named according to their color (Fig. 68). Thus we find on ascending the section from south to north the low *Chocolate Cliffs*, the higher *Vermillion Cliffs*, and the very massive *White Cliffs* (which form the rock at Zion Canyon). Surmounting them are the less massive, better stratified *Gray Cliffs* which are capped in the higher plateaus by the *Pink Cliffs* (the rock at Bryce Canyon).

Each of these cliffs is held up by a formation of the succession of Mesozoic and later rocks. The Chocolate Cliffs are made by the Triassic Shinarump Conglomerate, which is underlain and overlain by less resistant Triassic redbeds, the Moenkopi and Chinle Formations.

The Vermillion and White Cliffs are formed by the Wingate and Navajo Sandstones—the lower one reddish, the upper without pigment. For the most part the Wingate and Navajo are great fossil sand dune deposits formed in a desert of late Triassic and early Jurassic time, and by coincidence now exposed again in a desert region. In many parts of the plateau these sandstones have been sought out as dwellings and places of defense by the Indians of former times, who built their pueblos in great alcoves in the cliffs or on tops of the sheer-sided mesas.

The succeeding Gray Cliffs are formed of interbedded sandstones and shales of the later Jurassic and Cretaceous formations; the Pink Cliffs at the top are made by the continental deposits of the Eocene Wasatch Formation (Fig. 69).

EARLY MESOZOIC ROCKS. Triassic and Jurassic rocks similar to those just mentioned extend far across the Eastern Ranges and Plateaus. The lower part is nearly everywhere red colored, but changes to white or gray above; both parts were formed largely in a continental and probably a desert environment. The deposits thin eastward across the Rocky Mountains to a feather edge in the Great Plains, but thicken to 900 to 1,500 meters near the western edge of the Colorado Plateau toward the miogeosyncline, where some marine layers are interbedded. North of the plateau in the Central and Northern Rocky Mountains marine Jurassic deposits are widespread but attain no great thickness; they are known variously as the Sundance, Ellis, and Fernie Formations.

These Triassic and Jurassic deposits somewhat resemble the clastic wedges that spread from the Appalachian geosyncline into its foreland. The comparison is not perfect but has some basis in the Jurassic, whose thick sandstones had their source in the west, where the Cordilleran orogeny was beginning. It is in the succeeding Cretaceous deposits that the clastic wedges are best displayed, and to these we will now turn.

THE CRETACEOUS CLASTIC WEDGES. As a paleogeographic map in any of the textbooks of historical geology will show, during Cretaceous time, and especially during its last half, a broad seaway extended northward from the Gulf of Mexico to the Arctic Ocean along the eastern side of the Cordilleran region, covering most of the area of the Eastern Ranges and Plateaus and overlapping the Interior Lowlands as far as Kansas, Iowa, and Minnesota. Westward, the seaway extended no farther than central Utah, or only a little beyond the Colorado Plateau.

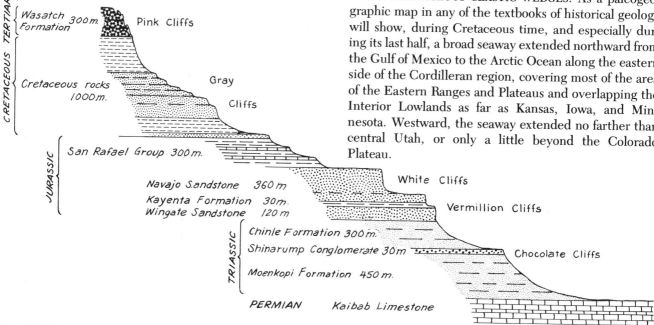

FIG. 68. Columnar section showing sequence of Mesozoic formations in southern Utah north of the Grand Canyon, and their topographic expression. Compiled from Gregory (1950) and other sources.

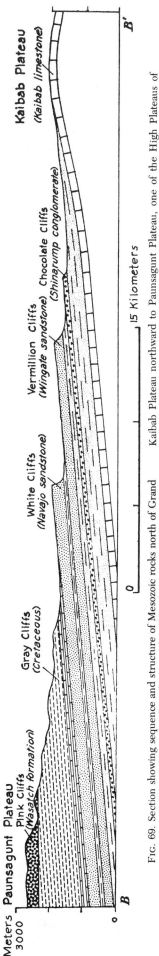

Fig. 69. Section showing sequence and structure of Mesozoic rocks north of Grand Canyon and the cliff lines that have been produced by their erosion. Section from Kaibab Plateau northward to Paunsagunt Plateau, one of the High Plateaus of Utah, along line B–B' of Fig. 67.

Cretaceous deposits laid down in this seaway are, in effect, a series of clastic wedges, related to the growth of the Cordillera on the west in later Mesozoic time, and are worth examining for that reason. Our analysis can best begin at their eastern edge in the Interior Lowlands and proceed westward (Fig. 70).

The present eastern edge of the Cretaceous is probably not far from the original eastern limits of the deposit. In Iowa and Kansas, the sequence is no more than a few hundred or thousand meters thick. It begins with a basal transgressive sandstone, the Dakota, above which are interbedded limestones and shales, including the Greenhorn Limestone and Niobrara Chalk below and the Pierre Shale above.

Farther west near the front of the Rocky Mountains in Colorado the deposits have thickened to 2,500 to 3,000 meters, most of the increase being in the shales. The two limestone units, the Greenhorn and Niobrara, persist but fade into shales a short distance to the west. At the top of the sequence is the marine Fox Hills Sandstone followed by the continental Laramie beds of latest Cretaceous age.

Beyond the front of the Rocky Mountains, ledge-making beds of sandstone appear in the shales and are generally grouped at certain levels. One group in the upper part of the sequence is the widespread Mesaverde Formation; a lower one, mainly developed in Wyoming, is the Frontier Formation. The eastern edges of the sandstone layers are marine, but where they thicken westward as wedges they include continental beds with layers of coal.

At the west edge of the Colorado Plateau, the Cretaceous deposits attain a thickness of 4,500 to 6,000 meters, and most of them are continental (Fig. 70). The marine shales have largely pinched out, and the sandstones and coal-bearing rocks have passed into coarse conglomerates made up of clasts of earlier Mesozoic and Paleozoic formations derived from the site of the present Great Basin immediately to the west. Unconformities develop beneath some of the units by which conglomerates lie on the eroded and upturned edges of the beds beneath. Along the edges of the Wasatch Mountains, the unconformable beds overlap a rough topography of much deformed earlier rocks; such beds are, in fact, piedmont deposits laid down along the bases of newly upraised mountain areas.

In our traverse across the deposits of the Cretaceous seaway we have observed the thin transgressive marine deposits of the eastern edge with much limestone; the thick, dominantly marine deposits at the present front of the Rocky Mountains, near the center of the seaway; and the even thicker, coarse continental beds at the western edge of the seaway, evidently laid down along the front of a mountain belt in process of growth.

Little information is available as to the extent of Cre-

111

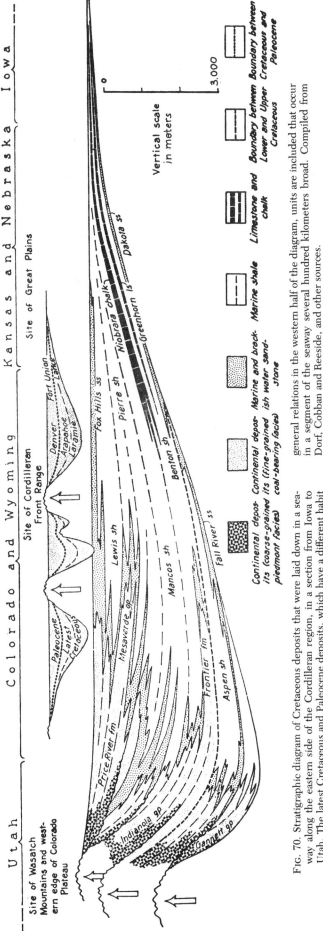

FIG. 70. Stratigraphic diagram of Cretaceous deposits that were laid down in a seaway along the eastern side of the Cordilleran region, in a section from Iowa to Utah. The latest Cretaceous and Paleocene deposits, which have a different habit from the remainder, are shown in a separate diagram above. In order to bring out general relations in the western half of the diagram, units are included that occur in a segment of the seaway several hundred kilometers broad. Compiled from Dorf, Cobban and Reeside, and other sources.

taceous deposits farther west in the Great Basin. Here and there in its eastern half as far as central Nevada, patches of coarse conglomerate and other continental beds lie on much deformed earlier rocks and in places contain fresh-water Cretaceous fossils. Very likely these deposits were not much more continuous than they now are, and formed in local depressions in the mountain belt rather than as widespread deposits; the main body of Cretaceous deposits with their clastic wedges probably thinned abruptly westward near the edge of the present Great Basin.

RELATION OF CRETACEOUS DEPOSITS TO OROGENY. The paleogeographic maps indicate a broad belt of land west of the Cretaceous seaway, which is labeled the "Cordilleran geanticline" in older textbooks. The term "geanticline" is misleading as it implies merely a broad upwarp of the crust, whereas, as we have seen, the belt was a product of much stronger deformation—orogenic rather than epeirogenic. During much of Cretaceous time it was probably hilly or even mountainous and was undergoing vigorous erosion.

Moreover, the several unconformities in the Cretaceous at the western edge of the Colorado Plateau, the coarse piedmont deposits that overlie them, and the successive wedges of continental beds and sandstone that extend far eastward into the seaway indicate that deformation was accomplished in a series of pulses, probably with intervening periods of relative quiesence.

West of the Great Basin, in the western part of the Cordillera, Nevadan orogeny had begun during Jurassic time. Orogeny at the eastern edge of the Great Basin took place in Cretaceous time, and mainly in the last half, or at a time intermediate between the Nevadan orogeny on the west and the Laramide orogeny on the east. This *Sevier orogeny* differs not only in time from the other two but in its manifestations. Whereas the Nevadan orogeny involved deep-seated deformation and plutonism and the Laramide orogeny produced great upfolds and downfolds of all the rocks into the basement, the visible effects of the Sevier orogeny were mainly eastward thrusting of plates of the miogeosynclinal rocks toward their foreland. By late Cretaceous time, all the Cordillera up to the edge of the Colorado Plateau had been transformed into a mountain belt. We will now examine further progress of deformation eastward into the Eastern Ranges and Plateaus during latest Cretaceous and Paleocene time.

LARAMIE AND PALEOCENE DEPOSITS. Overlying the main body of the Cretaceous in the Eastern Ranges and Plateaus, and extending eastward beyond the front of the Rocky Mountains for some distance into the Great Plains, are continental and coal-bearing deposits of latest Cretaceous age, which are succeeded conformably by similar deposits of earliest Tertiary or Paleocene age.

During early geologic work in Wyoming and Colorado

the latest Cretaceous deposits were termed the *Laramie Formation*, and this is still a useful general term for the whole. Farther north, similar beds termed the *Hell Creek, Lance,* and *Fort Union Formations* were also recognized, but their age was much disputed; the first two are now generally placed in the latest Cretaceous like the Laramie, the latter in the Paleocene. For our purpose we need not burden ourselves with the multiplicity of other local names that have arisen.

These deposits have a different pattern from the widespread deposits of earlier Cretaceous time. They occur in great thickness in local basins—in part between the ranges, as in the small Hanna Basin and the larger Bighorn and Powder River basins in Wyoming, in part in the Great Plains to the east, as in the Denver and Williston basins (upper part of Fig. 70). As we shall see, the deposits, although conformable within the basins, were being deposited while the ranges about them were in process of growth, so that their present extent corresponds somewhat to their original areas of deposition. Deformation, whose eastward spread had reached the edge of the Colorado Plateau during earlier parts of Cretaceous time, was by now active in the plateau itself and in the ranges of the Rocky Mountains beyond it.

This is the so-called *Laramide orogeny* of latest Mesozoic and earliest Cenozoic time, once thought to have been distinct from the Nevadan orogeny of mid-Mesozoic time farther west. From the record presented here, however, we can see that these are merely the beginning and end members of a nearly continuous process of deformation.

LARAMIE QUESTION. These latest Cretaceous and earliest Tertiary deposits have given rise to one of the former great controversies of American geology, the "Laramie question." Actually, this involved two questions that are not entirely related.

(a) Where is the Cretaceous-Tertiary boundary? The deposits are conformable and much alike, but the lower part contains *Triceratops* and other representatives of the last of the dinosaurs, whereas the upper part contains mammals and plants of more modern or Tertiary aspect. At some time during this depositional period there was a change-over from the characteristic life of Mesozoic time to that of Cenozoic time, the former becoming extinct, apparently with some abruptness. This question need not concern us greatly; it is a matter for paleontologists and stratigraphers and has now largely been resolved to their satisfaction.

(b) When did the Laramide orogeny take place, and when were the Rocky Mountains formed? The deposits are conformable, as stated, yet in their upper part they contain granitic debris from the cores of the ranges, indicating that the ranges had been greatly uplifted and deeply eroded (Fig. 71). Geologists have devoted much futile effort to a search for immense unconformities that

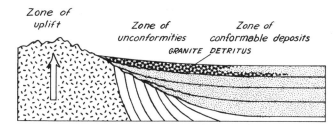

FIG. 71. Sketch section of the border of a typical mountain and basin in the Eastern Ranges during Laramie and Paleocene time, showing how conformable deposits could be laid down in the basin near the rising mountain area.

were supposed to have been overlooked in the seemingly conformable basin deposits. It was thought that such unconformities should be a necessary consequence of the formation of the Rocky Mountains.

As we have seen, however, orogeny had been in progress for a long period of Mesozoic time, advancing progressively eastward across the Cordilleran region. In later Cretaceous time, the ranges of the Rocky Mountains were gradually raised while deposition of the Laramie strata continued in the intervening basins. The ranges did not project in the manner they do now, but were eroded about as rapidly as they were uplifted, shedding detritus into the basins roundabout. Sediments in the basins and their contained fossils indicate a low-altitude, semi-tropical, moist climate; no great mountain barriers to the west shut off the flow of moisture-laden winds from the Pacific Ocean. The present lofty height of the Rocky Mountains did not develop until afterwards, and only by processes that were related to the waning stages of the formation of the Cordillera (see section 7 of this chapter).

UNCONFORMITY AT BASE OF WASATCH FORMATION. In contrast to the conformable sequences of deposits from the Cretaceous through the Paleocene, a considerable change took place from the Paleocene into the Eocene, or within the Tertiary. At the edges of the basins the coarse, bouldery Wasatch Formation oversteps and overlaps all the earlier formations with marked unconformity, extending in places far into the ranges. This relation has sometimes been said to indicate the climax of the Laramide orogeny. More properly, it was an anti-climax after the orogenic forces had largely spent themselves.

We have now carried our story of the Eastern Ranges and Plateaus through the great deformation, ending with the Laramide orogeny of late Cretaceous and Paleocene time. Events that followed the great deformation were many and varied, and are difficult to generalize because they are closely bound to local conditions. It is therefore appropriate that we now describe the structures of the several parts of the region that were formed mainly during the Laramide orogeny before resuming the history of the region from Laramide time to the present.

4. CENTRAL ROCKY MOUNTAINS

SUBDIVISIONS OF THE ROCKY MOUNTAINS. As noted earlier, the "Rocky Mountains" are more of a geographical than a geological entity, the name being used for any of the frontal ranges of the Cordillera that face the Great Plains. To give the expression geological meaning it is necessary to break the Rocky Mountains into several parts. Geologists differ as to how this subdivision should be made and what the various parts should be called; it would be tedious here to review the many usages. We will speak of a Northern, Central, and Southern Rocky Mountains, but the reader should be forewarned that these are units that differ in one or more particulars from those of other geologists.

The *Northern Rocky Mountains* extending from western Montana into Canada are ridges of sedimentary rocks that originated in the miogeosynclinal belt of the Cordillera; by subsequent deformation they have acquired a folded and faulted structure like that in the sedimentary Appalachians (see Chapter VIII, section 3).

The *Southern Rocky Mountains*, by contrast, are Eastern Ranges that belong to that part of the Cordilleran system east of the front of the main geosynclinal belt. They are the high, closely packed ranges that center in Colorado, but whose prongs extend northward into Wyoming, westward into Utah, and southward into New Mexico. The Laramide and later structure of these ranges is complicated by its superposition on structures of the later Paleozoic Colorado system.

Between the Northern and Southern Rocky Mountains is a more heterogeneous set of ranges lying mainly in Wyoming but extending northward into Montana and westward into Idaho. This middle or central part of the Rocky Mountains includes on the west ranges of deformed miogeosynclinal rocks, and east of them a set of rather simple uplifts and basins that, like the Southern Rocky Mountains, are Eastern Ranges that formed from rocks outside the main geosynclinal belt. For the mountains on the west, formed of the miogeosynclinal rocks, we can use a synthetic term, the *Wyomide Ranges* (from *Wyoming* and *Idaho*); those to the east we will term the *Central Rocky Mountains*. Unlike the Southern Rocky Mountains, their rocks and structures show little evidence of Paleozoic disturbance, and their ranges originated largely during the Laramide orogeny. Exposition of the structures of the Eastern Ranges can best begin with this part, where the structures are less confused by earlier deformations.

GENERAL GEOLOGY AND GEOGRAPHY. The Central Rocky Mountains are illustrated by the geologic maps of Wyoming and Montana. On these one can see that the ranges are broad-backed uplifts, many of which expose wide areas of Precambrian basement rocks in their cores; also that they are of diverse trends and widely spaced, with broader basin areas between, most of whose surface

rocks are of early Tertiary (Paleocene and Eocene) ages.

Some of the ranges of the Central Rocky Mountains rise to imposing heights; the Wind River Mountains, for example, include peaks more than 4,000 meters high. But the intervening basins form plains and plateaus much like the Great Plains farther east—so broad that in many places the mountains along their edges are only dimly visible. Although the state of Wyoming lies mainly in the Central Rocky Mountains, over half its area is plains country.

It was no accident, therefore, that most early western travel was through the Wyoming country, avoiding the more massive ranges of the Rocky Mountains to the north and south. Emigrant wagons could roll across the plains with few obstacles and without passing through any mountains, until they came to the Wasatch Range in Utah, far to the west. So also, some years after the great western emigrations, the first transcontinental railroad was laid out and built through the same area.

THE RANGES AND THEIR STRUCTURE. In most of this account I have not burdened the reader with local geography, but to explain the Eastern Ranges it is necessary to name at least the major physical features.

On the east side of the Central Rocky Mountains are the *Black Hills* athwart the boundary between Wyoming and South Dakota—an isolated domical uplift well out in the plains, yet showing many features of the main mountain structure. Although the Black Hills neither rise as high as the ranges farther west nor show as much structural uplift, Precambrian rocks are laid bare in their core.

Farther west are the more lofty *Bighorn Mountains* with peaks of Precambrian rocks along their crests. The Bighorn Mountains extend into other ranges at their ends, which together form a great arcuate uplift, convex toward the east.

Southwest of the Bighorn arc are the *Wind River Mountains*, again with high peaks of Precambrian rocks along their crests. The Wind River Mountains are merely a segment of a larger northwest-trending chain of ranges whose original Laramide structures were much modified later. Toward the southeast are the low *Granite Mountains*, half-buried by Tertiary sediments; but to the northwest, south of Yellowstone Park, the chain rises in the *Teton Mountains*. These overlook the flanking basin of Jackson Hole to the east in towering precipices with some of the most spectacular alpine scenery in the United States (end paper 2). Here, as in the part of the chain southeast of the Wind River Mountains, the topography is greatly influenced by structures younger than the Laramide deformation; the Teton Mountains were raised by block-faulting rather late in Tertiary time.

In northwestern Wyoming and extending into Montana are the *Beartooth Mountains* lying west of one end of the Bighorn arc and northeast of Yellowstone Park.

Like the Bighorn and Wind River Ranges, they have a high-standing Precambrian core.

The Eastern Ranges in Montana are smaller, more disconnected, with disordered trends. West of the Beartooth Mountains they include the Madison, Jefferson, Tobacco Root and other ranges, each with a Precambrian core and flanked by Paleozoic and Mesozoic sediments. The Precambrian is less widely exposed farther north, but it emerges in the cores of the *Big Belt* and *Little Belt Mountains*, where it is represented by sedimentary rocks of the Middle Proterozoic Belt Series.

over the rocks of the basins (Fig. 73C). These thrusts differ from the lengthy low-angle thrusts in the geosynclinal sedimentary rocks, as they are caused by very local bulging out of the uplifts as they arose.

(D) In still other places (notably along the southwest edge of the Wind River Mountains) the turned up rocks along the edges of the uplifts are masked by Eocene and later deposits younger than the uplifts; these overlap and overstep the older rocks from the basins toward the mountains (Fig. 73D).

THE BASINS AND THEIR STRUCTURE. Between the

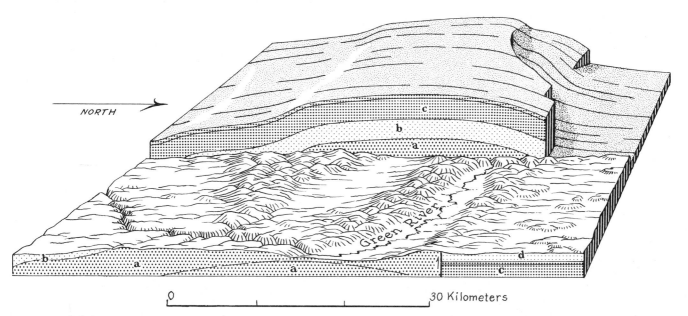

FIG. 72. Block diagram showing an uplift typical of those in the Central Rocky Mountains; eastern part of Uinta Mountains in northwestern Colorado and northeastern Utah. Rear half of the block shows structural form of uplift without erosion; the front half, the present landscape. (a) Precambrian (Uinta Mountain Group). (b) Paleozoic. (c) Mesozoic. (d) Tertiary. After Powell (1876).

The ranges are uplifts somewhat longer than wide, raised so high that in many places erosion along their crests has laid bare the basement of Precambrian rocks. Reconstruction of the sedimentary cover indicates that the uplifts are arch-like or block-like, with gentle dips over the crests and steep dips along the edges where the basement and immediately overlying strata descend to great depths in the adjoining basins (Fig. 72). The edges of the uplifts present several varieties of structure.

(A) The turned-up sedimentary cover may form a steeply dipping border along the core of exposed Precambrian rocks, carved by erosion into lines of hogbacks (Fig. 73A).

(B) In other places the sedimentary rocks are cut off by nearly vertical faults, along which Precambrian rocks of the core have been upthrust so that they adjoin directly the Cretaceous and early Tertiary rocks of the basins (Fig. 73B).

(C) In a few places the faults dip under the mountains, and the Precambrian rocks of the core have been thrust

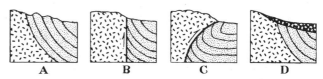

FIG. 73. Sketch sections illustrating four different sorts of structural features that occur along the edges of uplifts in the Central Rocky Mountains, as explained in text.

ranges are the basins, which cover the greater area (Fig. 74). Between the Black Hills and the Bighorn Mountains is the *Powder River basin*. Enclosed within the arc of the Bighorn Mountains is the *Bighorn basin*. Southwest of the arc and between it and the Wind River Mountains is the *Wind River basin*. Between the latter range and the northern prongs of the Southern Rocky Mountains is the very broad *Green River basin*. Some smaller basins are enclosed between the ranges elsewhere, of which we need mention only the *Hanna basin* on the southeast.

The basins have been more passive features than the ranges, and remained relatively stable while the latter

115

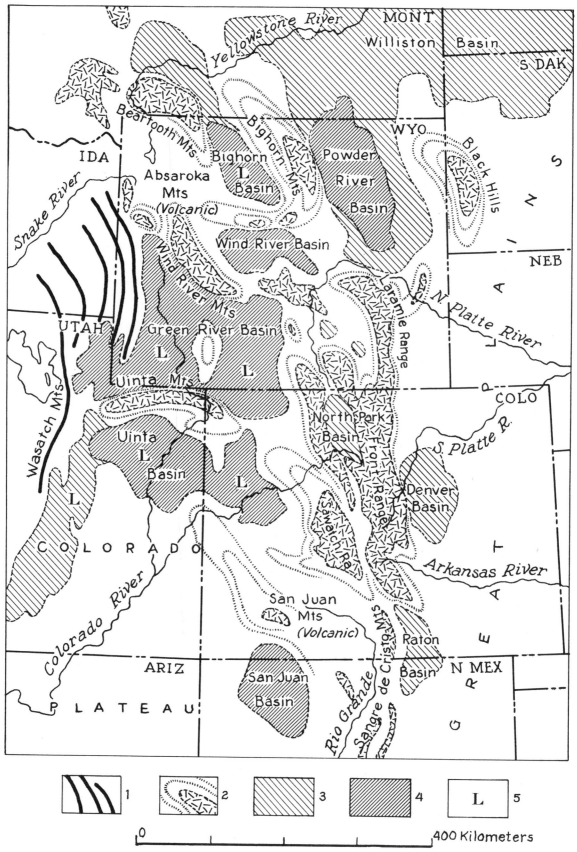

FIG. 74. Map of Central and Southern Rocky Mountains showing uplifts and basins of Paleocene and Eocene time. Compiled from Geologic Map of United States (1974) and other sources.

Explanation of symbols: 1–Folds and fault-blocks in geosynclinal sediments. 2–Uplifts east of geosynclinal area with outcrops of Precambrian basement rocks in their higher parts. 3–Basins which received Paleocene sediments. 4–Basins in which Eocene sediments were deposited over Paleocene sediments. 5–Areas of lake deposits, mainly of Eocene age.

were uplifted between them. Most of their surfaces are covered by Eocene formations that were laid down after the climax of the Laramide orogeny, hence have been little folded. But drilling indicates that in the central parts of the basins the older rocks—Paleocene, Mesozoic, and Paleozoic—are less disturbed than in the uplifts.

Nevertheless, on many places along the edges of the basins, close to the mountain uplifts, the pre-Eocene rocks are folded into anticlines. These have served as traps for oil and are the sites of many of the oil fields in this part of the Rocky Mountain region.

The Eocene deposits that form the surfaces of the basins are all of continental origin. The seas that had spread along the east side of the Cordillera had by then disappeared as a result of the vicissitudes of the Laramide orogeny. This orogeny for a time impeded the exterior drainage so that the deposits were laid down in enclosed basins. The Eocene sequence begins with the Wasatch Formation, a reddish, sandy stream deposit that becomes coarse and bouldery where it overlaps the edges of the mountains. It is succeeded in many of the basins by deposits of a series of great lakes (Fig. 74)—well-bedded clays, silts, and sands, with much oil shale—typified by the Green River Formation of contiguous parts of Wyoming, Colorado, and Utah.

VOLCANIC AREAS. The Central Rocky Mountains are not a notable volcanic region. Wide areas lack any igneous rocks except those in the projecting Precambrian basement, but there are some widely separated areas of volcanic rocks and shallow intrusives that contrast with the dominant terrane of sedimentary and basement rocks. The volcanic areas are of several sorts, have had varied histories, and show different degrees of destruction by erosion.

An older center forms the *Crazy Mountains* of southwestern Montana (Fig. 75). These mountains are made by the Livingston Formation, a mass of andesitic tuff derived from volcanic eruptions somewhere nearby, which was deposited during latest Cretaceous and Paleocene time and later downwarped gently into a basin. The relatively soft rocks of the Livingston Formation project as bold mountains because they are held together by several intrusive stocks and by great swarms of radiating dikes. Stocks and dikes were intruded during a second period of volcanism early in Tertiary time when the stocks were conduits that fed volcanoes and lava fields at a higher level, all traces of which have now been removed by erosion (Section A-A', Fig. 75). Apparently no volcanic activity occurred in the Crazy Mountains after early Tertiary time.

A more complex and persistent volcanic area occurs in the *Absaroka Mountains* and *Yellowstone National Park* between the Beartooth and Wind River uplifts in northwestern Wyoming, where flows, breccias, and tuffs were piled up to a thickness of many thousands of meters and

have not yet been removed by erosion; the area thus stands now as a high, deeply dissected lava plateau. Here volcanic eruptions began in late Eocene time toward the close of the sedimentary filling of the adjacent Bighorn and Wind River basins. Eruptions continued through the Tertiary. The many hot springs and geysers in the National Park indicate that the volcanic fires have not yet cooled.

IMPINGEMENT OF GEOSYNCLINAL FOLDS ON WEST SIDE OF CENTRAL ROCKY MOUNTAINS. A final item completes our outline of the structure of the Central Rocky Mountains.

The western part of the area that is defined geographically as the Central Rocky Mountains is a set of ranges of very different character from those we have considered; these are the *Wyomide Ranges* of westernmost Wyoming and southeastern Idaho. They consist of miogeosynclinal Paleozoic and Mesozoic sediments, which have been thrown into closely packed folds and thrust slices without exposing any Precambrian basement. Their structures trend for long distances in the same direction, running northwestward into Idaho and Montana and southward into the Wasatch and other ranges in Utah.

The Wyomide Ranges contrast with those to the east with their erratic trends, broad backs, and Precambrian cores. In many places the latter strike westward toward the miogeosynclinal structures and seem to be overridden by them. In northwestern Wyoming the miogeosynclinal structures are thus deflected around the Gros Ventre and Teton Mountains at the northwest end of the Wind River trend; and in Utah the Wasatch Mountains meet the westward trend of the Uinta Mountains at nearly right angles.

Contrasts between the structures of the Central Rocky Mountains and the Wyomide Ranges on the west result from deformation of unlike rock masses. In the Central Rocky Mountains the sedimentary cover is rather thin with basement rocks fairly near the surface. The area was a foreland, more resistant to deformation than the miogeosynclinal area, where the basement is thickly covered by sediments.

ECONOMIC PRODUCTS. General simplicity of the structure of the Central Rocky Mountains has influenced the economic products, inhibiting extensive metallic mineral deposits and enhancing the quantity of its mineral fuels.

Mineralized areas are few except in the uplifted bodies of Precambrian rocks. The Precambrian in some of the ranges in Wyoming contain beds of iron ore like those in the Lower Proterozoic of the Lake Superior Region. In the northern Black Hills the Precambrian also contains the great ore body of the Homestake Mine, the largest gold producer in North America. Opinion is divided as to whether this body was introduced into the

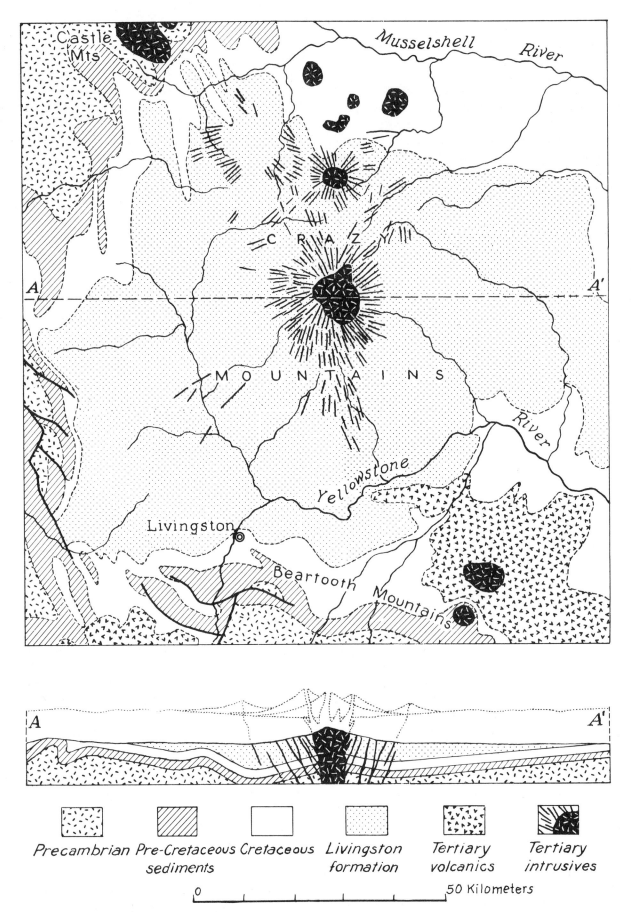

Precambrian Pre-Cretaceous Cretaceous Livingston Tertiary Tertiary
sediments formation volcanics intrusives

0   50 Kilometers

Fig. 75. Geologic map and sections of Crazy Mountains, southwestern Montana, showing Livingston Formation of latest Cretaceous and Paleocene age, and the stocks and dikes that intrude it. Dotted lines above the section indicate the volcanic field that probably lay on the site of the Crazy Mountains in early Tertiary time. After Weed (1899) and Geologic Map of Montana (1955).

Precambrian rocks during Precambrian time, or later on during the Tertiary, when igneous rocks were intruded nearby in plugs and laccoliths.

By contrast, mineral fuels in the prevailing sedimentary rocks are widespread.

The Laramie and Paleocene continental deposits contain many beds of coal, mostly low-quality lignite but attaining bituminous grade where deformation was greatest. The Hanna Basin of southeastern Wyoming with thick coal-bearing deposits of these ages is fortunately placed along the line of the Union Pacific Railroad and was a source of fuel for its locomotives before the days of the diesels.

Eocene lake beds such as the Green River Formation, which overlie the Paleocene in the western intermontane basins, contain thick beds of oil shale. Technology for its extraction has been studied for many years but still seems not to be economically or environmentally feasible. Some day when our liquid petroleum supplies are further depleted and our automobiles are grinding to a halt, and with uranium-powered family vehicles still a dream of the future, these great oil shale deposits may come into their own as a source of petroleum.

The Central Rocky Mountains of Wyoming and Montana are also more prolific and widespread producers of oil and gas than the more complex and closely crowded ranges of the Northern and Southern Rocky Mountains. Many of the oil fields of the region occur in structural traps formed by the little anticlines around the edges of the major uplifts.

We will see presently that in the Southern Rocky Mountains the proportion between the values of metallic and non-metallic mineral deposits is reversed because of the somewhat different structure of the two regions.

5. SOUTHERN ROCKY MOUNTAINS

We have learned something of the characteristic style of Rocky Mountain structure from consideration of the relatively simple Central Rocky Mountains. Now let us turn to the Southern Rocky Mountains, where many of the same kinds of structures occur, but with additional features that add to the complexity of the picture.

EXTENT OF SOUTHERN ROCKY MOUNTAINS. The main body of the Southern Rocky Mountains is in Colorado, where it forms a wide band across the central part of the state. Prongs extend northward into Wyoming and die out in a particularly extensive area of plains and basins. Another prong, the Uinta Mountains, extends westward into Utah and abuts against the Wasatch Mountains. Still others extend southward into New Mexico, one of which ends east of Santa Fe at Glorieta Pass, through which the Santa Fe Railroad has been built.

South of Santa Fe and Glorieta Pass shorter and more widely spaced ranges extend on each side of the Rio Grande to El Paso, Texas, but these are not truly part of the Rocky Mountains, as we will discover later in this chapter (section 6).

COMPARISON OF CENTRAL AND SOUTHERN ROCKY MOUNTAINS. General features of the Southern Rocky Mountains may be seen on the geologic maps of Colorado, Wyoming, and New Mexico. Using the maps alone let us observe resemblances between the Central and Southern Rocky Mountains.

(a) Both sets of mountains are bordered on the east by the Great Plains or western edge of the Interior Lowlands.

(b) In both areas Precambrian rocks are extensively exposed along the cores of the mountain uplifts.

(c) Broad basins of Paleocene and Eocene rocks occur alongside both sets of ranges.

(d) Both regions contain dispersed areas of volcanic rocks and shallow intrusives. In the Southern Rocky Mountains these are best displayed in contiguous parts of Colorado and New Mexico where plugs and attendant dike swarms occur in the east and dissected volcanic plateaus in the west (Fig. 71).

But let us note some obvious differences:

(a) The Southern Rocky Mountains are bordered on the west not by geosynclinal folds of the main Cordillera but by the Colorado Plateau.

(b) Ranges of the Southern Rocky Mountains are not widely dispersed; the whole mountain belt from Great Plains to Colorado Plateau is narrower than farther north.

(c) Individual ranges are more crowded, too, as shown by the close spacing of areas of Precambrian rocks that emerge along their cores. Crowding of the ranges is greatest at about mid-length in the latitude of Denver (Fig. 76).

(d) Basins between the ranges are correspondingly narrower than those farther north, and form high mountain valleys or "parks" rather than broad tracts of plains country.

(e) Large bodies of intrusive igneous rocks occur in the Southern Rocky Mountains, unlike any in the Central Rocky Mountains. The map legends call them "diorite porphyry," "quartz monzonite porphyry," and "granite porphyry," suggesting a fairly deep-seated plutonic habitat.

Other differences not evident from the maps alone will be apparent as the discussion proceeds.

RANGES ON THE NORTH. Let us observe the major physical features of the Southern Rocky Mountains in the same manner as we have those of the Central Rocky Mountains.

In the north half of Colorado and northward into Wyoming the Great Plains are faced on the west by the ramparts of the *Front Range* (Fig. 76), a broad-backed

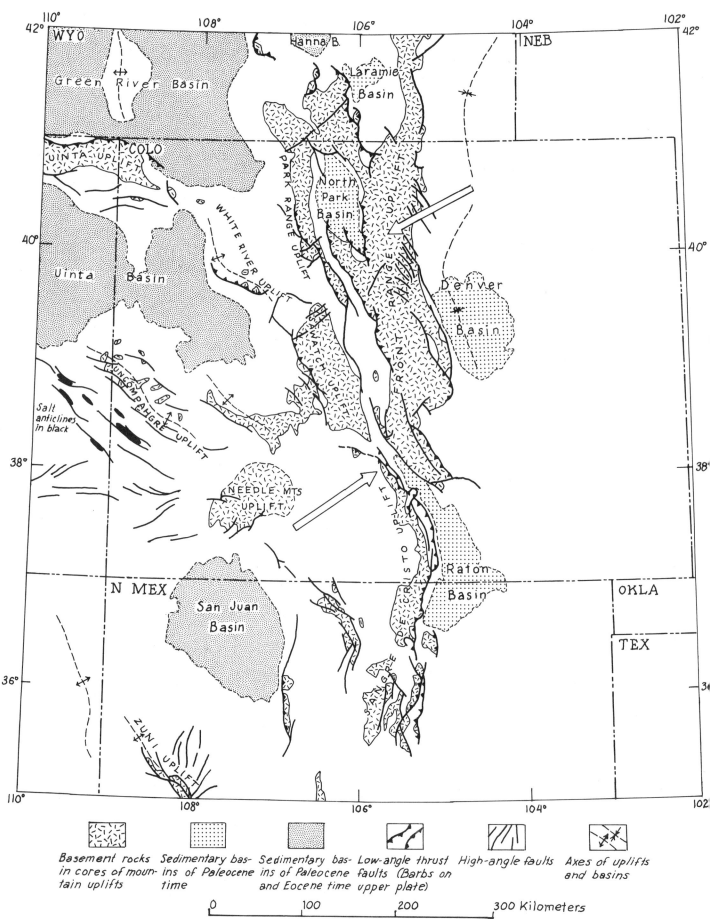

Basement rocks in cores of mountain uplifts

Sedimentary basins of Paleocene time

Sedimentary basins of Paleocene and Eocene time

Low-angle thrust faults (Barbs on upper plate)

High-angle faults

Axes of uplifts and basins

0   100   200   300 Kilometers

Fig. 76. Part III of a series showing structural development of Southern Rocky Mountains. Map shows structures formed by Laramide orogeny in late Cretaceous and Paleocene time. Large arrows indicate dominant directions of thrusting in the north and south. After Tectonic Map of United States (1962) and Geologic Map of United States (1974).

uplift along whose crest erosion has laid bare wide areas of Precambrian rocks; these project in such summits as Pikes Peak and Longs Peak, both named for leaders of early American exploring expeditions. Southward near Canon City the massif of the Front Range plunges beneath the plains, although a small prong, the *Wet Mountains*, extends a little farther. Northward in Wyoming the main ridge forms the *Laramie Range*, but a western branch extends into the *Medicine Bow Mountains*. The Front Range owes its present form largely to uplift during the Laramide orogeny, but its position corresponds to the main eastern part of the Front Range geanticline of the later Paleozoic Colorado system; as a consequence the lower Paleozoic rocks are nearly missing along the flanks.

West of the Front Range in central Colorado is the shorter but somewhat higher *Sawatch Range*, also a broad uplift that lays bare wide areas of Precambrian rocks. One of its peaks, Mount Elbert (4,389 meters), is the highest summit of the Rocky Mountains. The Precambrian of this range is penetrated by extensive bodies of much later Tertiary plutonic rocks such as the great stock of Mount Princeton at its south end. Unlike the Front Range, the Sawatch Range was newly born during the Laramide orogeny and rose from the Paleozoic trough betweeen the two geanticlines; it thus has its full quota of lower Paleozoic rocks along the flanks.

Northward the Sawatch structure fans out (Fig. 76). A branch to the north forms the *Park Range*, which continues into southern Wyoming before plunging beneath younger rocks. A branch to the northwest forms the *White River Plateau*, also a broad-backed uplift but still largely sheeted over by Paleozoic rocks. It is trenched by the gorge of the Colorado (formerly "Grand") River above Glenwood Springs, traversed by the Denver and Rio Grande Railroad, where the arched structure of the uplift is wonderfully exposed.

This branch descends into a sag northwest of the White River Plateau, beyond which it rises again into the *Uinta Mountains*. These extend westward into Utah, approaching the Wasatch Mountains of the main Cordillera nearly at right angles. Like many other ranges of the Central and Southern Rocky Mountains, the Uinta Mountains are a broad-backed uplift in which Precambrian rocks are exposed along the crest (Fig. 72), but here the Precambrian is not crystalline basement and is the Uinta Mountain Group, a thick mass of bedded supracrustal sandy rocks.

RANGES ON THE SOUTH. Near the latitude of Canon City the *Sangre de Cristo Mountains* develop behind the Front Range. Southward where the Front Range and Wet Mountains plunge beneath the Great Plains, the Sangre de Cristo Mountains form the frontal ridge and so continue into New Mexico. The Sangre de Cristo Mountains are not a broad-backed uplift like the Front and Sawatch Ranges (Fig. 78B). Precambrian rocks emerge in places, but much of the range is formed of strongly folded late Paleozoic sediments that were derived from the Uncompahgre geanticline of the Colorado system, and were laid down in the trough east of it.

In front of the Sangre de Cristo Mountains stand the *Spanish Peaks*, whose structure resembles that of the Crazy Mountains of Montana (Fig. 78)—a basin of early Tertiary sediments intruded by central stocks, or volcanic necks, and by a remarkable swarm of radiating dikes.

West of the Sangre de Cristo Mountains are the *San Juan Mountains*, a much larger volcanic center, with an area of 15,000 square kilometers (Fig. 79). As in the Absaroka Mountains of northwestern Wyoming, volcanic activity was long-persistent here. Volcanic rocks occur in the Paleocene at the base of the sequence, but main activity was during the Oligocene when a succession of great calderas and volcanic-tectonic depressions were created, each in turn erupting thick masses of lavas and ash-flow tuffs. Minor eruptions of lava continued into the Miocene. The mass of eruptive rocks has been deeply dissected into a mountainous plateau.

The volcanics of the San Juan Mountains have been built over an eroded surface of disturbed earlier rocks, part of which belonged to the Uncompahgre geanticline of Paleozoic time, and which was domed again during the Laramide orogeny. On the southwest side of the volcanic area Precambrian rocks project in the high peaks of the *Needle Mountains*. Northwest of the volcanic area the *Uncompahgre Plateau* extends into the Colorado Plateau past Grand Junction, Colorado. Like the White River Plateau, the Uncompahgre Plateau is largely sheeted over by sediments, here of Triassic age. Where these are breached by erosion the truncated earlier structure of the Uncompahgre geanticline is revealed, with Precambrian beneath the Triassic along the crest and Paleozoic rocks intervening along the flanks (Fig. 77).

BASINS OF SOUTHERN ROCKY MOUNTAINS. Basins of the Southern Rocky Mountains are most extensive east and west of the ranges.

East of the Front Range is the broad *Denver Basin*, thickly filled by Laramie and Paleocene deposits (Fig. 76). It became nearly inactive after Paleocene time, re-

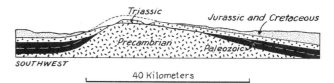

FIG. 77. Sketch section across Uncompahgre Plateau southwest of Grand Junction, Colorado, showing truncation of Paleozoic rocks by Triassic along the site of the Uncompahgre geanticline of later Paleozoic time, and the arching of both Paleozoic and Mesozoic rocks by Laramide deformation.

ceived no Eocene deposits, and is now partly masked by late Tertiary Great Plains deposits. Farther south in the angle between the Front Range and Sangre de Cristo Mountains is the similar but narrower *Huerfano Basin*, which contains the stocks and dikes of the Spanish Peaks.

Along the edge of the Colorado Plateau west of the Southern Rocky Mountains are the broad *Uinta* and *San Juan Basins*, the first lying south of the Uinta Mountains, the second south of the San Juan Mountains. Their rocks and structures resemble those of the intermontane basins of the Central Rocky Mountains, as they contain Eocene as well as Laramie and Paleocene deposits; the Eocene of the Uinta Basin includes lake beds like those farther north.

Basins between the ranges form a chain of high mountain valleys or "parks" filled by early Tertiary sediments. *North* and *Middle Parks* west of the Front Range are parts of a single basin; *South Park* is a separate structure along the same trend. South of the "parks" is the *San Luis Valley* between the Sangre de Cristo and San Juan Mountains at the headwaters of the Rio Grande (Fig. 79). It differs from the basins so far described in that it is filled by Pliocene rather than earlier deposits and has been shaped by block faulting, which dropped the east side against the Sangre de Cristo Mountains and tilted the volcanic rocks of the San Juan Mountains beneath it. Similar block-faulted depressions of about the same age extend southward along the Rio Grande across New Mexico, and the fault system extends well north of the San Luis Valley into central Colorado.

INFLUENCE OF EARLIER STRUCTURES ON PATTERN OF SOUTHERN ROCKY MOUNTAINS. So much for the "geological geography" of the Southern Rocky Mountains. Now let us analyze their structures more critically (Fig. 76).

In the Central Rocky Mountains the Laramide structures appear to have been newly born without deformational antecedents, but in the Southern Rocky Mountains they were much influenced by earlier structures. Effects of the Precambrian structures cannot be evaluated, but it is worth recalling that their dominant trends are northwestward to southwestward across the Laramide structures. Structures of the Colorado system of later Paleozoic time are more nearly comparable with those which developed later. Recall some of the details of this system: the Front Range geanticline, which lies near the site of the later Front Range; the Uncompahgre geanticline on the site of the later Uncompahgre Plateau and San Juan Mountains; and the deep sedimentary trough between, whose rocks were themselves raised into mountains later (Fig. 65).

LOW-ANGLE FAULTS. The rocks of the Southern Rocky Mountains are broken by low-angle faults as they are in places in the Central Rocky Mountains, but they

are more extensive—although never reaching the proportions of those in miogeosynclinal regions.

The eastern border of the Front Range is much like the borders of the uplifts in the Central Rocky Mountains. Paleozoic and Mesozoic strata are sharply unturned against the lofty Precambrian rocks of the range, and in places they are cut off by vertical upthrusts or high-angle faults so that the Precambrian lies directly against the strata of the Great Plains. But on the west side of the Front Range for much of its length Precambrian rocks are thrust westward on low-angle faults for as much as 6 or 7 kilometers over Cretaceous rocks (Fig. 78A). Similar low- to high-angle faults occur in the Sawatch and Park Ranges beyond, again with the Precambrian thrust toward the west.

Farther south, by contrast, the rocks of the Sangre de Cristo and related ranges are thrust toward the east. In Huerfano Park on the east flank of the Sangre de Cristo Mountains, complex thrusts in this direction have developed in the great mass of late Paleozoic clastic rocks, although these have been much confused by later upthrusts of the Precambrian basement (Fig. 78B).

These varied directions of thrust during the Laramide orogeny may be related to the Paleozoic structures of the Colorado system on which they were imposed. The westward thrust of the ranges of northern Colorado was from the site of the Front Range geanticline of Paleozoic time toward the Colorado trough that lay west of it; the eastward thrust of southern Colorado was from the Uncompahgre geanticline of Paleozoic time toward the trough that lay east of it.

TRANSVERSE ZONE OF CENTRAL COLORADO. A final item of structure of the Southern Rocky Mountains remains—the transverse zone or *Colorado Mineral Belt*, which extends diagonally northeastward across all the mountains, from the San Juan Mountains to the Front Range (Fig. 79).

The transverse zone is most prominently expressed on the map by distribution of the larger bodies of intrusive igneous rocks, which occur in all the ranges but are especially concentrated in or near the Sawatch Range. The intrusive rocks are diorite, quartz monzonite, and granite porphyries, and are of plutonic habit, unlike the shallow stocks and laccoliths that occur elsewhere in the region. Radiometric dating indicates that they have a considerable spread in ages, from 70 million years to 40 million years, or from near the Cretaceous-Paleocene boundary into the Oligocene.

Other features of the zone are short northeast-trending faults and shear zones, crossed in places by a minor set trending northwest. These have had a long antecedent history—the northeast-trending shear zones represent a reactivation of shear zones that developed in the Precambrian basement toward the end of its defor-

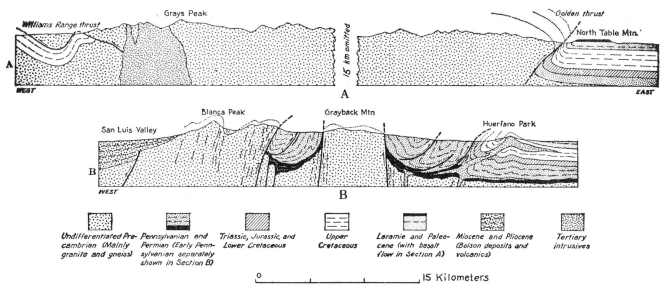

FIG. 78. Sections that compare the structure of the Front Range with that of the Sangre de Cristo Mountains in the north and south parts of the Rocky Mountains of Colorado. (A) Section of Front Range in latitude of Denver. (B) Section of Sangre de Cristo Mountains in latitude of Walsenburg. After Lovering (1935), Van Tuyl and McLaren (1933), and Burbank and Goddard (1937).

mational history, and created a line of weakness that influenced the Laramide and early Tertiary movements.

MINERAL DEPOSITS. The Southern Rocky Mountains are noted for their metallic mineral wealth, which for many years made Colorado one of the great mining states of the west. Curiously, first discovery of gold (or of any other metal) in Colorado was in the alluvial deposits of Cherry Creek, a stream that heads in the Great Plains and enters the South Platte River near the present city of Denver. It was only after prospectors had flocked to Colorado on the strength of this find that the vastly richer deposits in the bedrock of the mountains to the west became known.

As discoveries followed each other through the years, the pattern of the bedrock deposits became clearer. Almost all lie on or near the transverse zone just discussed (Fig. 79), as though its structures were such as to permit the rise of mineralizing solutions as well as of igneous magmas. Few important deposits lie north or south of the zone, the only exception being at Cripple Creek far to the south in the Front Range near Pikes Peak, where the throat of a former caldera has been mineralized.

That part of the transverse zone in the Front Range includes such great mining camps as Central City and Georgetown. Farther southwest is Leadville between the Front and Sawatch Ranges; beyond are the camps of Ouray, Telluride, and Silverton in the western San Juan Mountains.

Unlike some other productive regions, the Colorado mineral belt contains ores of a great variety of metals. The first attraction, of course, was the gold deposits, but in 1879 lead-carbonate silver ores were discovered at Leadville, and thereafter silver was extensively mined as well. It was only later that the value of the baser metals

such as lead, copper, and zinc began to be appreciated, and it was found that much of the waste discarded in dumps and tailings was almost as valuable as the material that had been saved. Among the later discoveries were the molybdenum at Climax near Leadville, probably the richest occurrence of this metal in North America.

In its time, mining activity had a dominant influence in the shaping of the history of Colorado, but (sad to relate) it is now on the wane. Many of the large low-grade metallic deposits in which reserves can be blocked out for years ahead are still being actively worked, but the days of the bonanza discovery and the small rich mine appear to be in the past. Mining camps picturesquely set in gorges far back in the mountains are now moribund; the narrow-gauge railroads which once connected them with the world have been dismantled. Colorado has learned to prosper on its less glamorous resources of agriculture, timber, and mineral fuels, and its superb mountain environment, which each year draws increasing numbers of visitors.

6. LESS DEFORMED PARTS OF EASTERN RANGES AND PLATEAUS; NEW MEXICO RANGES AND COLORADO PLATEAU

We pass now to the western and southern parts of the Eastern Ranges and Plateaus, which have been less deformed, on the whole, than the Central and Southern Rocky Mountains. Much of this region is table-land and constitutes the *Colorado Plateau*; on the southeast in New Mexico it is broken into a succession of block mountains, which we can designate as the *New Mexico Ranges*.

NEW MEXICO RANGES. Prongs of the Rocky Mountains extend into New Mexico, but they die out south-

123

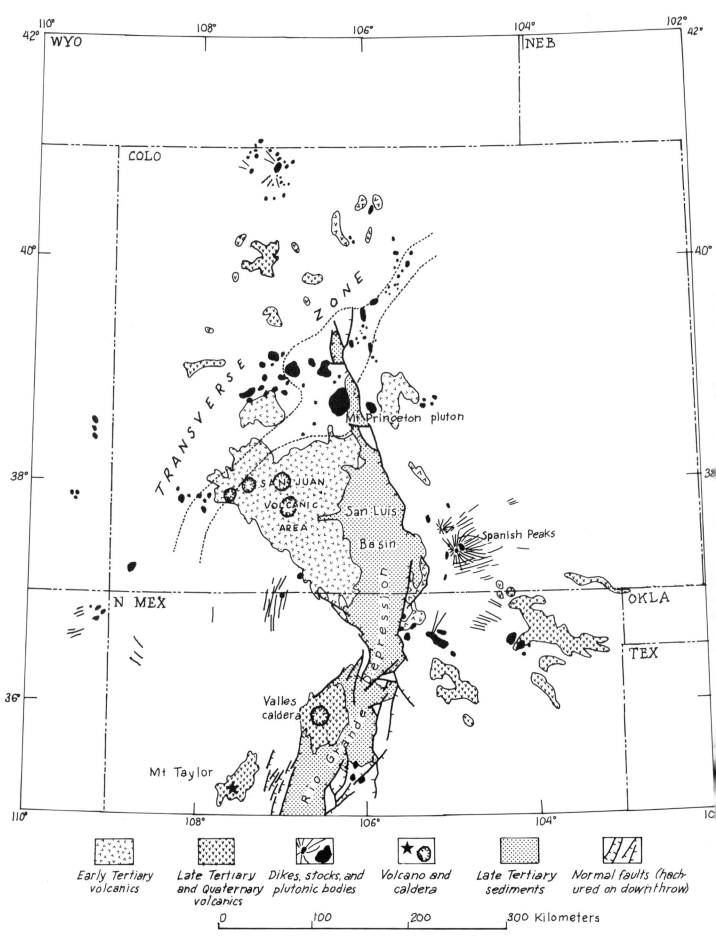

Early Tertiary volcanics

Late Tertiary and Quaternary volcanics

Dikes, stocks, and plutonic bodies

Volcano and caldera

Late Tertiary sediments

Normal faults (hachured on downthrow)

0   100   200   300 Kilometers

FIG. 79. Part IV of a series showing structural development of Southern Rocky Mountains. Shows Tertiary and Quaternary structures, igneous rocks, and deposits. Some of the features shown are nearly contemporaneous with those of Fig. 76; others are much younger. Compiled from Tectonic Map of United States (1962) and Geologic Map of United States (1974).

ward; the Sangre de Cristo Mountains or easternmost prong ends east of Sante Fe at Glorieta Pass. Farther south shorter, lower, more dispersed ranges continue across New Mexico into western Texas, where they merge with the Sierra Madre Oriental of Mexico. These ranges have little of the characteristic style of the Rocky Mountains and are not truly extensions of them.

Quite as significant as the ranges in New Mexico are the intervening basins, part of which are traversed by the Rio Grande in its course southward from the Rocky Mountains toward the Gulf of Mexico (Fig. 80D). The river breaks out of the southernmost basins through a spectacular set of gorges in the Big Bend country of Texas.

We learned earlier that New Mexico was part of the continental backbone of Paleozoic time, and that over wide areas later Paleozoic strata directly overlie Precambrian basement. Compared with the sequence of Paleozoic and Mesozoic rocks in the Central and Southern Rocky Mountains, that in the New Mexico Ranges is relatively thin. Traces of Laramide orogeny with development of thrusts, uplifts, and basins may be observed in various parts of the area (Fig. 80A, B, and C), but disturbances of this time affected it only lightly.

The modern topography of New Mexico, instead of being inherited from the Laramide orogeny, is largely a product of block-faulting in late Tertiary time and afterward (Fig. 80)—one of the processes that modified the surface aspect of the Cordillera after the great deformation of Mesozoic time. The mountains were raised or tilted by movements along the faults that outline their bases, and the basins have been depressed and filled by great thicknesses of Pliocene and younger deposits derived from the wasting of the mountains.

We have already noted similar block-faulting younger than the Laramide deformation in local areas farther north—in the Teton Mountains of Wyoming and the San Luis Valley of Colorado. Features of this sort are termed *Basin and Range structure*; we will analyze them more fully when we discuss the Basin and Range province as a whole (Chapter IX, section 2).

GEOGRAPHY OF COLORADO PLATEAU. The Colorado Plateau or "Plateau province" of Powell lies northwest of the New Mexico ranges and is a great, high-standing crustal block, nearly square and 800 kilometers broad on the sides, whose center is close to the "Four Corners" of the states of Colorado, Utah, Arizona, and New Mexico. Westward and southwestward the plateau breaks off in escarpments that overlook the more diversified and broken country of the Basin and Range province—the Great Basin of Utah and Nevada and the similar terrain in Arizona. The escarpments on these sides meet in northwestern Arizona south of the Grand Canyon, where they form a right-angled corner of the plateau. By contrast, the eastern and northeastern sides of the plateau are flanked by more elevated country, the ranges of the Southern Rocky Mountains.

The western and southwestern rims of the Colorado Plateau attain altitudes of 3,000 to 3,500 meters, and form the High Plateaus of Utah and the Mogollon Plateau of Arizona and New Mexico, large parts of which are heavily forested. Most of the remaining area is also lofty, but somewhat less so, and is a thinly inhabited, bare, desert country—the part of the region that ordinarily comes to mind when one hears the phrase "Colorado Plateau."

The Colorado Plateau is a region of plateaus, escarpments, and canyons, all laid out on a vast scale. Except where volcanic piles have been built on its surface or intrusives have disturbed its rocks, there are no mountains in the usual sense, but rather a series of tables, benches, and steps. Also, the stream valleys are not the familiar valleys of other regions, but steepsided canyons, narrow or wide, shallow or deep. The deep, wide Grand Canyon of the Colorado River is familiar to all, but the same river farther upstream is canyoned likewise, as are all tributaries that enter it, each canyon having a distinctive form conditioned by the country rocks and their structures.

Rocks of the plateau have been flexed or folded, but for the most part gently and on a grand scale. Wide areas of nearly flat-lying rocks are separated by abrupt bends in the strata along folds or monoclinal flexures (Fig. 81). Nearly all systems of the geologic column from Paleozoic to Tertiary occur at one place or another in the plateau but are not uniformally distributed. In the Grand Canyon, as we have seen, are many hiatuses or lost intervals in the record; other hiatuses occur elsewhere at the same or different levels.

HISTORICAL SETTING. The distinctive features of the Colorado Plateau have been conditioned to a large extent by its prior history.

We have seen that the plateau in early Paleozoic time was as much a part of the stable continental platform as the Interior Lowlands, both of them sharing the overlap of Paleozoic strata from the Cordilleran geosyncline on the west (see section 2 of this chapter). Later in Paleozoic time the plateau became separated from the rest of the platform by increasing mobility of the Colorado system on the site of the present Southern Rocky Mountains.

In Mesozoic time the plateau area was overspread, first by Triassic redbeds and Jurassic dune deposits, later by Cretaceous clastic wedges related to onset of the Sevier orogeny in the main Cordillera farther west (see section 3 of this chapter). Afterwards, during the Laramide phase of the Cordilleran orogeny, principal crustal activity shifted east of the plateau and deformed the Central and Southern Rocky Mountains. Nevertheless, much of the broad folding and flexing of the rocks in

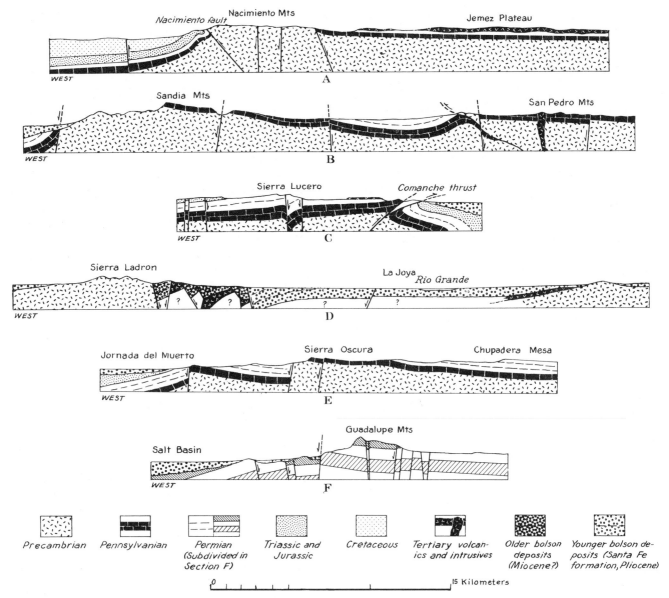

FIG. 80. Sections of the New Mexico Ranges, which show their block-faulted structure produced by deformation late in Tertiary time. Section D shows faulting and tilting of later Tertiary sediments and volcanics. In sections A, B, and C are thrust faults older than the block-faulting, probably formed during the Laramide orogeny. Note relatively small thickness of sedimentary cover in most of the sections, with basement rocks close to the surface. (A) Nacimiento Mountains, northern New Mexico. (B) Sandia Mountains northeast of Albuquerque, north-central New Mexico. (C) Lucero Mountains southwest of Albuquerque, central New Mexico. (D) Rio Grande depression east of Sierra Ladron, central New Mexico. (E) Sierra Oscura, south-central New Mexico. (F) Guadalupe Mountains, northern trans-Pecos Texas. Compiled from Wood and Northrop (1946), Read and others (1944), Kelley and Wood (1946), Denny (1940), Wilpolt and Wanek (1951), and King (1948).

the plateau itself is also a product of Laramide movements, and growth of the Uinta and San Juan Basins on the border between the plateau and Rocky Mountains took place during the waning stages of that orogeny.

BASINS AND UPLIFTS. The characteristic structure of the plateau is a series of broad uplifts and intervening basins.

To the northeast are the *Uinta* and *San Juan Basins*, thickly filled by Paleocene and Eocene sediments derived from the waste of the Southern Rocky Mountains (Fig. 76). Other shallower basins occur farther south-

west, in which early Tertiary deposits, if they ever accumulated, have been removed by erosion. The *Black Mesa Basin* in the Navajo country of northeastern Arizona is almost as large as the first two; the remainder are smaller.

Uplifts between the basins are not unlike those in the ranges of the Central and Southern Rocky Mountains, but they show less structural relief, so that they are still sheeted over by sedimentary formations. On the uplifts, denudation has removed the poorly resistant higher strata down to some resistant stratum such as the Kaibab

126

Limestone, so that they are expressed topographically as broad swells or plateaus whose surfaces reflect the warping of the resistant rocks.

One of the most lofty of these is the *Kaibab uplift*, which forms the Kaibab and Coconino Plateaus of the Grand Canyon district; it can serve as a type of the rest. It forms a great arch in the strata, 160 kilometers long and 40 kilometers wide trending northwest, on whose crest the top of the Kaibab Limestone rises to heights of 2,500 meters or more. Its original structural surface has been reduced by the great denudation of the plateau, which has removed the poorly resistant Mesozoic formations from its summit while they still remain in surrounding areas. Nevertheless, the surface of the uplift still projects several hundred meters above its surroundings. Other parts of the plateau project higher, it is true, and preserve younger sedimentary strata or volcanic rocks.

The Grand Canyon is "grand," in fact, because of the Kaibab uplift, into whose south end it has been cut. Upstream and downstream the Colorado River flows in canyons, but these are not as deep because the Kaibab Limestone stands at a lower level and the formations beneath it are not as deeply penetrated by the river. Upstream from the Grand Canyon, for example, the river flows in the narrower Marble Canyon, whose walls are formed of Kaibab and Redwall Limestones.

We are thus presented with a paradox. The Kaibab uplift is one of the highest in the Colorado Plateau, yet the main drainage of the region, the Colorado River, has cut its way across it. We will consider this problem in section 7 of this chapter.

MONOCLINAL FLEXURES. A striking feature of the uplifts of the Colorado Plateau is the manner in which the strata along their edges are flexed abruptly downward along monoclinal flexures. For the most part this is accomplished by bending of the strata, although locally they are faulted. Flexing and faulting seem to be closely related forms of yielding of the rocks; possibly the flexed sedimentary layers are draped over breaks in the stronger basement rocks beneath.

Along the east side of the Kaibab uplift the Kaibab Limestone is bent down abruptly several hundred meters on the *East Kaibab monocline*, whose steeply tilted strata form an escarpment (Fig. 81A). Along the river the descent is from the rim of the high Grand Canyon to the

rim of the lower Marble Canyon. On the downflexed side red Triassic formations of the Painted Desert are preserved above the Kaibab Limestone.

Several kilometers farther east the strata are again bent down abruptly along the *Echo Cliffs monocline*, which carries Triassic formations beneath Jurassic sandstones at the edge of the Black Mesa basin; here erosion has carved the flexed strata into an escarpment that faces the upraised side of the flexure rather than the depressed side (Fig. 81B).

Elsewhere in the Colorado Plateau the monoclinal flexures stand out well in the topography as a result of etching by erosion of less resistant formations between the more resistant. Topographic expression is diverse, as in the two examples cited, and depends on the nature of the formations that happen to be preserved at any locality.

BLOCK-FAULTING IN WESTERN PART OF PLATEAU. Westward from the Kaibab uplift toward the lower end of the Grand Canyon the strata descend also, but in a different manner; they form a set of giant steps, each dropped on the west side by a fault (Fig. 82). Proceeding in this direction from the Kaibab uplift the Colorado River thus crosses the *West Kaibab monocline* (in part faulted), and the *Toroweap*, *Hurricane*, and *Grand Wash faults*.

The faults are followed by escarpments on their upthrown sides that extend far north and south of the river. Northward in Utah the escarpments on the faults intersect and offset the variously colored cliff lines (the Chocolate, Vermillion, White, Gray, and Pink Cliffs of section 3 of this chapter), which are the products of erosion of tilted strata. In central Utah, where the highest units of the succession are preserved, the faults outline various parts of the High Plateaus.

The fault blocks of the western part of the Colorado Plateau resemble those of the Basin and Range province to the west, which we will consider later (Chapter IX, section 2). The structure of this western part of the plateau appears, in fact, to be transitional between that of the typical plateau on the east and the Great Basin part of the Basin and Range province on the west.

LACCOLITHS AND SALT STRUCTURES. Two other items complete the roster of significant structures of the Colorado Plateau:

Several clusters of mountain peaks in its central part are carved from intrusive bodies or the sedimentary rocks that were arched above the intrusives. One of the clusters near the Colorado River was sighted by Powell during his exploration of the canyons and named the *Henry Mountains* after his sponsor Joseph Henry of the Smithsonian Institution. Somewhat later Powell's colleague, G. K. Gilbert, determined that the intrusives were "pools of rock" of a hitherto unknown structural type—laccoliths that were formed by magmas injected at shal-

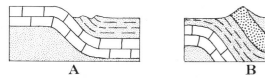

FIG. 81. Diagrammatic sections illustrating topographic expression of monoclinal flexures in Colorado Plateau. (A) With scarp facing downflexed side as in East Kaibab monocline. (B) With scarp facing upflexed side as in Echo Cliff monocline.

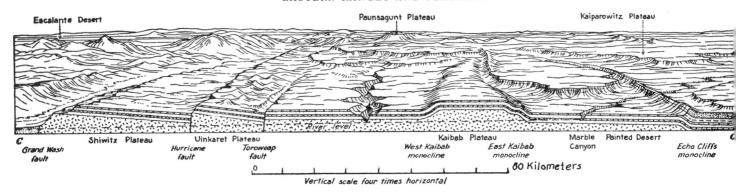

FIG. 82. Block diagram of western part of Colorado Plateau north of Grand Canyon showing monoclinal flexures to east and fault blocks to west. Section on front of block is a little north of Grand Canyon along line C–C' of Fig. 67; landscape behind extends across northern Arizona to High Plateaus of Utah. After Powell (1876).

low depth along the bedding planes of the sedimentary rocks, doming the strata above and leaving a horizontal floor beneath. Later work has shown that many of the larger intrusives of these mountains are actually stocks without floors, which were conduits that fed the adjacent laccoliths.

Similar stocks and laccolithic clusters form the La Sal, Abajo, and other groups of mountains in the vicinity. They were intruded rather late in the history of the plateau, all probably at about the same time and in much the same manner. They formed after the gross features had been developed, and they bear slight relation to them.

The salt structures were not observed during the early explorations and were only discovered later. The Paradox Formation, an evaporite deposit of Pennsylvanian age, underlies part of the east-central plateau southwest of the Uncompahgre uplift. The salt and other incompetent layers of the evaporite sequence became mobile shortly after deposition, were wrinkled into anticlines, and intruded or flowed into the overlying rocks along their crests, their form accentuated during the Laramide deformation. Subsequent collapse and solution greatly accentuated the structures. Two or three of these long narrow anticlines fringe the Uncompahgre Plateau along its southwestern side.

ECONOMIC PRODUCTS. The central part of the Colorado is bare desert country, probably one of the most empty and thinly inhabited regions in the United States. I recall vividly plane flights over it in past years, when for interminable distances little or nothing was visible of the works of man.

But even this remote region has its attraction for developers. A sizable amount of the uranium produced in the United States is mined in the region. It occurs in the form of the yellow mineral carnotite, a hydrous vanadate of potassium and uranium, which impregnates sandy sedimentary layers in the Mesozoic part of the sequence, and is extracted by following out the strata.

Oil is also being produced in the Four Corners area,

and in the same area steam plants are producing electric power from coal mined in the Black Mesa basin. The Glen Canyon Dam on the Colorado River just above the Utah-Arizona line has backed up the waters for long distances northward in Lake Powell, which has made many remote sections of the canyon lands accessible by boat.

All this is sufficient to make conservationists unhappy, and perhaps there is more to come. Even so, large parts of the plateau are still an empty wilderness, and let us hope that much of it will so remain.

7. EVENTS AFTER THE GREAT DEFORMATION

Let us now return to the history of the Eastern Ranges and Plateaus, which we left at the close of the great deformation of the Cordillera that ended with the Laramide orogeny of late Cretaceous and Paleocene time.

Laramide orogeny rather fully shaped the structures of the region—the folds and faults, the uplifts and basins—although these were accentuated later and other structures were superposed upon them. Compared with the modern landscape of the Eastern Ranges and Plateaus, however, that produced by the climactic orogeny was still primitive. The modern landscape evolved during later phases of Cordilleran history in Tertiary and Quaternary time. Again it is worth emphasizing the distinction between geological and topographic "mountains."

EARLY TERTIARY ENVIRONMENTS. As we have indicated in our discussion of the rocks formed during the great deformation (section 3 of this chapter), the ranges produced by Laramide orogeny did not project in the manner they do today, but were eroded about as rapidly as they were uplifted. Regional altitudes remained low; floors of the basins stood no more than 300 meters above sea level, and the intervening mountains projected only a few hundreds of meters higher. The climate was uniformly moist and semi-tropical; no great mountain barriers to the west cut off the flow of moisture-laden winds from the Pacific Ocean.

128

This record can be deduced from the Paleocene and Eocene sediments of the Central and Southern Rocky Mountains and from their contained plant and animal fossils. The somber-colored, coal-bearing Paleocene deposits of the basins formed in a region of forests and swamps, and their mammals were a forest-dwelling community. The red-banded deposits of the succeeding Eocene contain a larger number of mammals that lived in open grasslands, indicating a spreading of that environment, but apparently without a significant change in altitude or climate. Eocene deposits of the different basins contain the same species of mammals, indicating that the mountain uplifts between them did not project high enough to create barriers to migration.

Laramide orogeny expelled the seas from the region and marine deposits appear no more except for a brief incursion of the sea during later Paleocene time in the northern Great Plains (the Cannonball Formation of North and South Dakota). All the succeeding deposits were laid down in a continental environment.

The extensive basin deposits of Eocene time, partly laid down on flood plains of streams, partly in a series of great lakes, might suggest that Laramide orogeny also made the region one of interior drainage. A little reflection suggests that this is implausible. The region was not made lofty by the orogeny, yet its summits must have projected to some height above the Interior Lowlands on the east and formed a drainage divide; the probable rainfall of Paleocene and Eocene time was such that it could not have been tapped entirely by basins without outlets. Even the deposits of the lakes, which were formed when basin subsidence was so great as to pond the drainage, are such as to indicate that these lakes possessed outlets through much of their history. *Laramide orogeny initiated the modern drainage pattern of the Eastern Ranges and Plateaus.*

Compare, now, these Paleocene and Eocene landscapes of the Eastern Ranges and Plateaus with the landscape of present times. Today the region is one of rugged mountain ranges, whose summits reach heights of 4,000 to 4,500 meters. Not only are the mountains high but also the remainder of the region: the edge of the Great Plains at Denver is two kilometers above sea level, and many of the plains in Wyoming and Montana are even higher. The modern rivers cut through the ranges of the Rocky Mountains in rugged gorges, and those that traverse the Colorado Plateau are canyoned through most of their length. The climate of the Eastern Ranges and Plateaus is marked by harsh contrasts: plains, basins, and lower plateaus are arid or semi-arid, and only the mountains and higher plateaus receive heavy rainfall.

How was this change brought about? Clearly the whole region—from Great Plains across the Rocky Mountains into the Colorado Plateau—was raised as a unit 1,500 meters or more since Eocene time. Geologists are not fully agreed as to the manner in which this was accomplished, or by what stages, as their conclusions depend on interpretation of the elusive evidence furnished by the Tertiary and Quaternary land forms and deposits. The following pages outline what appears to be the most plausible story.

MIDDLE AND LATE TERTIARY DEPOSITS. During middle and late Tertiary time deposits were laid down as widely in the Eastern Ranges and Plateaus, or more so, than during early Tertiary time. The pattern is different, however; they are preserved as erosion remnants of original broad sheets of sediments rather than as downfolds in original depositional and structural basins. Total thickness at any locality is generally a few hundred meters rather than more than 300 meters as with the earlier deposits.

Our discussion can best begin with the middle and later Tertiary deposits of the Great Plains, which extend from South Dakota to Texas and 650 kilometers eastward from the mountain front.

During Laramide orogeny the Great Plains were a foreland area much like the Allegheny synclinorium and other foreland areas on the continentward side of the Appalachians. During Laramie and Paleocene time such basins as the Williston and Denver basins developed east of the mountain front; these became inactive during the Eocene and received few or no deposits during that period.

The Laramie and Paleocene deposits have little to do with the present surface configuration, which is a long slope on the later Tertiary deposits away from the mountains and toward the Missouri River. Some years ago when I traveled westward with my family, the slope of the Great Plains was a matter of puzzlement to them. How could we leave the Missouri River at an altitude of less than 300 meters, travel over a featureless, level country for 950 kilometers, yet arrive in Denver at the west edge of the plains at an altitude of more than two kilometers above sea level? Without apparently climbing we had been climbing all the way—up the great slope of the plains.

Much of the surface of the plains is covered by the Ogallala Formation of Pliocene age. Despite its extent, it is a relatively thin sheet of deposits, in part fine-grained, but containing lenses of coarser gravels carried eastward from the Rocky Mountains in the channels of withering streams. In many places, its layers are peculiarly cemented by caliche as a result of soil-forming processes in an arid climate, so that they are resistant to erosion and create the caprock of the plains.

Deposits beneath the Ogallala emerge in the northern part of the plains, the most extensive of which form the White River Group of Oligocene age, eroded into the extensive badlands of South Dakota. The White River Group also extends westward as smaller remnants between and into the Central Rocky Mountains of Wyoming.

During the first geological investigations of the Great Plains it was assumed that the later Tertiary deposits there—the Ogallala, the White River, and the rest—were laid down in a series of vast shallow lakes, hence that their depositional surfaces were nearly level and were later tilted regionally eastward. Later investigations proved that the deposits were dominantly of fluviatile origin, and also that the texture of their gravels was such, under semi-arid conditions, that they must have moved down a gradient nearly as great as the present slope of the country. The plains were tilted eastward as a part of the regional arching of the Eastern Ranges and Plateaus, but this tilting preceded the laying down of the later Tertiary deposits.

During later Tertiary time deposits were spread, not only over the Great Plains east of the Rocky Mountains but also over the Colorado Plateau southwest of it. These deposits, the Bidahochi Formation, are preserved as remnants in the Navajo and Hopi country of northeastern Arizona and contain gravels from at least as far away as the San Juan Mountains. Part of the Bidahochi is of lacustrine origin, indicating that on this side of the mountains the drainage was at times obstructed.

The fossil plants and mammals contained in the middle and later Tertiary deposits record an increasing regional altitude and aridity. By late Miocene time many of the early browsing herbivorous mammals had disappeared; those that survived, such as the horses, were adapted to feeding on the harsh grasses of semi-arid plains. The transition to more arid conditions in later Tertiary time resulted partly from a world-wide secular change toward cooler, more arid, more contrasting climates, which foreshadowed the onset of the Pleistocene ice ages. In part it was a result of the raising of higher mountains on the west, which produced a rain shadow over the plains country. By Pliocene time the climate of the Great Plains was apparently about as arid as that of the present.

EROSION SURFACES IN THE RANGES. So much for middle and late Tertiary conditions in the plains and lowlands around the mountain ranges. What were conditions in the ranges which were the sources of the rivers and hence of the detritus deposited roundabout?

Most of the ranges in the Central and Southern Rocky Mountains possess a widespread subsummit surface—a series of accordant crests that extends across the deformed bedrock structure, above which chains and clusters of higher peaks project on the divides, and below which the streams have cut valleys and gorges to depths of hundreds of meters. It apparently marks a time of widespread planation of the ranges, and it can be proved that this time was the same as that during which the later Tertiary formations were deposited in the Great Plains.

Where the original profile of the subsummit surface can be reconstructed, it is steeper and more concave than would have been formed during an erosional regime in a humid climate; like the Great Plains deposits it was formed in a semi-arid or arid climate.

In later Tertiary time during the climax of deposition in the Great Plains and of planation in the mountains, a landscape had developed in the Eastern Ranges and Plateaus that differed not only from that of earlier Tertiary time, but from that of the present. The region had by then attained an altitude only slightly lower than today's, yet the local relief was probably as subdued, or more so, than that of earlier Tertiary time. Extensive areas not now covered by later Tertiary deposits were then buried, including the earlier Tertiary intermontane basins and the lower mountain ends and spurs. Most of the emergent areas were planed off to form the subsummit surface; the only mountainous areas remaining were the unreduced peaks along the axes of the ranges.

QUATERNARY DENUDATION AND DISSECTION. At some time late in Tertiary or early in Quaternary time this subdued landscape began to be destroyed by more vigorous stream erosion. Formerly this erosion was believed to have been activated by a regional uplift greater than any that preceded it, but the steep gradients, which we now know must have existed on the depositional surface of the plains, and the erosional surfaces in the mountains suggest that such regional uplift was less than that which occurred earlier in the Tertiary. Quickening of stream erosion at the time was actuated not only by uplift, but by the more rainy glacial periods of Pleistocene time.

Regardless of causes, the drastic effects of the change in stream habit on the landscape are evident to all. Later Tertiary deposits were stripped off of large areas where they had been laid, and the streams excavated the rocks beneath by varying amounts according to their resistance to erosion. Weak Cretaceous and early Tertiary rocks of the basin areas were etched out; strong Precambrian crystalline rocks and Paleozoic stratified rocks of the ranges were left projecting above them.

It was at this time, apparently, that the rivers of the region acquired their anomalous courses. We have noted that Powell was puzzled by the crossing of the Green River through the great arch of the Uinta Mountains, which the river could have avoided by making a slightly longer traverse around the end of the uplift (Chapter VI, section 3). Powell concluded that the Green and similar rivers were antecedent—that they were in existence before the orogeny and were able to continue cutting down as the uplifts were raised across them. We now believe, however, that most such streams in the region were superimposed—that they had wandered at will down the slopes of the subdued erosional and depositional surfaces of later Tertiary time, but when they again cut downward they excavated wide valleys where they discovered weak rocks beneath them, and were confined to narrow gorges where they encountered belts of stronger rock.

HISTORY OF RIVER SYSTEMS IN EASTERN RANGES AND PLATEAUS. All this is very well, the reader may say, but what was the specific history of the rivers in the Eastern Ranges and Plateaus? The more specific we become, the more the doubts and confusions multiply.

In general, modern drainage of the region was initiated by Laramide orogeny, but there is little assurance that any particular stream held its course through the vicissitudes that followed that orogeny. Some rivers can be proved to have shifted greatly through time; for example, rivers on the eastern slope of the Northern and Central Rocky Mountains once flowed northeastward into Hudson Bay, but were deflected southward by the Pleistocene continental glaciers and coalesced to form the Missouri River, which now drains to the Gulf of Mexico. Could there not have been equally great shifts of other streams that have left less obvious records?

Especially puzzling is the history of the two great rivers that flow south and southwest from the Rocky Mountains—the Rio Grande and the Colorado—passing through long reaches of mountains, plateaus, and deserts on their way to the sea.

Waters no doubt flowed southward and southwestward from the mountain area for much of the time since the Laramide orogeny; the Miocene and Pliocene basin deposits of northern New Mexico contain gravels of such south-flowing rivers. But the basin deposits of this age farther south in New Mexico and Texas and in Nevada and Arizona below the end of the Grand Canyon are made up of locally derived detritus, and contain no gravels of the sort that would have been brought in by any large, through-flowing river.

The greatest problem pertains to that part of the Colorado River in the southwestern Colorado Plateau, where it has carved the Grand Canyon across the lofty Kaibab uplift. The river could not be antecedent to this uplift; the uplift was produced by Laramide orogeny, and it passes unconformably beneath early Tertiary deposits at its north end. Moreover, Miocene and Pliocene deposits downstream from the lower end of the canyon are all locally derived and show no evidence of the presence of a large, through-flowing river. Also, on the canyon rim west of the high part of the uplift are Pliocene lavas that were spread out on a subdued erosion surface.

It has been suggested that the river coursed across such uplifts as that of the Kaibab Plateau when they were

in an early stage of growth, that renewed uplift ponded the drainage on their upstream sides, until the river overflowed through its original valley and cut this to its present depth. But this proposed sequence of events cannot be reconciled with the evidence just stated. It has also been suggested that the Colorado River formerly flowed southward through the area of the Bidahochi Formation and to the sea, but was later directed westward by uplift of the southern rim of the plateau. It is believed that filling of the area upstream from the Kaibab Plateau to a depth of about 200 meters would be sufficient to allow the river to drain westward, utilizing the smaller consequent and subsequent stream valleys that had already been established between the Kaibab Plateau and Grand Wash Cliffs.

In any event, all the evidence seems to point to the astonishing conclusion that the Grand Canyon was cut largely in the two million years or so of Pleistocene and later time, or a time when men were already on the earth. *If primitive man had been living in North America, he would have witnessed the formation of the Grand Canyon.*

EFFECT OF MODERN ENVIRONMENT ON WATER ECONOMY OF THE WEST. Bearing in mind the low relief, low altitude, and well-distributed rainfall of early Tertiary times in the Eastern Ranges and Plateaus, let us consider how the changes of later Tertiary and Quaternary time affected the economy of the region—how people must live and adjust to this environment and especially to its unevenly distributed rainfall.

The heights of the Rocky Mountains are areas of abundant rainfall and give rise to the great rivers that flow east and west from the continental divide. The plains roundabout are semi-arid, yet they are the places where people must farm and build their cities. Water in the mountains must be conserved and carried by flumes and ditches to the plains country for irrigation and water supply.

This is not merely the dilemma of a few mountain states. Even in faraway southern California an increasing amount of water must come from the Colorado River, which originates in the Central and Southern Rocky Mountains. If Denver, to meet its growing needs, plans to tap the streams flowing westward from the continental divide, it immediately conflicts with southern California, because this would use water that would otherwise be available there. The peculiar rainfall and water supply conditions of the Rocky Mountains affect the economy of the whole western country.

REFERENCES

2. *Rocks and Events before the Great Deformation*
   Mallory, W. W., ed., 1972, *Geologic Atlas of the Rocky Mountain Region*: Rocky Mountain Assoc. Geol., pp. 52-165.
   Maxson, J. H., 1961, *Geologic map of the Bright Angel quadrangle,*

Grand Canyon National Park, Arizona: Grand Canyon Nat. Hist. Assoc.
Noble, L. F., 1914, *The Shinumo quadrangle, Grand Canyon district, Arizona*: U.S. Geol. Survey Bull. 549.

Peterman, Z. E., and Hedge, C. E., 1968, Chronology of Precambrian events in the Front Range, Colorado: *Canadian Jour. Earth Sci.*, v. 5, no. 3, pp. 749-756.

Tweto, Ogden, 1968, Geologic setting and interrelationships of mineral deposits in the mountain province of Colorado and south-central Wyoming, *in* Ridge, J. D., ed., *Ore deposits of the United States, 1933-1967 (Graton-Sales Volume)*: Am. Inst. Mining, Metall., and Petroleum Eng., v. 1, pp. 551-588.

3. *Rocks and Events during the Great Deformation*

Baker, A. A., Dane, C. H., and Reeside, J. B., Jr., 1936, *Correlation of Jurassic formations of parts of Utah, Arizona, New Mexico, and Colorado*: U.S. Geol. Survey Prof. Paper 183.

McGookey, D. O., and others, 1972, Cretaceous system, *in* Mallory, W. W., ed., *Geologic Atlas of the Rocky Mountain Region*: Rocky Mountain Assoc. Geol., pp. 190-228.

Spieker, E. M., 1946, *Late Mesozoic and early Cenozoic history of central Utah*: U.S. Geol. Survey Prof. Paper 205, pp. 117-161.

Tweto, Ogden, 1975, Laramide (late Cretaceous-early Tertiary) orogeny in the Southern Rocky Mountains, *in* Curtis, B., ed., *Cenozoic history of the Southern Rocky Mountains*: Geol. Soc. America Mem. 144, pp. 1-44.

4. *Central Rocky Mountains*

Bradley, W. H., 1948, Limnology and the Eocene lakes of the Rocky Mountain region: *Geol. Soc. America Bull.*, v. 59, pp. 635-648.

Darton, N. H., and Paige, Sidney, 1925, *Description of the central Black Hills*: U.S. Geol. Survey Geol. Atlas, folio no. 219.

Foose, R. M., Wise, R. U., and Garbarini, G. S., 1961, Structural geology of the Beartooth Mountains, Montana and Wyoming: *Geol. Soc. America Bull.*, v. 72, no. 8, pp. 1143-1172.

Horberg, Leland, Nelson, Vincent, and Church, Victor, 1949, Structural trends in central western Wyoming: *Geol. Soc. America Bull.*, v. 60, pp. 183-216.

Keefer, W. R., 1972, *The geological story of Yellowstone National Park*: U.S. Geol. Survey Bull. 1374.

Pierce, W. G., Heart Mountain and South Fork detachment thrusts of Wyoming: *Am. Assoc. Petrol. Geol. Bull.*, v. 41, no. 4, pp. 591-626.

Thom, W. T., Jr., 1923, The relation of deep-seated faults to the surface structural features of central Montana: *Am. Assoc. Petrol. Geol. Bull.*, v. 7, pp. 1-13.

5. *Southern Rocky Mountains*

Burbank, W. S., and Goddard, E. N., 1927, Thrusting in Huerfano Park, Colorado, and related problems of orogeny in the Sangre de Cristo Mountains: *Geol. Soc. America Bull.*, v. 48, pp. 931-976.

Knopf, Adolph, 1956, Igneous geology of the Spanish Peaks region, Colorado: *Geol. Soc. America Bull.*, v. 49, pp. 1727-1784.

Larsen, E. S., Jr., and Cross, Whitman, 1956, *Geology and petrology of the San Juan region, southwestern Colorado*: U.S. Geol. Survey Prof. Paper 258.

Litsey, L. R., 1958, Stratigraphy and structure of the northern Sangre de Cristo Mountains, Colorado: *Geol. Soc. America Bull.*, v. 69, no. 9, pp. 1143-1178.

Lovering, T. S., and Goddard, E. N., 1950, *Geology and ore deposits of the Front Range, Colorado*: U.S. Geol. Survey Prof. Paper 223.

Powell, J. W., 1876, *Report on the eastern portion of the Uinta Mountains, and a region of country adjacent thereto*: U.S. Geol. Geograph. Survey Terr., 2nd Div.

Steven, T. A., Mehnert, H. H., and Obradovich, J. D., 1967, Age of the volcanic activity in the San Juan Mountains, Colorado: *U.S. Geol. Survey Prof. Paper* 575-D, pp. 47-55.

Tweto, Ogden, 1968, Geologic setting and interrelationships of mineral deposits in the mountain province of Colorado and south-central Wyoming, *in* Ridge, J. D., ed., *Ore deposits of the United States, 1933-1967 (Graton-Sales Volume)*: Am. Inst. Mining, Metall., and Petroleum Eng., v. 1, pp. 551-588.

Tweto, Ogden, and Sims, P. K., 1963, Precambrian ancestry of the Colorado mineral belt: *Geol. Soc. America Bull.*, v. 70, no. 8, pp. 991-1014.

6. *Less Deformed Parts of Eastern Ranges and Plateaus*

Hunt, C. B., and others, 1953, *Geology and geography of the Henry Mountains region, Utah*: U.S. Geol. Survey Prof. Paper 228.

———, 1956, *Cenozoic geology of the Colorado Plateau*: U.S. Geol. Survey Prof. Paper 279.

Kelley, V. C., 1952, Tectonics of the Rio Grande depression of central New Mexico: *New Mexico Geol. Soc. Guidebook*, 3rd Ann. Field Conf. (Rio Grande country, central Mew Mexico), pp. 93-105.

Kelley, V. C., and Silver, Caswell, 1952, *Geology of the Caballo Mountains*: New Mexico Univ. Publ. Geol. no. 4.

———, 1955, *Regional tectonics of the Colorado Plateau and relationship to the origin and distribution of uranium*: New Mexico Univ. Publ. Geol. no. 5.

Powell, J. W., 1873, Geologic structure of a district of country lying to the north of the Grand Canyon of the Colorado: *Am. Jour. Sci.*, 3rd ser., v. 5, pp. 456-465.

Strahler, A. N., 1948, Geomorphology and structure of the West Kaibab fault zone and Kaibab Plateau, Arizona: *Geol. Soc. America Bull.*, v. 59, pp. 513-540.

7. *Events after the Great Deformation*

Atwood, W. W., and Atwood, W. W., Jr., 1938, Working hypothesis for the physiographic history of the Rocky Mountain region: *Geol. Soc. America Bull.*, v. 49, pp. 957-980.

Johnson, W. D., 1901, The High Plains and their utilization: *U.S. Geol. Survey 21st Ann. Rept.* (1900), pt. 4, pp. 601-741.

Mackin, J. H., 1937, Erosional history of the Bighorn Basin, Wyoming: *Geol. Soc. America Bull.*, v. 48, pp. 813-894.

Robinson, Peter, 1972, Tertiary history, *in* Mallory, W. W., ed., *Geologic Atlas of the Rocky Mountain Region*: Rocky Mountain Assoc. Geol., pp. 233-242.

Van Houten, F. B., 1948, Origin of red-banded early Cenozoic deposits in Rocky Mountain region: *Am. Assoc. Petrol. Geol. Bull.*, v. 32, pp. 2083-2126.

CHAPTER VIII

THE MAIN PART OF THE CORDILLERA: ITS GEOSYNCLINE
AND THE MOUNTAIN BELT THAT FORMED FROM IT

1. COMPARISONS AND COMPLICATIONS

In Chapter VII we explored an extensive part of the western Cordillera, yet this part is a set of Eastern Ranges and Plateaus that did not originate from a true geosynclinal area—as a well-behaved mountain belt should—and whose features are a novel structural element, not exactly comparable to any in the Paleozoic mountain belt on the southeastern side of the continent.

We turn now to that part of the Cordillera farther west that has had a more conventional history, originating as a geosyncline along the border of the continent and developing through time into a mountain belt. Some of the features will prove to resemble those of the Appalachian mountain belt, and we can account for many of the differences as local peculiarities one would expect on passing from one far-separated mountain belt to another. We will find that greatest differences are in the happenings after the climactic orogeny, which have been more profound in the western region than the eastern. For this reason these postorogenic features are reserved for discussion in Chapter IX.

Even the fundamental features of the geosyncline and the orogenic belt possess such a wealth of detail that our discussion had best be restricted to instructive examples of the whole region selected from various parts of the United States and southern Canada.

2. CORDILLERAN MIOGEOSYNCLINE

GENERAL RELATIONS. During Paleozoic time, the Cordilleran miogeosyncline, like the Appalachian miogeosyncline, was the scene of a long-continued, little interrupted sedimentation, largely in shallow water. Sedimentation in the miogeosynclinal area thus differed little from that on the continental platform, but there was more subsidence of its floor so that deposits accumu-lated to greater thickness and formed a more complete sequence.

In the Cordilleran miogeosyncline, as in the Appalachian miogeosyncline, the side toward the continent (here toward the east rather than the west) is marked by an abrupt thinning of the sedimentary section, partly by overlap and wedging out of the Cambrian deposits at the base, partly by thinning and disappearance of the systems above. On the side away from the continent, as in the Appalachians, the zone of transition from miogeosynclinal into eugeosynclinal rocks is seldom well preserved; in Nevada, for example, it has been overridden from the west, and concealed, by thrust sheets of eugeosynclinal rocks. Relations in a few other places suggest, however, that it may originally have been an abrupt shelf break from shallow water into the deeper water of the eugeosynclinal area.

Within the miogeosynclinal area itself, as in the Appalachians, the lowest part of the Cambrian consists of clastic deposits and the upper part of limestones and dolomites. Other and younger limestones and dolomites follow in great thickness, and the sequence is topped by clastic wedges that spread across the miogeosynclinal area into the foreland; these were derived from quickening orogeny in the eugeosynclinal part of the system.

Nevertheless, the parallelism between these two miogeosynclinal areas on opposite sides of the continent is not complete:

(a) In the Appalachian geosyncline some sediments and volcanics of Late Proterozoic age underline the Cambrian. In the Cordillera, Middle and Upper Proterozoic sediments attain much greater thickness and extent, especially in the north.

(b) In the Cordilleran miogeosyncline, climax of the orogeny was considerably later than in the Appalachian miogeosyncline; the characteristic miogeosynclinal se-

133

quence—from basal clastics into carbonates into clastic wedges—is offset upward in the section. Crustal disturbances in later parts of Paleozoic time were minor; in places they created clastic formations, but in others the carbonate part of the sequence continued high into the Paleozoic. Mississippian limestones spread over large parts of the miogeosyncline, and in places limestones extend through the Pennsylvanian and even the Permian. True clastic wedges make their appearance only above the Paleozoic in the Triassic and Jurassic and especially in the Cretaceous.

BELT SERIES. Let us first consider the segment of the miogeosyncline in the Northern Rocky Mountains—from western Montana northward across the International Boundary into the Canadian Rockies of western Alberta and eastern British Columbia.

A striking feature of this segment of the Cordillera is the wide surface extent of the *Belt Series*. The Belt (called the Purcell Series in Canada) is named for the Big Belt and Little Belt Mountains of west-central Montana, which are part of the Eastern Ranges of the Cordillera, but these mountains lie near the edge of its sedimentary basin; the Belt wedges out between basement and Paleozoic rocks a short distance farther east. Westward into the Cordillera the Belt has a much greater thickness and extent and forms most of the ranges of the Northern Rocky Mountains in northwestern Montana, northern Idaho, southwestern Alberta, and southeastern British Columbia. Here it forms the surface over an area of at least 100,000 square kilometers, and thickens from about 3,000 meters on the east to more than 16,000 meters in northern Idaho and southeastern British Columbia (Fig. 83).

Toward the east the Belt Series includes several thick limestone formations, but farther west the limestones fade out and various units of sandstone make their appearance. Nevertheless, the great bulk of the series is argillite or siltite—slightly altered shaly and silty rocks—mostly dull gray or green, but red-colored in certain parts. Various sedimentary structures, such as mud cracks and salt crystal impressions indicate that most of its great mass was laid down in shallow water. The Belt contains no indications of life except stromatolites, which are believed to have been built by lime-secreting algae. Although most of the series is sedimentary, a flow, the Purcell Lava, occurs high in the sequence in many of the ranges.

The sedimentary rocks of the Belt Series much resemble those of later ages—so much so that the early geological explorers supposed the series to be of early Paleozoic or even younger age, and until recently many geologists have doubted that it could be much older than the Cambrian. So far as its relation to overlying rocks is concerned it might be Early Cambrian, as the first strata that lie on it through most of its extent are Middle

134

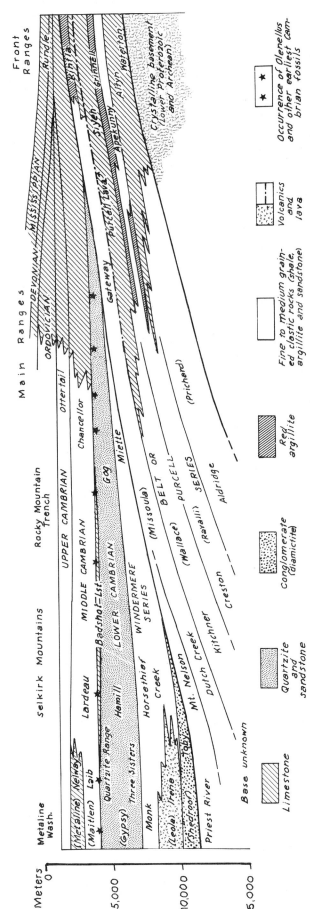

FIG. 83. Stratigraphic diagram showing relations of Cambrian System of Northern Rocky Mountains to Windermere and Belt Series. Diagram covers a zone about 320 kilometers in length immediately north of International Boundary. Equivalents of Canadian formation names in the United States shown in parentheses. Compiled from many sources, including Okulitch (1949, 1956), Price (1964), and Harrison (1972).

Cambrian or younger. Nevertheless, accumulating evidence indicates overwhelmingly that it is much older and is Middle Proterozoic:

(a) Several hundred kilometers north of the main area of the Belt Series along the strike of the mountains is a thick sequence of fossiliferous Cambrian rocks, the Lower Cambrian part of which consists of the usual clastics below and carbonates above. Nothing in this sequence is comparable to the Belt Series.

(b) About the same distance west of the front of the Rocky Mountains, in the Purcell Mountains far back in the geosynclinal area, the Belt is overlain unconformably by another thick mass of clastic rocks, the *Windermere Series* (Fig. 83). Fossils of various early Paleozoic ages have been found in the upper part of the Windermere as first defined, but its lower part is unfossiliferous and is of Upper Proterozoic age; lavas in its lower part have been dated as between 800 and 900 million years old. The Belt is thus not the youngest Precambrian in the Northern Rocky Mountains.

(c) Radiometric determinations from various levels in the Belt itself have ages ranging from 900 to 1,300 million years; the Purcell Lava has been dated at 1,100 million years. This indicates that Belt sedimentation persisted for 400 million years or so, a rather surprisingly lengthy period, equivalent to all Phanerozoic time back to the Ordovician—all in a period long before the beginning of the Cambrian.

These considerations indicate that the geosyncline in which the Belt Series was deposited was distinct from and older than the true Cordilleran geosyncline, with the deposits of the latter lying unconformably upon it. Along the eastern border of the Cordilleran miogeosyncline the first deposits above the Belt are of Middle Cambrian age. Farther west nearer the eugeosyncline, the first deposits above the Belt are much older and of Upper Proterozoic age. In the Windermere area sedimentation in the true Cordilleran geosyncline began before the Cambrian and Paleozoic time in a sort of "Eocambrian" epoch.

YOUNGER ROCKS OF THE NORTHERN SEGMENT. Above the Belt Series lie the Paleozoic miogeosynclinal deposits. In northwestern Montana, except along the mountain front, they are preserved only as occasional outliers or infolds. It is thus difficult to determine their former extent, although it may be presumed that they once covered the area of the present exposures of the Belt Series.

Across the International Boundary in Canada exposures of the Belt Series become narrower, and the series plunges northward beneath younger strata. Paleozoic miogeosynclinal rocks form most of the surface of the Northern Rocky Mountains about 250 kilometers north of the boundary along the main line of the Canadian Pacific Railroad west of Calgary, Alberta.

We can best begin our discussion of these miogeosynclinal rocks at Banff, the beautiful mountain resort on the railroad, lying in a valley between the high Front Ranges of the mountains. These ranges are formed of the upper part of the Paleozoic succession, about 2,500 meters thick and largely limestone (as one might expect in a miogeosynclinal area). The most prominent formation is the massive Rundle Limestone, whose 750-meter bulk crowns all the mountain ridges in the vicinity (shown by the black pattern on Fig. 84). It is of middle Mississippian age, or about equivalent to the Madison Limestone of the northwestern states and the Redwall Limestone of the Grand Canyon. Below are more than 1,500 meters of shales, thin-bedded limestones, and dolomites of earlier Mississippian and Devonian ages, which rest on Middle Cambrian strata; the latter come to the surface only in narrow exposures at the bases of the thrust blocks. Above the Rundle is the 200-meter Rocky Mountain Quartzite, a sandy deposit that forms the top of the Paleozoic section. It is overlain by Triassic and Jurassic shaly rocks, which have been eroded to form the valleys between the ridges; we will say more about them shortly.

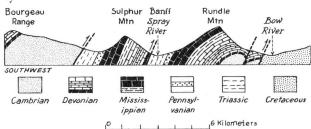

FIG. 84. Section across ridges and valleys of the Rocky Mountains in the vicinity of Banff, Alberta, showing miogeosynclinal sequence. After Warren (1927).

Eastward the Paleozoic formations thin and wedge out. Even at Banff, large breaks occur in the record between the Devonian and Middle Cambrian, between the middle Mississippian and the Pennsylvanian, and between the Pennsylvanian and the Triassic. In the Alberta basin, the foreland east of the miogeosyncline, many of the units of the Banff section are thin or missing. Only the Devonian is surprisingly persistent and contains some of the great productive oil fields of the basin.

West of Banff the lower part of the Paleozoic is raised to the surface and forms the Main Ranges of the inner part of the Rocky Mountains (Fig. 86). Devonian and Ordovician rocks occur, but the most extensive rocks are of Cambrian age and attain a thickness of 3,000 meters or more. The Cambrian begins with about 1,000 meters of sandstone, but the remainder is a great mass of limestone and dolomite interrupted only in places by shaly beds.

The Paleozoic miogeosynclinal rocks in this segment of the Cordillera thus total about 6,000 meters, of which the Cambrian accounts for nearly half. Whether all this mass accumulated at any one place cannot be proved, as the later Paleozoic is thick in the Front Ranges where the Cambrian has thinned, and the later Paleozoic is now missing in the Main Ranges where the Cambrian is thick.

Be this as it may, the Paleozoic rocks possess many features like those in the Appalachian miogeosyncline—the Early Cambrian sandstones at the base, the great mass of carbonates above them, and wedging of all the units toward the foreland. The sequence differs in that the carbonates continue well through the Paleozoic instead of ending in the middle of the Ordovician; the Pennsylvanian is sandy, yet we look in vain for Paleozoic clastic wedges of the sort characteristic of the upper part of the miogeosynclinal section in the Appalachians. Along the western side of the Main Ranges, however, close to the Rocky Mountain Trench, the great tabular mountains of Cambrian and Ordovician carbonate rocks end abruptly, and these rocks change rapidly into shale. Evidently the carbonate embankment of the miogeosyncline ends in this direction in a shelf break, on the side toward the eugeosyncline.

The upward change in sedimentation from carbonates to clastic deposits that were derived from erosion of the interior parts of the Cordilleran geosyncline began after Paleozoic time. Valleys between the frontal ridges of the Northern Rocky Mountains are underlain by shales of Triassic and Jurassic age—the marine Spray River and Fernie Formations. Drilling in the plains east of the mountains indicates that these do not extend far into the foreland east of the miogeosyncline.

Some of the deeper downfolds in the frontal ranges of the Rocky Mountains also contain remnants of lowest Cretaceous strata—the Kootenay continental deposits. These and higher Cretaceous beds are more completely developed in the foothills along the mountain front. The Cretaceous has a true clastic wedge structure—a replica of that we described earlier in the Eastern Ranges and Plateaus—with tongues of continental and marine sandstones projecting eastward into marine shales.

Finally, in the foreland along the mountain front in the deeper parts of the Alberta basin are the latest Cretaceous and Paleocene continental deposits (Edmonton and higher formations), which are comparable to the Laramie and overlying formations farther south, and like them were laid down during the concluding phases of the Laramide orogeny.

MIOGEOSYNCLINAL ROCKS OF SOUTHERN GREAT BASIN. To continue our story, let us turn our attention to another part of the miogeosyncline about 1,500 kilometers south of the International Boundary—the region west of the Grand Canyon and Colorado Plateau extending 250 kilometers across the Great Basin into the Inyo Mountains of eastern California (Fig. 85).

In the Grand Canyon the whole Paleozoic sequence is

136

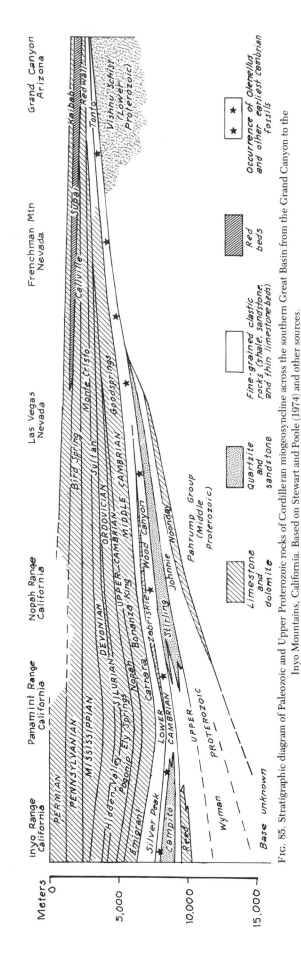

FIG. 85. Stratigraphic diagram of Paleozoic and Upper Proterozoic rocks of Cordilleran miogeosyncline across the southern Great Basin from the Grand Canyon to the Inyo Mountains, California. Based on Stewart and Poole (1974) and other sources.

encompassed within the walls of the canyon and does not exceed 1,200 meters. As we have seen (Chapter VII, section 2), strata of Cambrian, Mississippian, and Permian ages are represented. While there are minor occurrences of other systems in the region, most of the Ordovician, Silurian, Devonian, and Pennsylvanian are missing, their place being taken by disconformities below and above the Redwall Limestone.

The familiar Grand Canyon formations extend with little change westward down the Grand Canyon past the Grand Wash Cliffs and thence across the eastern Great Basin to Las Vegas, Nevada, but the section thickens by wedging in of formations at the positions of the disconformities in the Grand Canyon. Between the Supai Formation and the Redwall Limestone appears the thick body of Bird Spring Limestone of Pennsylvanian and early Permian age. Between the Redwall Limestone and the Tonto Group a Devonian formation occurs. Finally, on the unconformity at the base of the Paleozoic, Lower Cambrian rocks wedge in beneath the Middle Cambrian Tonto Group (Fig. 85).

Still greater thickening of the Paleozoic rocks into the miogeosyncline takes place west of Las Vegas, where the rocks attain more than 8,000 meters. Typical sections are exposed in the Nopah Range east of Death Valley and in the Inyo Range east of Owens Valley, both in California.

Nearly half of the miogeosynclinal sequence in the Nopah and Inyo Ranges is Cambrian and Upper Proterozoic. In the Nopah Range the Lower Cambrian and Upper Proterozoic are 4,000 meters thick, and consists of the Noonday Dolomite at the base (lying unconformably on earlier rocks), the Johnnie Formation (shales and thin sandstones), the Stirling Quartzite, and the Wood Canyon Formation (shales and thin limestones). In the Inyo Range the sequence thickens to more than 6,500 meters and the base is not visible. Here the whole sequence is rather fine-grained; the quartzites have faded out, and there are more carbonates; apparently the area is farther out in the depositional trough. The whole Lower Cambrian-Upper Proterozoic sequence is conformable, without prominent changes in sedimentation, and there is no clearly marked boundary between the Cambrian and the Precambrian. Lower Cambrian *Olenellus* and other shelly fossils occur in the upper part (as in the Wood Canyon Formation) and traces of fossils extend some distance lower, but the lower half of the sequence is barren except for equivocal algal remains. Like the Windermere Series north of the International Boundary, the Upper Proterozoic here marks the beginning of development of the Cordilleran geosyncline in a sort of "Eocambrian" epoch.

Where the base of the Upper Proterozoic is visible, it lies in places on a crystalline basement with Lower Proterozoic radiometric ages of about 1,700 million years. Intervening in southern Death Valley is the intermediate sedimentary body of the Pahrump Group, which is 1,500 to 2,500 meters thick and lithically like the Middle Proterozoic Unkar Group of the Grand Canyon Series to the east.

Miogeosynclinal rocks of northern Great Basin. In the northern Great Basin, the miogeosyncline broadens into a tract 320 kilometers wide between the Wasatch Mountains in Utah and central Nevada. Here, the Lower Cambrian is a basal quartzite 900 meters or more thick, variously called Prospect Mountain, Tintic, or Brigham, which overlies, more or less comformably Upper Proterozoic supracrustal clastic rocks.

The remainder of the lower Paleozoic sequence is largely limestone and dolomite about 3,000 to 4,000 meters thick. A notable sandy unit near the middle, the Middle Ordovician Eureka Quartzite, spreads over much of the region, and not only lies on carbonate rocks but is followed by more carbonates of Upper Ordovician, Silurian, and Devonian ages.

Above them, peculiarities develop in the section. Overlying the lower Mississippian Joana Limestone is the Chainman Shale which interfingers westward with the Diamond Peak Quartzite. These are a clastic wedge that thickens westward, related to the mid-Paleozoic Antler orogeny in the eugeosynclinal area beyond, and the Diamond Peak contains chert pebbles eroded from the eugeosynclinal rocks. Following the Diamond Peak are Pennsylvanian and Permian carbonates and interbedded clastics with many unconformities. We will discuss their relations to the eugeosyncline to the west in section 4 of this chapter.

The Mississippian clastic wedge fades out eastward, but in northwestern Utah is another notable thickening of the upper Paleozoic rocks into the Oquirrh basin, where they attain more than 6,000 meters. Nearly half of this is accounted for by the Pennsylvanian and lower Permian Oquirrh Formation of limestone and interbedded fine-grained sandstone. The sediments of the Oquirrh basin differ little from those of surrounding parts of the miogeosyncline and foreland except for their inordinate thickness; they express an unusual area of excessive subsidence in the miogeosyncline; their sandstones were probably derived from distant parts of the continental platform to the east.

Mesozoic rocks of eastern Great Basin. Above the Paleozoic miogeosynclinal sequence in the eastern part of the Great Basin, the record becomes more fragmentary. In places the Paleozoic is succeeded by marine Triassic, which is followed by Jurassic farther east. There is, however, a wide gap between these Triassic and Jurassic rocks and those of the western part of the Great Basin; strata of the two regions are so different that they were probably laid down in separate seaways.

Here and there in the eastern part of the Great Basin

patches of continental and fresh-water sandstone, shale, and conglomerate lie on the eroded surfaces of the deformed earlier rocks. Some of these are proved by fossils to be of Cretaceous age; others are probably Paleocene or Eocene. Unlike the Paleozoic and earlier Mesozoic deposits, they were formed in discontinuous basins during or after the main orogeny of the region, and were not a part of the deposits of the Cordilleran miogeosyncline.

SOUTHWARD EXTENSION OF CORDILLERAN MIOGEOSYNCLINE. We have followed the miogeosynclinal belt of the Cordillera, with its characteristic deposits forming a wide band along the edge of the continental platform, from Canada southward through the Great Basin to southern Nevada, but beyond this it mysteriously disappears. What happened to it?

Professor Schuchert, in making his paleographic maps half a century ago, extended his Paleozoic seaways from the Great Basin southwestward through his "borderlands" on the site of the present Transverse Ranges through a "Los Angeles portal" to the Pacific Ocean, but this scheme ignored the realities of the local geology, and is clearly impossible.

The Cordilleran miogeosyncline south of the Great Basin has somehow become obliterated and lost in the confused structures of southeastern California, mostly of later age. In the Mojave Desert region, most of the ranges are Mesozoic granitic rocks and their Tertiary volcanic cover. Some remnants of Paleozoic rocks remain, both here and southward in the San Bernardino Mountains, which are fragments of the miogeosynclinal sequence. Upper Paleozoic carbonates are recognizable in some places, and lower Paleozoic carbonates and quartzites in others, but all these end southwestward at the San Andreas fault, beyond which the rocks have been shifted for undetermined distances to the northwest. A possible equivalent of the Paleozoic miogeosynclinal rocks forms the Sur Series of the central Coast Ranges south of San Francisco, but this has been so heavily metamorphosed and fragmented that its original stratigraphy is no longer recognizable.

A patch of miogeosynclinal rocks northeast of the San Andreas fault zone occurs in the Caborca area of northwestern Sonora, 500 kilometers southeast of the last miogeosynclinal rocks in the United States. Here, lying on a Lower Proterozoic crystalline basement, are fragmentary representatives of Upper Proterozoic, Cambrian, Devonian, Permian, and Triassic formations nearly identical with those of the Death Valley region of the southern Great Basin. They might have been shifted here by transcurrent faulting, but this appears unlikely as it would require left-lateral displacement, whereas the dominant movement sense in the Pacific border region is right-lateral. An alternative would be that the miogeosynclinal belt originally bent southeastward into the Caborca area.

3. STRUCTURE OF EASTERN PART OF MAIN CORDILLERA

During the Laramide orogeny and the disturbances that preceded it—from Paleocene until well back in Cretaceous time—the stratified rocks laid down in the Cordilleran miogeosynclinal area were strongly deformed. Before taking up details of the structures thereby produced we will compare them with those of other regions we have already considered. In this comparison we will use one segment as representative of the whole: the Northern Rocky Mountains.

COMPARISON WITH SOUTHERN ROCKY MOUNTAINS.— The eastern edges of the Northern and Southern Rocky Mountains resemble each other in several respects:

(a) In both areas mountainous topography ends toward the east along an abrupt front that faces the Great Plains or edge of the Interior Lowlands.

(b) Structurally this front corresponds to a boundary between much deformed and little deformed rocks.

(c) The Great Plains were the foreland of both mountain areas, received Cretaceous and Paleocene deposits, and were warped down into basins.

(d) In both mountain areas rocks lower stratigraphically than those of the plains were raised so high that they have been uncovered by erosion. These lower rocks are of earlier Mesozoic, Paleozoic, and Precambrian ages.

Here the resemblances end and we must note some significant differences:

(a) In front of the ranges of the Southern Rocky Mountains the rocks of the Great Plains are little disturbed almost to the mountain front. Between the front of the Northern Rocky Mountains and the Great Plains the rocks have been intensely crumpled and sliced in a foothill belt.

(b) At the edges of the uplifts of the Southern Rocky Mountains the sedimentary section has been turned up steeply or cut off by high-angle faults associated with the upthrust of the range. In the Northern Rocky Mountains the older sedimentary rocks have been carried eastward over the younger rocks for many kilometers along great low-angle thrusts.

(c) In the Southern Rocky Mountains the Paleozoic sedimentary rocks are a relatively thin sequence laid down on the continental platform; those of the Northern Rocky Mountains are a thick sequence that formed in the Cordilleran miogeosyncline.

(d) In the Southern Rocky Mountains the Precambrian rocks are a metamorphic and plutonic basement; those of the Northern Rocky Mountains are geosynclinal sediments.

These differences between rocks and structures along the edges of the Northern and Southern Rocky Mountains are matched by contrasts farther back in the two systems. The ranges of the Southern Rocky Mountains are mainly broad-backed uplifts that raise Precambrian basement rocks to view, separated by narrow to wide basins containing much younger rocks. The ranges of the Northern Rocky Mountains are formed from long, narrow, closely spaced folds and thrust blocks made up of geosynclinal sedimentary rocks alone, not of basement rocks. These contrasts reflect the manner in which the unlike rocks of the two areas have responded to deformation.

COMPARISON WITH SEDIMENTARY APPALACHIANS. The Northern Rocky Mountains are a region of lofty peaks unlike the subdued landscape of the Appalachians whose Valley and Ridge province consists of low, rounded ridges and broad limestone valleys. Moreover, the Appalachian ridges are bordered toward the continental interior by plateaus as high or higher, rather than by plains.

We should not be deceived by these superficial contrasts, as the geological resemblances are much greater. The Northern Rocky Mountains and the Valley and Ridge province are analogous parts of mountain systems on opposite sides of the Central Stable Region; both are made up of sedimentary rocks that were laid down in a miogeosyncline and were afterward folded, faulted, and thrust toward the interior of the continent. Both regions contain great low-angle thrusts of the same sort, and in neither do basement rocks emerge, suggesting that deformation was largely confined to the sedimentary rocks above it.

The differences in topography are partly climatic, as the great limestone masses have been worn down more readily in the genial southeastern climate of the Appalachians than in the harsh northwestern climate of the Rocky Mountains. Partly, too, the Appalachians were deformed several periods earlier than the Cordillera, so that they have been exposed to the weather for a longer period and have attained greater topographic maturity. Finally, the crustal movements that followed deformation of the rocks of the sedimentary Appalachians were of less magnitude, for the most part, than those in the eastern part of the Cordillera.

SECTION IN THE NORTHERN ROCKY MOUNTAINS OF SOUTHERN CANADA. Let us now take up details of the structure of the Northern Rocky Mountains, or that part of the eastern Cordillera that we have used for comparison with structures of other regions.

We will deal first with a cross-section about 250 kilometers north of the International Boundary along the main line of the Canadian Pacific Railroad west of Calgary, Alberta—the segment whose miogeosynclinal Paleozoic and Mesozoic rocks we have already discussed in section 2 of this chapter. Proceeding west from Calgary we encounter in succession the following structures (Fig. 86A):

(1) The Great Plains east of the mountains, whose rocks are warped down into the Alberta basin. The surface rocks are flat-lying continental deposits of late Cretaceous and Paleocene age, beneath which (as shown by drilling) is a foreland section of Mesozoic and Paleozoic rocks.

(2) A foothill belt as much as 35 kilometers wide, whose surface rocks are mainly Upper Cretaceous shales and sandstones which, in contrast to the rocks of the Great Plains, have been steeply tilted and sliced into a great multitude of thrust blocks, each displaced by small amounts to the east (Fig. 86A and Fig. 87).

(3) West of the foothill belt the topographic eastern front of the Rocky Mountains, a bold escarpment of Paleozoic limestone. Near the railroad the contact between the Paleozoic of the mountains and the Cretaceous of the foothills is the *McConnell thrust*, along which the Paleozoic has been carried eastward over the Cretaceous at least eight kilometers.

(4) Behind the mountain front a belt of *Front Ranges* about 50 kilometers broad (Fig. 87A). These are high, parallel mountain ridges separated by longitudinal valleys, in one of which Banff is located (Fig. 84). Each ridge is supported by later Paleozoic limestone and especially the massive Rundle Limestone; each valley is cut on Mesozoic sandstones and shales. The whole has been thrown into a succession of long narrow folds and thrust slices that repeat the section many times, the thrusts dipping westward and probably joining the sole fault (McConnell thrust) at depth.

(5) Behind the Front Ranges the higher, more massive *Main Ranges* about 65 kilometers broad (Fig. 87A). They are made up of earlier Paleozoic miogeosynclinal rocks, mainly Cambrian, which have been less faulted and more openly folded than those of the Front Ranges, so that many of the mountains have the form of lofty plateaus. The powerful forces to which the rocks of the Main Ranges have been subjected are attested, however, by their much greater uplift than those of the Front Ranges, and by presence of slaty cleavage in the more argillaceous layers.

Seismic reflection traverses across the Rocky Mountains made by the oil companies demonstrate that none of the surface structures in the sedimentary rocks of the Front Ranges and Main Ranges involves the underlying basement, whose top is found to be a surface that slopes smoothly westward from the Great Plains to the Rocky Mountain Trench, or even beyond. All the complex thrust slicing in the overlying sediments is a décollement structure originating from slippage along the sedimentary layers. Estimates have been made that the crustal shortening resulting from these décollement thrusts amounts to 150 kilometers.

(6) At the west edge of the Rocky Mountains in this latitude, and separating them from the Purcell and other interior ranges beyond, is a peculiar, long, narrow val-

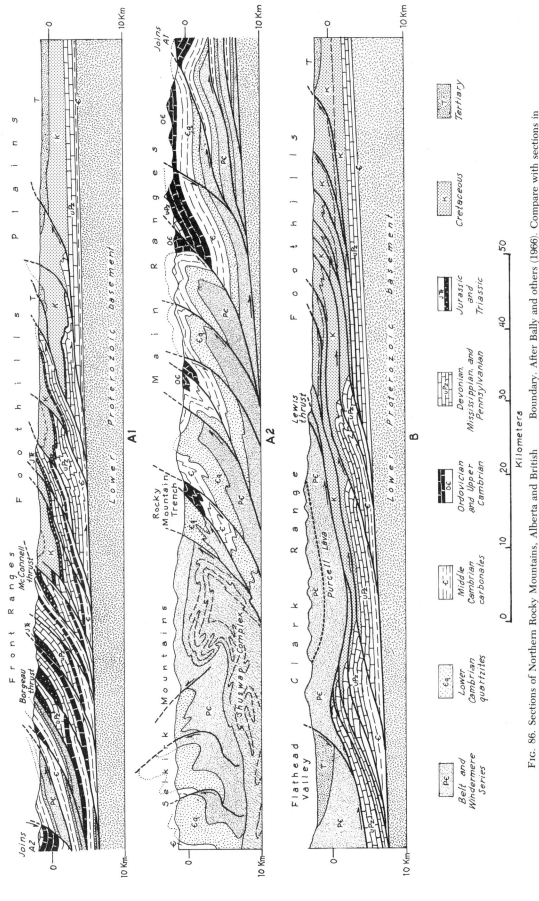

FIG. 86. Sections of Northern Rocky Mountains, Alberta and British Columbia. (A1 and A2) Section extending northeastward, a little north of the line of the Canadian Pacific Railroad. After Price and Mountjoy (1970). (B) Section immediately north of the International Boundary. After Bally and others (1966). Compare with sections in the comparable Valley and Ridge province of the Appalachians in Fig. 29.

Kilometers

Belt and Windermere Series — Pꞓ

Lower Cambrian quartzites — ꞓq

Middle Cambrian carbonates — ꞓ

Ordovician and Upper Cambrian — Oꞓ

Devonian, Mississippian, and Pennsylvanian — uPz

Jurassic and Triassic — JꞆ

Cretaceous — K

Tertiary — T

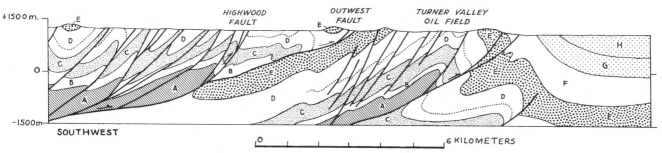

FIG. 87. Section across Turner Valley area 40 kilometers southwest of Calgary, Alberta, showing typical foothill structures of Northern Rocky Mountains where subsurface structure has been extensively determined by drilling. After Gallup (1951) and Hume (1957).

Explanation of symbols: (A) Banff and Rundle Limestones (Missis-sippian). (B) Fernie Formation (Jurassic). (C) Blairmore Formation. (D) Alberta Shale. (E) Belly River Formation. (F) Bearpaw Shale, and (G) Edmonton Formation (Cretaceous). (H) Paskapoo Formation (Paleocene).

ley, the *Rocky Mountain Trench*. This is no mere erosional feature, for it is not drained by a single river; most of the great rivers of the northern Cordillera flow in it at one place or another—the Kootenai, the Columbia, the Fraser, the Peace, and many more. The trench extends at least 1,500 kilometers northward from the International Boundary, nearly parallel to the trends of the ranges (Plate I).

Along the line of the railroad the Rocky Mountain Trench seems to be a synclinorium in which Ordovician and younger strata are downfolded between the Cambrian of the Rocky Mountains on the east and the Proterozoic (Belt and Windermere) of the Purcell Mountains on the west (Fig. 87A). But the true nature and origin of the trench remain elusive, as the visible structures along it differ from place to place. Some geologists have suggested that it marks a zone of transcurrent faulting, others that it forms the boundary between structures of different ages, those on the west being earlier than the dominantly Laramide structures in the Rocky Mountains to the east. Neither of these explanations of the trench nor any other can be proved with certainty.

SECTION AT INTERNATIONAL BOUNDARY. Farther south near the International Boundary is another significant section of the Northern Rocky Mountains; its eastern part is splendidly exposed in Glacier National Park and adjacent parts of the Lewis, Livingston, and Clark Ranges (Fig. 86B).

Here the mountains are composed of Middle Proterozoic sedimentary rocks of the Belt Series, which have been raised so high that nearly all the former cover of Paleozoic miogeosynclinal strata has been removed by erosion. The Belt Series has been broadly folded at most; characteristic features of the landscape are the lines of gently dipping ledges on the mountainsides. The mountains face eastward in bold escarpments upon a foothill belt where, as farther north, intensely faulted Cretaceous rocks lie at the surface.

The Belt Series of the mountains overlies the Cretaceous rocks of the foothills on the *Lewis thrust*, one of the most prominently exposed of the great low-angle thrusts

of North America. The low dip of the fault and the superposition of the Belt on Cretaceous can be proved by following the fault out onto the points of the ridges or up the intervening valleys. Besides, Chief Mountain, a peak projecting from the foothills some kilometers in front of the mountains, is a klippe or erosional outlier of the thrust sheet (Fig. 88). Like the main mountain front it is composed of Belt strata that lie on the Cretaceous. Sinuosities of the trace of the thrust—from its exposures farthest up the valleys to those on the points of the ridges and in the klippe—indicate that the rocks above the thrust have ridden eastward over those beneath for a distance of at least eleven kilometers.

Altyn formation
upper member

lower member, with
minor thrusts

Lewis
thrust

FIG. 88. Chief Mountain a klippe at the eastern edge of the Rocky Mountains in northwestern Montana. View is from the south, the mountains being to the left and the plains to the right. This is probably the most striking example in the United States of a klippe or thrust-outlier. The Altyn Formation of the Belt Series (Precambrian) lies on Cretaceous strata on the sole of the Lewis thrust. From a photograph by Willis (1902).

Actual movement on the Lewis thrust is certainly much greater. North of the International Boundary well back in the mountains are several windows in the thrust sheet where deep valleys have cut through the Belt strata into those of the Cretaceous beneath the thrust. In many parts of the mountains oil seeps issue from the Belt rocks and probably originated in the Mesozoic and Paleozoic rocks beneath. On the strength of these seeps several holes have been drilled for oil in the mountains. One of these, the Pacific-Atlantic, Flathead no. 1 well passed from Belt Series at 1,370 meters into highly dis-

141

turbed Paleozoic and Mesozoic strata (Fig. 86B); it lies 30 kilometers southwest of the nearest emergence of the Lewis thrust along the mountain front.

Windows, oil seeps, and drill holes indicate that the Lewis thrust underlies the whole of the Lewis, Livingston, and Clark Ranges, and that the rocks above it have been transported at least 30 milometers eastward, and probably very much more. They have, moreover, moved without rupture, in contrast to the rocks in the segment farther north where those in the Front Ranges above the McConnell thrust have been split into many slices.

One might infer a comparison and a correlation between the Lewis thrust and the McConnell thrust, as both are master low-angle faults along the mountain front. The comparison is apt but the correlation is not. To the north the Lewis thrust changes into a high-angle fault that passes behind the front of the mountains; the McConnell thrust develops out of folds and fault blocks east of it. Thrusting of rocks of the mountains over those of the foothills is a continuous feature, but at one place movement is concentrated on one low-angle fault, elsewhere on another.

LEWIS AND CLARK TRANSVERSE ZONE. Between Helena and Missoula, Montana, on the east, and Spokane, Washington, on the west, the continuity of the Cordillera is interrupted by a series of west-northwest-trending transverse valleys. This topographic interruption has made its mark on human affairs, as it furnished the route for the historic journey of Meriwether Lewis and William Clark in 1805 to the Pacific Coast, by which the Oregon Country was gained for the United States; today it is followed by U.S. Highway 10. The topographic interruption expresses a fundamental discontinuity in Cordilleran structure that appropriately has been termed the *Lewis and Clark line* or transverse zone.

The transverse valleys are followed by discontinuous high-angle faults of the same trend, of which the best known is the *Osburn fault* of northern Idaho. Along the same trend in the Eastern Ranges, zones of abrupt flexing and belts of en echelon faults seem to express draping of the sedimentary cover over faults in the basement rocks. On the Osburn fault and others near it there is a proved right-lateral displacement. Curiously, however, the en echelon fault belts in the Eastern Ranges indicate movements in the opposite sense, suggesting that there were many complex adjustments in different directions in the transverse zone from one place to another and from one time to another.

Interesting though these faults may be, they are merely one feature of a much larger discontinuity. North of the transverse zone the ranges and valleys of the Cordillera are like those we described at the International Boundary and northward. They extend north-northwest

and consist of geosynclinal sediments of Belt and later ages that have been thrown into folds and thrust blocks, or were transported eastward on low-angle faults like the Lewis and McConnell thrusts.

South of the transverse zone the ranges are more disordered and some trend north-northeast—an odd direction in the Cordillera. Folded and faulted Paleozoic and Mesozoic sediments occur in patches, but many of the mountains consist of Archean basement rocks older than the Belt Series, of Mesozoic felsic plutonic rocks, and of Tertiary volcanics. A part of the character of the area south of the transverse zone was determined early in geologic time, as the Belt Series appears to have been deposited over it thinly, if at all, and near it overlaps abruptly on the Archean rocks toward a shoreline with coarse marginal deposits.

PLUTONIC ROCKS SOUTH OF LEWIS AND CLARK ZONE. The most striking of the new features that appear south of the Lewis and Clark zone in the eastern Cordillera are great masses of felsic plutonic rocks.

To the west is the vast *Idaho batholith* that forms the rough mountain country of most of central Idaho. It had its inception during the Nevadan orogeny, but plutonic activity in the mass was prolonged; parts have yielded Cretaceous radiometric ages of about 100 million years (about the same as some of those in the Sierra Nevada) but others have yielded later ages. The batholith may have been sufficiently consolidated by the time of the Laramide compression to disorder the structures of the eastern part of the Cordillera that were forming in front of it.

During Laramide orogeny the region east of the Idaho batholith became a plutonic realm also; numerous masses of granitic rocks, large and small, were emplaced in western Montana south of the transverse zone.

Largest of these is the *Boulder batholith* southwest of Helena, a through-breaking mass that has ascended high in the crust from its place of origin. At the surface it has an oval outline 100 kilometers long and 30 kilometers wide, but it probably originated at its southwestern end as a broad stock and spread thence northeastward as a floored intrusive in a downwarp of the latest Cretaceous deposits. The Boulder batholith is notable because it can be dated more closely by both stratigraphic and radiometric means than most of the plutonic bodies in the Cordillera:

(a) It invades lavas and tuffs which contain fossil plants of late Cretaceous age, with radiometric dates of 73 to 78 million years; and is overlain unconformably by other tuffs whose fossil plants are of middle Eocene age.

(b) Radiometric determinations on the plutonic rock itself show that it was emplaced between 71 and 82 million years ago, that is, at about the same time and only slightly later than the Cretaceous lavas and tuffs that it intrudes.

METALLIC MINERAL DEPOSITS OF THE LEWIS AND CLARK ZONE AND TO THE SOUTH. Western Montana and northern Idaho—with their transverse zone, the discontinuity it expresses, and the plutonic realm south of it—are also the locus of the largest metallic mineral deposits of this part of the Cordillera. Exploitation of these deposits has contributed much to the wealth of the region.

The great copper deposits of Butte, Montana, occur in veins in the fractured western part of the Boulder batholith; they have been worked for many years and are still actively producing. Farther west are the mining camps of Philipsburg, Montana, and those in the Coeur d'Alene Mountains of northern Idaho.

It is worth recalling that the principal mineral deposits of Colorado are in another zone of transverse structures and plutonic rocks that crosses the Southern Rocky Mountains. Relation between the mineral deposits and the other features of these transverse zones is probably more than coincidence; the weakness of the crust that permitted the emplacement of magmas must also have allowed an ascent of mineral-bearing solutions.

WYOMIDE RANGES OF SOUTHEASTERN IDAHO AND WESTERN WYOMING. South of the region just discussed, in south-central Idaho, structures of the Mesozoic and older rocks are obscured across the *Snake River Plain*. This is another transverse zone that extends across the Cordillera, but it is much younger than the Lewis and Clark zone in west-central Montana—a broad downwarp that has been filled by Pliocene and Pleistocene lava flows.

South of the Snake River Plain the structures of the eastern part of the main Cordillera emerge again in the Wyomide Ranges—the western part of the Central Rocky Mountains as defined physiographically. Here the topography and structure are again like those in the Northern Rocky Mountains—a series of parallel ridges made up of folds and thrust blocks of Paleozoic and Mesozoic miogeosynclinal sediments. The Wyomide Ranges, however, do not make the front of the Cordilleran system, but pass behind the uplifts and basins of the Central Rocky Mountains; we have already mentioned their impingement on the latter (Chapter VII, section 4).

Various west-dipping, low-angle thrust faults occur in the Wyomide Ranges, the easternmost of which face the Green River Basin in southwestern Wyoming. But the most famous is the *Bannock thrust* farther west in the system, which was credited by its overenthusiastic discoverers with an eastward displacement of more than 50 kilometers. At its type area near the southeastern corner of Idaho, the rocks above the Bannock have clearly been moved for many kilometers, but the Bannock probably changes character and loses displacement northward and southward in the same manner as the Lewis thrust. A more fundamental thrust is probably the *Paris thrust*, or

next one to the west, which brings up lower Paleozoic over Triassic; it seems to correlate southward with the Willard thrust of the Wasatch Mountains, which is part of the system along the eastern edge of the Great Basin (see below). The significant feature here, as in the Northern Rocky Mountains, is not a single dominant low-angle thrust, but the whole complex of thrusts along which eastward movement has been distributed.

Various lines of evidence, including the sediments involved and their relations to the tectonics, indicate that the Wyomide Ranges grew progressively eastward. Thrusting apparently began in the west in late Jurassic time, and was completed at the eastern edge in early Eocene time.

EASTERN GREAT BASIN. Southward from Idaho and Wyoming in northern Utah, structures of the eastern part of the main Cordillera run out into the Great Basin, through which they extend into southern Nevada and southeastern California.

This is, however, a region of Basin and Range topography and structure, of discontinuous ranges separated by broad alluvial basins produced by block faulting late in geologic time—one of the modifications of Cordilleran structure of which we have spoken and of which we will have much more to say in Chapter IX, section 2. Here the pattern of fundamental earlier structures has been obscured and disordered into bits and pieces of a jigsaw puzzle, but with many parts missing where older rocks are covered by the younger in basins between the mountain ranges (Fig. 89). Knowledge of the region also lagged behind because for many years most of the geological data were obtained during spot jobs in local mining districts or on scattered mineral deposits. It has only been in the last few decades that the entire region has been satisfactorily mapped, and a regional picture has emerged.

Many of the ranges in the eastern part of the Great Basin expose segments of great low-angle thrust faults comparable to the frontal thrusts farther north; these segments can be pieced together into features that are continuous the length of the region. They lie close to the western edge of the Colorado Plateau and to the zone of westward thickening of the strata into the miogeosyncline. For the most part they are in the ranges of the basin, but to the north segments of them extend eastward into the Wasatch Mountains, where they bring the thick sequence of the Oquirrh basin over the thinner sequence of the autochthon. One segment is the *Willard thrust* north of Ogden, which has been tilted eastward and connects underground northward with the Paris thrust of the Wyomide Ranges, already noted. Its upper plate contains a thick Upper Proterozoic and Cambrian sedimentary sequence and its lower plate a thin lower Paleozoic sequence that directly overlies Lower Proterozoic metamorphic basement, the Farmington Can-

EXPLANATION

Rocks of the mountain areas
(Tertiary and older)

Rocks of intermontane basins
(mainly Quaternary)

Sevier thrusts
(middle Cretaceous)

Metamorphic infrastructure
(probably related to Sevier
thrusting)

Roberts thrust (late Devonian to early Mississippian)

Golconda thrust (late
Permian to early Triassic)

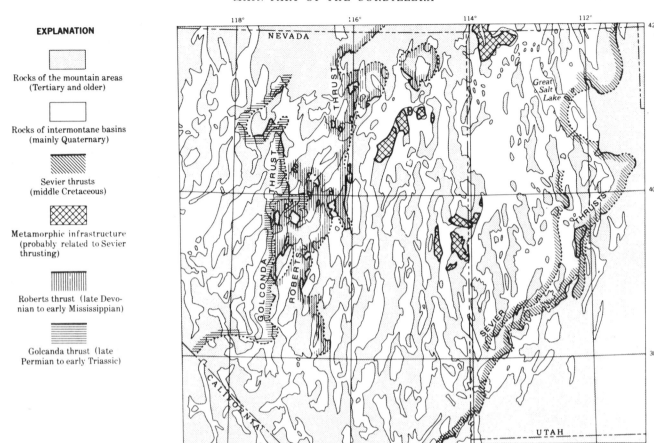

0   50   100   150 Kilometers

FIG. 89. Map of part of Great Basin in Nevada and Utah, showing patterns of major thrusts. The regional traces of the thrusts have been
obtained by connecting the short segments of exposed outcrop
through the intervening areas. The Sevier thrusts and the infrastruc-
tural areas are features of the miogeosynclinal area. The Roberts and
Golconda thrusts are in the eugeosynclinal area and are treated in
section 4 of this chapter. After King and Beikman (1974); data from
Geologic Map of United States (1974).

yon Complex. In the Las Vegas, Nevada, area, 650
kilometers farther south the frontal fault is the *Keystone
thrust*, spectacularly exposed in the east-facing escarpment of the Spring Mountains, with dark Cambrian
dolomites of the upper plate lying on cliff-making yellow
or orange Aztec Sandstone of Jurassic age.

These thrusts, and others immediately behind them,
are décollement thrusts that have moved older rocks of
the upper plates along bedding planes until they lie on
much younger autochthonous rocks. Many of them, like
the Keystone thrust, bring lower Paleozoic over Mesozoic. The Willard thrust plate has been moved more
than 65 kilometers eastward over its autochthon, and
displacements of similar magnitude probably occurred
on the frontal thrusts farther south.

The thrusts are manifestations of the *Sevier orogeny*,
which transformed the site of the present eastern Great
Basin into a mountain belt during Cretaceous time. As
already noted, thrusting in the Wyomide Ranges began
in the late Jurassic and persisted into the Eocene, but
the climax was certainly during the last half of the Cre-

taceous, before the climax of the Laramide orogeny to
the east. The Upper Cretaceous piedmont deposits of
the western edge of the Colorado Plateau in northeastern Utah overlap westward on a deformed terrane produced by the Sevier orogeny. In southern Nevada east of
Las Vegas the frontal thrust is bordered on the east by
the clastic continental Willow Tank and Baseline Formations containing middle Cretaceous plants, which are followed by the Overton Fanglomerate containing large
clasts and blocks of Paleozoic limestones derived from
the thrust sheet.

In western Utah and eastern Nevada, about 125
kilometers west of the frontal thrusts, the Paleozoic
rocks of the ranges contain another set of structures—
numerous décollement thrusts in which younger rocks
are carried over older, or the reverse of the usual relation, and resulting in considerable thinning of the original sequence. Probably these structures are the root
zone of the frontal thrusts. In the northern Snake Range,
the Ruby Range, and some other mountains the lowest
décollement thrust emerges, and carries unaltered

144

Paleozoic rocks over an infrastructure of highly meta-morphosed, plastically folded lower Paleozoic rocks. Radiometric dating indicates that the infrastructure was formed during the Mesozoic, but somewhat before the thrust structures that overlie it. At present it cannot be determined whether this infrastructure underlies all the thrusted but otherwise unaltered Paleozoic rocks, or whether it represents local spots of exceptional crustal heating.

EXTENSION OF STRUCTURES TO THE SOUTH. As indicated in section 2, the great sequences of miogeosyncli-nal rocks of the eastern Great Basin lose themselves in the Mojave Desert south of Nevada, where they become entangled with younger rocks and structures. The char-acteristic structures of the eastern Great Basin also disappear or change their character. Low-angle thrusts persist but are no longer confined to the sedimentary column. Instead, they extend into the basement, so that many of the thrust sheets have metamorphic Lower Pro-terozoic rocks at their bases. They also bend toward the southeast and trend toward the cratonic rocks of south-western Arizona, where their extent is still poorly known.

4. CORDILLERAN EUGEOSYNCLINE AND STRUCTURES THAT FORMED FROM IT

COMPARISON WITH CRYSTALLINE PART OF THE AP-PALACHIANS. In our earlier summary of the Cordillera (Chapter IV) we pointed out that the oceanward part of the system away from the continental interior possesses many of the same features as the oceanward part of the Appalachians—it was a eugeosynclinal area during the geosynclinal stage, and its rocks were afterwards con-solidated by metamorphism and plutonism into a terrane like that in the crystalline Appalachians.

The differences are expectable between two widely separated mountain systems. Here, the oceanward side is on the west rather than the southeast, and the ocean is the Pacific rather than the Atlantic; the Cordilleran eugeosyncline is the child of the Pacific Ocean, just as the Appalachian eugeosyncline is the child of the Atlan-tic Ocean. Here, in contrast to the Appalachians, there were no impinging continental plates to complicate the relations; the Pacific was ocean throughout the life of the Cordillera. Partly as a consequence of this, eugeosyncli-nal conditions in the Appalachians largely ceased by the end of the Devonian, whereas in the Cordillera they continued into the Jurassic, so that the eugeosyncline contains large volumes of late Paleozoic and early Mesozoic deposits.

The crystalline area of the Appalachians is concealed in many places by later supracrustal deposits; that of the Cordillera is equally so. Up to its climactic orogeny this western belt of the Cordillera must have been continu-ous along the Pacific border. Now it is widely covered by sediments and lavas, mainly continental in origin and Tertiary in age, so that it is exposed only in fragments.

THE SIERRA NEVADA. We can introduce the eugeo-synclinal rocks and the structures that formed from them by considering a typical segment, that in the Sierra Nevada of California—where they were first encoun-tered by Americans.

We must do so, however, with a word of caution. The present Sierra Nevada is a great tilted block (Fig. 91) shaped accidentally in Tertiary and Quarternary time out of a more extensive earlier eugeosynclinal and crys-talline terrane that extended far northward and south-ward, as well as eastward and westward. The present range is merely a fragment of the original structure.

Let us recall how gold was discovered in the western foothills of the Sierra Nevada in 1848—in the tailrace of Sutter's Mill at Coloma—and how it was exploited by the Forty-niners. Most of the Forty-niners obtained their gold from placers; that is, from the alluvial deposits of streams flowing out of the Sierra. But as the placers be-came depleted, the more experienced prospectors and miners began following the alluvial gold up to its source in the older rocks.

They found a great concentration of gold in quartz veins along a narrow zone in the foothills where the bed-rock was intensely sheared and faulted, and so gave it the name of Veta Madre or *Mother Lode*. Here they began the more difficult task of vein or lode mining, which their successors profitably carried on for genera-tions. More considered judgment in later years has indi-cated that this zone was only one source of the placer gold; much of it came from other sources in the bedrock or from older placer deposits of Tertiary age. The name Mother Lode has persisted, nevertheless, in popular legend.

Geologic investigation of the gold belt in the Sierra Nevada lagged far behind the feverish searchings of the prospectors. The belt was first studied between 1860 and 1874 by the Geological Survey of California under J. D. Whitney, and later by parties of the U.S. Geological Survey under G. F. Becker, which included Waldemar Lindgren, F. L. Ransome, and W. H. Turner; the U.S. Geological Survey produced a dozen geologic folios covering the western slope of the Sierra Nevada that are still classic.

The geologists found that the rocks of the gold belt fell into two great subdivisions which were called in the folios the *Superjacent Series* and the *Bedrock or Au-riferous Series*.

SUPERJACENT SERIES. The Superjacent Series com-prises those deposits that lie with little disturbance on the eroded edges of the Bedrock Series. Along most of the western slope of the Sierra Nevada these are of Ter-tiary age, but at the north end of the Sacramento Valley somewhat older strata, the Upper Cretaceous Chico Formation, have a similar relation to the rocks beneath, hence may be included. The Chico establishes the climax of the deformation of the Bedrock Series as having occurred before the end of Mesozoic time and as having been produced by an orogeny earlier than the one which deformed the Rocky Mountains farther east. The Chico is, moreover, merely the highest overlapping part of a much more extensive upper Mesozoic sequence that includes lower and older beds to the west; we will say more about this *Great Valley sequence* later (Chapter IX, section 4).

The Tertiary deposits of the Superjacent Series fringe the western base of the Sierra Nevada, and extend far up its slopes in old swales in the topography or on ridge tops between the present streams. They include gravels that were laid down along the courses of vanished rivers that flowed westward from sources somewhere east of the modern crest line, across the site of the Sierra Nevada before it was raised to its present heights. The gold prospectors found that these old river gravels contained placer gold like the modern ones, and they worked them extensively by hydraulic mining.

Volcanic eruptions occurred from time to time in the region, and lavas flowed down the river valleys; these formed a capping of the gravels that resisted erosion; when renewed downcutting took place, the former valleys were thus left standing in the higher parts of the country (Fig. 90).

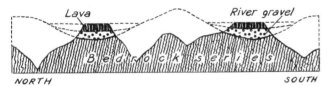

FIG. 90. Sketch section in the western part of the Sierra Nevada showing relation of Tertiary gravels and lava (Superjacent Series) to the bedrock and to present topography.

Detailed study of the Superjacent gravels and lavas indicates that they had a more complex history than was first supposed, and were formed at intervals from Eocene to Pliocene time. But that is another story; our interest here is in the Bedrock Series.

BEDROCK SERIES. The Bedrock Series comprises the pre-Tertiary rocks of the Sierra Nevada—the supracrustal eugeosynclinal rocks, now deformed, upended, and altered, and the plutonic rocks that invade them; the latter include great masses of granitic rocks collectively known as the *Sierra Nevada batholith*. The supracrustal rocks were early recognized to be of both Paleozoic and Mesozoic ages, the former being termed the *Calaveras Formation*, and the latter the *Mariposa Slate*. Besides these, the folios indicate numerous bands of "diabase porphyrite," "augite porphyrite," "quartz porphyrite," and "amphibolite," which one would suppose were

igneous intrusives; they are, instead, surface lavas and pyroclastics that are interbedded in the Mesozoic stratified succession. Later work has shown that the supracrustal sequence is actually more complicated than this original simple classification would imply.

The supracrustal rocks of the Bedrock Series form a belt as much as 100 kilometers broad in the northern Sierra Nevada, between the Great Valley on the west and the Sierra Nevada batholith on the east. However, the trend of their structures is south-southeastward, whereas the trend of the west side of the batholith is more nearly southward, so that the supracrustal rocks are gradually truncated and end as a coherent belt south of the Merced River. In the southern Sierra Nevada they are preserved only as roof pendants or inclusions in the batholith.

The supracrustal rocks are traversed by a series of great high-angle reverse faults, thrust toward the west (of which the original Mother Lode is a part). The eastern, or Melones fault, generally separates the Paleozoic rocks on the east from the Mesozoic rocks on the west; one of the major breaks farther west, the Bear Mountain fault, divides the Mesozoic rocks into two different sequences.

THE PALEOZOIC ROCKS. The *Calaveras Formation* forms the southern part of the Paleozoic terrane and is a monotonous sequence of black carbonaceous slate and siltstone, with several large lenses of limestone and a few rare volcanics. It seems to be a homoclinal eastward-dipping sequence that might be as thick as 40,000 meters, although it is probably considerably duplicated by folding. The Calaveras is traditionally believed to be upper Paleozoic, but this is no more than a guess, and is based only on a few fossils discovered early and not duplicated since.

North of the latitude of Sacramento the Calaveras is adjoined on the east by a different and equally thick terrane, the *Shoo Fly Formation*, a sequence of weakly metamorphosed phyllites, siltstones, chert, and quartzose sandstone. The Shoo Fly Formation is generally considered to be older than the Calaveras, although the contact is mostly faulted. Silurian fossils have been collected from its northern exposures, and it is overlain unconformably on the east by dacitic and andesitic volcanics that contain Devonian ammonoids. In another structural belt on the east side of the Sierra Nevada near the head of Owens Valley is a thick sequence of fossiliferous Ordovician slates.

The Paleozoic record in the Sierra Nevada is thus incompletely known in detail, but the occurrence of fossiliferous rocks as old as Ordovician or Silurian indicates that eugeosynclinal conditions began here at a very early period. The basement on which these rocks were laid down is undetermined, but the bands of serpentinite along the faults in the foothills are probably ophiolites, or relics of an original oceanic crust; no Precambrian rocks (that is, continental crust) are known west of the miogeosynclinal belt in eastern Nevada.

THE MESOZOIC ROCKS. The type *Mariposa Slate* is in the belt immediately west of the Melones fault, and is part of a 5,000-meter sequence with the Amador Group beneath, also partly sedimentary but with extensive flows of basaltic and andesitic lava. West of the Bear Mountain fault is another sequence, which has been given another set of formation names, mainly basaltic, andesitic, and rhyolitic pyroclastic rocks and lava, but with slates near the middle. Both sequences contain middle to upper Jurassic fossils (Callovian to Kimmeridgian), and no older rocks are known; in places they seemingly lie on ophiolitic or oceanic crust. (Older Jurassic, and Triassic rocks are known in other belts in the northern Sierra Nevada). The nature of the volcanic rocks in both sequences indicates that they are island-arc deposits.

In the northern half of the outcrop belt, the two sequences are separated by the 20-kilometer broad *Smartville terrane*, an ophiolite assemblage with pillow basalts that overlie a sheeted-dike complex and intrusive gabbro—the earmarks of an oceanic crust. The Smartville terrane narrows southward and pinches out between the two sequences, leaving only a narrow belt of melange containing a wide variety of tectonic blocks of sedimentary and volcanic rocks, including limestone masses with Permian fusulinids.

Thus, in the Mesozoic belt of the western Sierra Nevada, as in the eugeosynclinal area of the Northern Appalachians, there are fragments of terranes that were originally widely separated, now closely juxtaposed by deformation, and much of the intervening part subducted and lost. The two island-arc sequences formed far apart and were separated by an oceanic area represented by the Smartville terrane. The main subduction zone probably lay to the west and is now concealed beneath the younger sediments of the Great Valley; the high-angle reverse faults in the foothill belt probably originated as westward-directed thrusts above it.

DEFORMATION OF THE EUGEOSYNCLINAL ROCKS. The Calaveras and Shoo Fly are more deformed and metamorphosed than the Mesozoic rocks, and were seemingly involved in one or more orogenies before the end of Paleozoic time. The evident deformation of both Paleozoic and Mesozoic rocks, however, occurred after the formation of the latter. A striking feature of their structure is their steep or vertical dip. Steep dips in other regions are common enough on the flanks of folds, but here they are well-nigh universal. Moreover, except for a few steep isoclinal folds, the sequence is almost invariably upward toward the east, toward the heart of the Sierra Nevada (Fig. 91C). The only duplication is created by the Melones and other faults of the foothill

belt, which raise the older rocks on their eastern sides.

On the opposite or eastern side of the Sierra Nevada, south of Mono Lake, the structure is similar but reversed. Paleozoic and Mesozoic rocks dip steeply, but with the sequence upward toward the west, again toward the heart of the Sierra. The two steeply dipping and opposing belts appear to be the flanks of a much greater feature—a great crustal downfold whose trough is now obliterated by the masses of granitic plutonic rocks of the Sierra Nevada batholith that form the core of the range (Fig. 91D and E).

The supracrustal rocks were metamorphosed, probably at the time of deformation, so that their constituents were recrystallized into chlorite and other low-grade metamorphic minerals, and their more argillaceous parts were converted into slates and phyllites. During the plutonic invasions that followed, a higher-grade thermal metamorphism was imposed that locally converted the rocks into hornfels or even into gneiss.

THE PLUTONIC ROCKS. Felsic (granitic) plutonic rocks are embedded in the earlier eugeosynclinal rocks throughout the length of the Sierra Nevada (Fig. 91C, D, E). Broadly, these can be called "granitic," although true granites in the technical sense are rather minor, most of them being the somewhat more mafic quartz monzonites, granodiorites, and quartz diorites. Unlike many felsic plutonic rocks of other regions, those of the Sierra Nevada are prevailingly of light gray or white color from lack of red coloration in their feldspars. Their shining peaks and bare rock faces inspired John Muir's poetic designation of the region as "the range of light."

The mass of plutonic rocks is referred to collectively as the *Sierra Nevada batholith*, but this is an oversimplification. Actually, it was never a single great lake of magma, but was composed of many individual plutons of various shapes and sizes, of different compositions, and of different ages, that were emplaced over a span of nearly 100 million years. East and west of the axis of the range are Jurassic plutons with ages of 160 to 180 million years; those on the west form equidimensional bodies embedded in the country rocks, but merge eastward into a more continuous body that forms the western part of the main batholith, as at the lower end of Yosemite Valley (Fig. 91C). Along the crest of the range for its entire length is a wide band of Cretaceous granitic rocks, the first part of which has ages of 104 to 121 million years, and the succeeding main part ages of 79 to 80 million years or Upper Cretaceous (Fig. 91D). The oldest part of this long sequence of plutonic rocks is the more mafic, but becomes more felsic with time and into the center of the batholith, where there are some true granites.

The Jurassic and Cretaceous ages of the plutonic rocks raise interesting questions regarding their relation to the accumulation of the adjoining supracrustal rocks. The Cretaceous granitic rocks are especially troublesome,

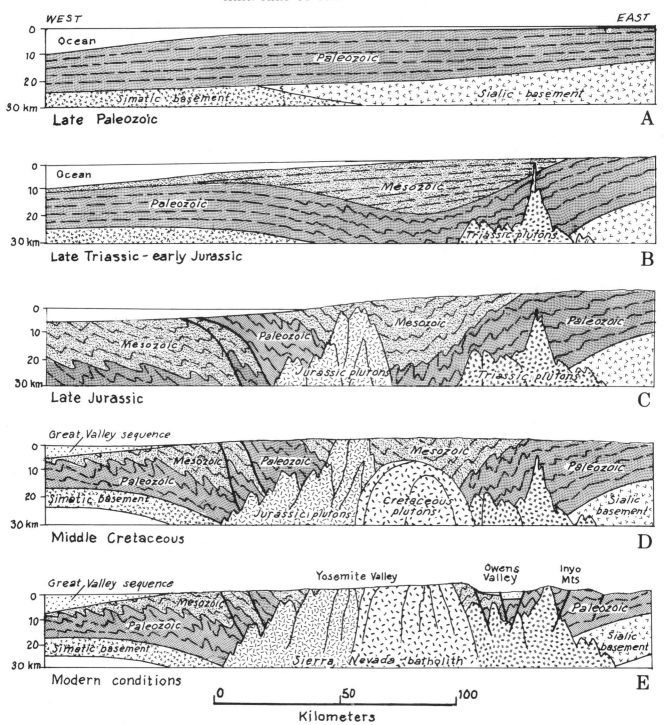

FIG. 91. Sections showing sequential development of the site of the Sierra Nevada from Paleozoic time to the present: A–Late Paleozoic. B–Late Triassic to early Jurassic. C–Late Jurassic. D–Middle Cretaceous. E–Modern conditions. Modified from Bateman and Wahrhaftig (1966). Other more complex (and more speculative reconstructions have been published later.

because they were being emplaced at the same time the postorogenic Great Valley sequence was accumulating to the west. During emplacement of the Cretaceous batholithic rocks, the site of the Sierra Nevada was probably being raised and eroded, producing large volumes of debris that were incorporated in the Great Valley sediments.

All the plutons of the Sierra Nevada are massive and cross-cutting rather than foliated and concordant, and they were emplaced largely after the deformation of the eugeosynclinal rocks had ceased. Apparently they rose as true magmas from the depths to their present levels in the crust, breaking through the strata and forcing them aside. Elsewhere in the western part of the Cordillera, structural relations of the plutonics are more varied; they include not only massive and cross-cutting bodies such as those in the Sierra, but also foliated and concordant bodies and magmatic permeations in a prevailing, highly altered country rock.

Viewing the western belt of the Cordillera as a whole, we observe that the felsic plutonic rocks occupy a much greater surface area than their counterparts in the Appalachians and pose, even more compellingly, some fundamental geologic questions:

(a) What was the source of the enormous volumes of granitic material?

(b) Why are the granitic rocks mainly emplaced in the former eugeosynclinal areas?

(c) What became of the eugeosynclinal rocks whose place they have taken?

These questions are much debated, and final answers are still elusive. The association of the felsic batholiths with eugeosynclinal rocks has led to the suggestion that the felsic rocks were generated from melting of the eugeosynclinal rocks themselves, when their lower parts were folded down to great depths, as in the Sierra Nevada. This cannot be the whole answer, however. The eugeosynclinal rocks east of the Sierra Nevada, which we will examine next, do not contain plutons of batholithic proportions. Moreover, batholithic rocks extend southeast from the end of the Sierra Nevada into the Mojave Desert, where they lie in miogeosynclinal rocks. Instead, both the eugeosynclinal and the batholithic domains seem to owe their origin to the junction between the American plate and the Pacific plate on the west, which has been a subduction zone through much of its history. The lithosphere of the Pacific plate is being thrust under the American plate, and being carried down many kilometers below the normal crust of the earth along a Benioff zone. At these great depths the lithosphere and its associated mantle are partially melted, giving rise to sialic differentiates that rise as magmas into the overriding American plate. Some of the magmas reach the surface to form andesitic lavas and lines of andesitic volcanoes; those beneath consolidate as felsic batholiths.

AGE OF NEVADAN OROGENY. These events—deformation of the eugeosynclinal rocks and their subsequent invasion by plutonic rocks—represent the *Nevadan orogeny* in its type area. When did this orogeny take place?

Within the Sierra Nevada itself the timing of the deformation of the eugeosynclinal rocks is bounded only by wide limiting dates; youngest strata involved are of late Jurassic age (Kimmeridgian and older), and the oldest strata not involved are of late Cretaceous age (Chico Formation); Nevadan deformation occurred during the intervening hiatus. Farther west in the Sacramento Valley, the Great Valley sequence includes earlier Creta-

ceous strata (Horsetown and Paskenta Formations), as well as late Jurassic strata (Knoxville Formation), none of which is metamorphosed or invaded by plutonic rocks. All this sequence has been supposed to have been altogether younger than the deformation of the supracrustal rocks of the Sierra Nevada.

Modern data require large modifications of this simple concept. Most of the Knoxville is of Portlandian (= Tithonian) age, or a stage younger than the Kimmeridgian age of the youngest strata of the Sierra Nevada. However, the lower part of the Knoxville is now known to contain a species of *Buchia* of Kimmeridgian age, so that accumulation of the two sequences actually overlaps in time. Moreover, radiometric dating of the plutonic rocks of the Sierra Nevada indicates that they were being implaced during a long period, from Jurassic to late in the Cretaceous, so that these also overlap the time of accumulation of the Great Valley sequence. The sediments of the Great Valley sequence that were formerly thought to have accumulated in a new trough west of the Sierra Nevada orogen after its deformation were actually accumulating during the Nevadan orogeny, with intensity of deformation diminishing westward.

Elsewhere in the western belt of the Cordillera, where deformed and plutonized eugeosynclinal rocks occur, it has commonly been assumed on the basis of relations in California that the rocks were likewise deformed in late Jurassic time. In many places decisive evidence is lacking, the limiting dates being as great or greater than in California. But where evidence is obtainable, the record turns out to be complex and varied. In the Hawthorne-Tonopah area of southwestern Nevada, major thrust faulting was in progress during deposition of adjacent early Jurassic sediments. In northern Baja California early and middle Cretaceous rocks are involved in the orogeny and plutonism and are overlain unconformably by late Cretaceous rocks. In the northern Cascade Range of Washington there was major deformation and regional metamorphism before the middle Jurassic, followed by folding and thrusting in middle Cretaceous time. Nevadan orogeny in the western part of the Cordillera was thus a prolonged event that began in mid-Mesozoic time and approached or overlapped the time of Laramide orogeny in the eastern part of the Cordillera.

WESTERN GREAT BASIN. The rocks of the Sierra Nevada are only a small sample of the large and diversified eugeosynclinal realm. To explore it further, and to elucidate its earlier history, let us drop back to the east, into western Nevada. One of the sequences of miogeosynclinal rocks we mentioned earlier is that in the Inyo Mountains of the southern Great Basin, a range that is separated from the Sierra Nevada on the west merely by the trough of Owens Valley. Here, the change from miogeosynclinal rocks and their dominant carbonates to eugeosynclinal rocks with their dominant clastics and volcanics takes place across a single desert valley in a zone immediately east of the present front of the Sierra Nevada. North of the Inyo Mountains, however, the boundary diverges northward or northeastward from the front of the Sierra and passes into the middle of the Great Basin.

A contrast between the pre-Tertiary rocks of the eastern and western part of the Great Basin in northern Nevada has been known since the days of Clarence King's Fortieth Parallel Survey—the rocks of the eastern half are largely Paleozoic carbonates, and those to the west are clastic rocks with considerable volumes of interbedded volcanics and embedded granitic plutons like those in the Sierra Nevada. Originally it was thought that the supracrustal rocks of the western area were mainly of Triassic age, but it is now known that they include large thicknesses of Paleozoic rocks as well, of the same age but of a different facies from those of the miogeosyncline. Their complex history has been worked out only during the last few decades (Fig. 92).

Many different sequences of contrasting origins and ages have been juxtaposed in this region by processes of thrusting, overlap, and block-faulting, producing a most complex map pattern (Fig. 93). Samples of the internal structure of some of the ranges are shown in Figure 94.

Immediately west of the belt of miogeosynclinal rocks, in a wide band across central Nevada, are lower Paleozoic eugeosynclinal rocks, which have an aggregate thickness of 13,000 meters (although this is not preserved in sequence at any one place). The most extensively exposed of these rocks are Ordovician—shale, chert, and minor lavas of the Vinini Formation and a more sandy facies to the northwest, the Valmy Formation, both containing graptolites of many zones. Cambrian eugeosynclinal rocks are preserved in a few places—Lower Cambrian chert, argillite, and greenstone with archeocyathids (Scott Canyon Formation), and Upper Cambrian arkosic turbidites (Harmony Formation). But these occur in separate thrust slices and are in sequence neither with each other nor the younger eugeosynclinal rocks (Fig. 94C). Above the Ordovician, but more scantily preserved, are Silurian and Devonian formations of cherts, shales, sandstones, and minor lavas. All these are deep-water, sea-floor deposits, probably laid down on oceanic crust.

The lower Paleozoic eugeosynclinal rocks have been transported eastward over the miogeosynclinal rocks for as much as 160 kilometers along the low-angle *Roberts thrust*. Because of the cover of younger rocks and the extensive disruption of the whole terrane by basin and range faulting, no clearly defined thrust front is now preserved, but the miogeosynclinal rocks are exposed in windows beneath the eugeosynclinal rocks from one range to the next across the 160-kilometer breadth (Fig.

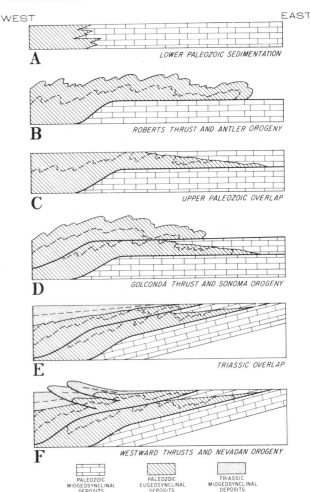

FIG. 92. Diagrammatic sections illustrating structural history of north-central Nevada in Paleozoic and Mesozoic time. (A) Early to middle Paleozoic. (B) Late Devonian and early Mississippian; Roberts thrust and Antler orogeny. (C) Pennsylvanian and Permian; upper Paleozoic overlap. (D) Late Permian and early Triassic; Golconda thrust and Sonoma orogeny. (E) Triassic; overlap of miogeosynclinal deposits. (F) Mid-Mesozoic; westward thrusts and Nevadan orogeny.

89). Emplacement of the Roberts thrust occurred in late Devonian and early Mississippian time during an event termed the *Antler orogeny*.

This orogeny raised the deformed terrane to the level of erosion, creating the clastic wedge of Chainman Shale and Diamond Peak Quartzite that was spread over the miogeosyncline (see section 2 of this chapter). Younger Paleozoic shallow-water conglomerates, sandstones, and limestones overlapped westward over the deformed terrane, including the Battle Conglomerate and Antler Peak Limestone in Battle Mountain, of Pennsylvanian and early Permian age (Fig. 94C), followed nearby by the later Permian Edna Mountain Formation. Angular unconformities occur between some of these younger overlapping formations, attesting a waning instability in the area.

West of this belt of lower Paleozoic eugeosynclinal

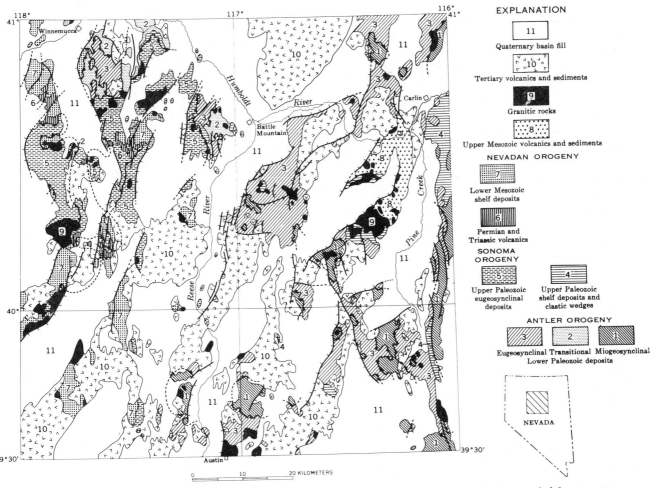

EXPLANATION

11
Quaternary basin fill

10
Tertiary volcanics and sediments

9
Granitic rocks

8
Upper Mesozoic volcanics and sediments

NEVADAN OROGENY

7
Lower Mesozoic shelf deposits

6
Permian and Triassic volcanics

SONOMA OROGENY

5
Upper Paleozoic eugeosynclinal deposits

4
Upper Paleozoic shelf deposits and clastic wedges

ANTLER OROGENY

3   2   1
Eugeosynclinal   Transitional   Miogeosynclinal
Lower Paleozoic deposits

NEVADA

Fig. 93. Map of part of north-central Nevada, showing confused pattern and small outcrops of structural units of widely different origins and ages, resulting from shuffling on thrust slices, from overlaps, and from block-faulting. After King (1969); compiled from county geologic maps of Nevada and from publications of U.S. Geological Survey.

rocks is another belt of upper Paleozoic eugeosynclinal rocks. In the Sonoma Range and others near Winnemucca these are the Pumpernickel and Havallah Formations of Pennsylvanian and Permian age, the first dominantly cherts and greenstone lavas, and the second a more sandy deposit (Fig. 94A). In other ranges to the west and north, similar deposits are older, and contain Mississippian fossils. Partial sections of these rocks attain 4,000 meters, and the whole must be much thicker. Like the lower Paleozoic eugeosynclinal rocks to the east, they are deep-water, sea-floor deposits, probably laid down on oceanic crust; small outcrops of serpentinite along their eastern border suggest an ophiolitic basement.

The upper Paleozoic eugeosynclinal rocks, like the lower Paleozoic eugeosynclinal rocks, were transported eastward, this time over the latter and their cover of overlapping shallow-water upper Paleozoic deposits. The surface of movement was the low-angle *Golconda thrust*, which was emplaced during a late Permian and early Triassic event termed the *Sonoma orogeny*. The

Golconda thrust, like the Roberts thrust, has been greatly disrupted by basin and range faulting, but fragments are preserved along a distance of 200 kilometers or more (Fig. 89)—frequently identifiable by its characteristic trademark of upper Paleozoic eugeosynclinal rocks overlying nearly contemporaneous shallow-water deposits of the Antler belt.

A still further chapter in the tectonic history of western Nevada began in Triassic time. Unconformably on the upper Paleozoic rocks of the Sonoma orogenic belt are the lavas of the Koipato Formation of late Permian and early Triassic age, followed by younger Triassic marine miogeosynclinal deposits that overlap eastward toward a land barrier created by the Sonoma and Antler orogenies. This barrier separated them from the Triassic and Jurassic deposits of the eastern Great Basin, already mentioned (see section 2, this chapter).

The Triassic rocks, like the Paleozoic rocks, were subjected to low-angle thrusting, probably during a phase of the Nevadan orogeny (Fig. 94B). Thrusting was, curiously, mainly from east to west, or the reverse of the

151

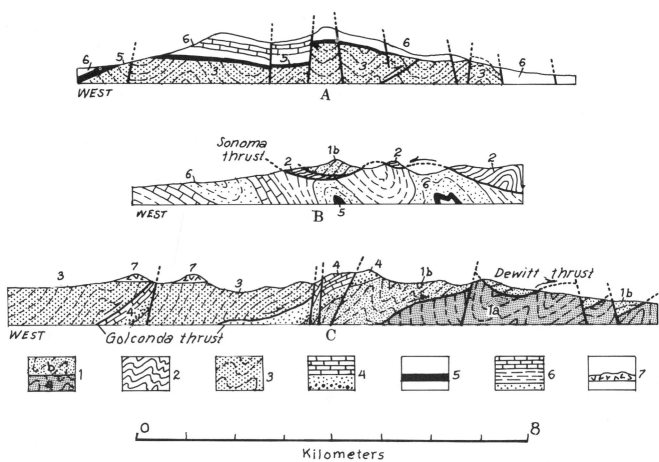

FIG. 94. Sections showing internal structure of some of ranges in north-central Nevada and their deformed Paleozoic and Mesozoic rocks: (A) North end of Tobin Range; little deformed Triassic of Augusta sequence on Paleozoic rocks deformed during Sonoma orogeny. (B) West side of Sonoma Range; Paleozoic rocks thrust westward on Sonoma thrust over deformed Triassic of Winnemucca sequence during Nevadan orogeny. (C) Battle Mountain and its deformed Paleozoic rocks; pre-Pennsylvanian Dewitt thrust of Antler orogeny, and post-Permian Golconda thrust of Sonoma orogeny. After Ferguson, Muller, and Roberts (1951, 1952), with modifications from later sources.

Explanation of symbols: 1–Cambrian: 1a, Scott Canyon Formation (eugeosynclinal deposits); 1b, Harmony Formation (arkosic turbidite). 2–Ordovician: Sonoma Range Formation (eugeosynclinal deposits). 3–Pennsylvanian and Permian: Pumpernickel and Havallah Formations (eugeosynclinal deposits). 4–Pennsylvanian and Permian: Battle Conglomerate and Antler Peak Limestone (overlap assemblage). 5–Early Triassic: Koipato Formation (terrestrial volcanics). 6–Middle and upper Triassic (miogeosynclinal deposits of Augusta and Winnemucca sequences). 7–Tertiary volcanics.

previous relations. In the ranges south of Winnemucca the thrusts separate the Triassic into an eastern, or Augusta sequence and a western, or Winnemucca sequence—the first a near-shore deposit with much sandstone and conglomerate below, passing upward into limestone, the second again with limestone formations below but passing upward into shales that include early Jurassic at the top. The Triassic deposits of both sequences attain 3,000 meters or more. Westward, the Winnemucca sequence passes into a deeper-water shaly sequence and finally in western Nevada into sedimentary and volcanic rocks of the Mesozoic eugeosyncline that we have described in the Sierra Nevada.

The history of this segment of the Cordilleran eugeosyncline records the accretion of a band 400 kilometers or more broad to the North American continent during Paleozoic and the first half of Mesozoic time,

out of what was originally the eastern part of the Pacific Ocean basin. No Precambrian rocks are known, either in outcrop or subsurface, west of eastern Nevada, and their western terminus probably marks approximately the western edge of the North American continent at the beginning of Paleozoic time (Fig. 95). During early Paleozoic time the edge of the continent was the shelf break along the western side of the miogeosyncline, beyond which was a deep-water area floored by oceanic crust. Probably the ocean basin within the present state of Nevada was separated from the main ocean by volcanic island arcs along the site of the Sierra Nevada and Klamath Mountains; the Mesozoic island arcs in the western Sierra Nevada have already been mentioned. During the mid-Paleozoic Antler orogeny, the depth differences between the miogeosyncline and eugeosyncline were reversed, and the eugeosynclinal rocks were raised

152

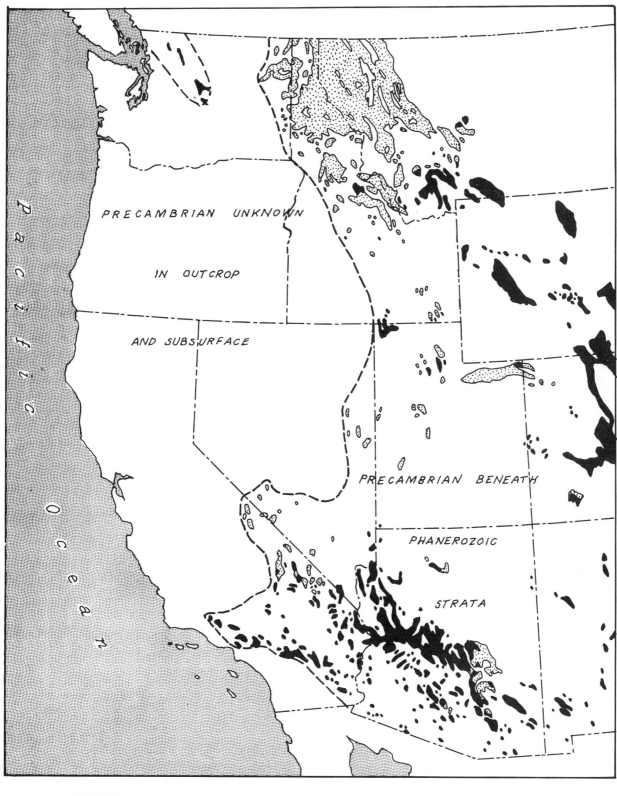

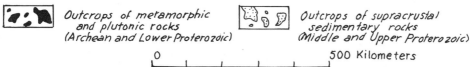

Outcrops of metamorphic
and plutonic rocks
(Archean and Lower Proterozoic)

Outcrops of supracrustal
sedimentary rocks
(Middle and Upper Proterozoic)

0   500 Kilometers

FIG. 95. Map of western United States, showing outcrops of Precambrian metamorphic rocks and supracrustal rocks. No Precambrian rocks are known in outcrop or subsurface outside of the dashed line, and this line is probably near the western edge of North American continental crust at the beginning of Phanerozoic time. The exten-sion of the Precambrian westward to the Pacific Coast in southern California is the result of shifting of crustal blocks during the Cenozoic; the small areas in the metamorphic complex of northwestern Washington are probably stray continental fragments.

and carried over the edge of the miogeosyncline. During the end-Paleozoic Sonoma orogeny, the process was repeated a little farther to the west. As a final phase of accretion, the Mesozoic eugeosynclinal rocks beyond were deformed by the Nevadan orogeny and made continental by the emplacement of extensive granitic plutons.

REGIONAL RELATIONS OF THE CORDILLERAN EUGEOSYNCLINE. The segment of the eugeosyncline just described is merely a sample of a long and complex belt for which detailed treatment would be tedious. Before leaving the subject, however, it would be desirable to make a regional summary.

Northwest of the north end of the Sierra Nevada, and separated from it by a short gap covered by younger deposits, are the Klamath Mountains of Paleozoic and Mesozoic eugeosynclinal rocks, which form a west-bulging arc that extends from northern California into southwestern Oregon. Here, the rocks are broken into a series of broad thrust slices, each moved to the west, with older rocks on the east and younger rocks on the west, the last slice to the west being thrust over the Franciscan of the Coast Ranges (Chapter IX, section 4). Serpentinites and other ultramafic rocks are more extensive areally than in the Sierra. Some are low-dipping sheets, probably ophiolites at the bases of the supracrustal rocks of the thrust sheets. A few small intrusive stocks have been dated radiometrically as late Paleozoic, but all the large granitic plutons are Jurassic; none is Cretaceous.

At the north end of the Klamath Mountains the eugeosynclinal rocks plunge northeastward under Tertiary lavas. In Oregon and Washington, the lavas extend eastward to the Idaho border in a great reentrant, the older eugeosynclinal rocks bordering it on the southeast, east, and north in the *Columbia arc*; the reentrant itself may have been floored by oceanic crust until Cenozoic time.

North of the arc the eugeosyncline is exposed in a broad band through British Columbia and Yukon Territory into Alaska. Paleozoic components in the eastern part of the belt in British Columbia form the Cache Creek Series, which is reminiscent of the Paleozoic eugeosynclinal rocks of Nevada. It was deformed and metamorphosed before the accumulation of lower Mesozoic eugeosynclinal rocks. Later Jurassic and Cretaceous deposits in successor basins within the belt are partly non-marine and are unmetamorphosed. Granitic plutonic rocks reach their climax in the mighty *Coast batholith*, which extends 1,700 kilometers through the high mountains along the Pacific Coast. Like the Sierra Nevada batholith, it is a complex of plutons of different ages, from late Triassic to late Cretaceous. The tectonic history of this segment of the eugeosynclinal belt is too complex to set forth in detail here; there were many orogenic periods, but the main deformation appears to have been in early Cretaceous time.

South of the Sierra Nevada the eugeosynclinal belt is interrupted by the Transverse Ranges of southern California, which are part of a fault-block network associated with the San Andreas fault, and which bring crystalline rocks of Precambrian, Paleozoic, and Mesozoic ages nearly to the Pacific Coast. The belt is resumed again to the south in the Peninsular Ranges of southern California and Baja California, whose Mesozoic eugeosynclinal rocks are extensively invaded by the *Peninsular batholith*. The many plutons of the batholith are principally of middle Cretaceous age, and in Baja California they invade eugeosynclinal rocks as young as Lower Cretaceous.

REFERENCES

2. *Cordilleran Miogeosyncline*

Gabrielse, Hugh, 1972, Younger Precambrian of the Canadian Cordillera: *Am. Jour. Sci.*, v. 272, no. 6, pp. 521-536.

Harrison, J. E., 1972, The Precambrian Belt basin of northwestern United States; its geometry, sedimentation, and copper occurrences: *Geol. Soc. America Bull.*, v. 83, no. 5, pp. 1215-1240.

Lockman-Balk, Christina, 1956, The Cambrian of the Rocky Mountains and southwestern deserts of the United States and adjoining Sonora province, in Rodgers, John, ed., *El sitema Cambrico, su paleogeographia y el problema de su base*: XX Int. Geol. Cong. (Mexico), v. 2, pp. 529-661.

Nolan, T. B., Merriam, C. W., and Williams, J. S., 1956, *The stratigraphic section in the vicinity of Eureka, Nevada*: U.S. Geol. Survey Prof. Paper 276.

Roberts, R. J., Crittenden, M. D., Tooker, E. W., Morris, H. T., and Cheney, T. M., 1965, Pennsylvanian and Permian basins in northwestern Utah, northeastern Nevada, and south-central Idaho: *Am. Assoc. Petrol. Geol. Bull.*, v. 49, no. 11, pp. 1926-1956.

Stewart, J. H., and Poole, F. G., 1974, Lower Paleozoic and uppermost Precambrian Cordilleran miogeosyncline, Great Basin, western United States, in Dickinson, E. R., ed., *Tectonics and sedimentation*: Soc. Econ. Paleontologists and Mineralogists Spec. Paper 22, pp. 28-57.

3. *Structure of Eastern Part of Main Cordillera*

Armstrong, F. C., and Oriel, S. S., 1965, Tectonic development of Idaho-Wyoming thrust belt: *Am. Assoc. Petrol. Geol. Bull.*, v. 49, no. 11, pp. 1849-1866.

Armstrong, R. L., 1968, Sevier orogenic belt in Nevada and Utah: *Geol. Soc. America Bull.*, v. 79, no. 4, pp. 429-458.

Bally, A. W., Gordy, P. L., and Stewart, G. A., 1966, Structure, seismic data, and orogenic evolution of southern Canadian Rocky Mountains: *Canadian Petrol. Geol. Bull.*, v. 14, no. 3, pp. 337-381.

Burchfiel, B. C., and Davis, G. A., 1972, Structural framework and evolution of the southern part of the Cordilleran orogen, western United States: *Am. Jour. Sci.*, v. 271, no. 2, pp. 97-118.

———, 1975, Nature and controls of Cordilleran orogenesis, western United States; extensions of an earlier synthesis: *Am. Jour. Sci.*, v. 275-A (John Rodgers Volume), pp. 363-396.

Crittenden, M. D., Jr., 1961, *Magnitude of thrust faulting in northern Utah*: U.S. Geol. Survey Prof. Paper 424-D, pp. 128-131.

Daly, R. A., 1912, *Geology of the North American Cordillera at the forty-ninth parallel*: Canada Geol. Survey Mem. 38, 799 p.

Hewett, D. F., 1931, *Geology and ore deposits of the Goodsprings quadrangle, Nevada*: U.S. Geol. Survey Prof. Paper 162.

Longwell, C. R., 1949, Structure of the northern Muddy Mountains area, Nevada: *Geol. Soc. America Bull.*, v. 60, no. 5, pp. 923-968.

Misch, Peter, 1960, Regional structural reconnaissance of central-northeast Nevada and some adjacent areas; observations and interpretations: Intermountain Assoc. Geol. 11th Ann. Field Conf., *Guidebook to the geology of east-central Nevada*, pp. 17-42.

Price, R. A., and Mountjoy, E. W., 1970, Geologic structure of the Canadian Rocky Mountains; a progress report, *in* Wheeler, J. O., ed., *Structure of the southern Canadian Cordillera*: Geol. Assoc. Canada Spec. Paper 6, pp. 7-25.

Robinson, G. D., Klepper, M. R., and Obradovich, J. D., 1968, Overlapping plutonism, volcanism, and tectonism in the Boulder batholith region, *in* Coats, R. R., Hay, R. I., and Anderson, C. A., eds., *Studies in volcanology*: Geol. Soc. America Mem. 116, pp. 557-576.

Willis, Bailey, 1902, Stratigraphy and structure, Lewis and Livingston Ranges, Montana: *Geol. Soc. America Bull.*, v. 15, pp. 305-352.

4. *Cordilleran Eugeosyncline and Structures That Formed From It*

Bateman, P. C., and Wahrhaftig, Clyde, 1966, Geology of the Sierra Nevada, in Bailey, E. H., ed., *Geology of northern California*: California Div. Mines and Geol. Bull., v. 190, pp. 107-172.

Clark, L. D., 1964, *Stratigraphy and structure of part of the west-ern Sierra Nevada metamorphic belt, California*: U.S. Geol. Survey Prof. Paper 410.

Evernden, J. F., and Kistler, R. W., 1970, *Chronology of emplacement of Mesozoic batholithic complex in California and western Nevada*: U.S. Geol. Survey Prof. Paper 623.

Hotz, P. E., 1971, *Geology of the lode gold deposits in the Klamath Mountains, California and Oregon*: U.S. Geol. Survey Bull. 1290.

Misch, Peter, 1966, Tectonic evolution of the northern Cascades in Washington State: a west Cordilleran case history, *in Tectonic history of mineral deposits of the western Cordillera*: Canadian Inst. Min. and Metall. Spec. Vol. 8, pp. 101-148.

Roberts, R. J., Hotz, P. E., Gilluly, James, and Ferguson, H. G., 1958, Paleozoic rocks of north-central Nevada: *Am. Assoc. Petroleum Geol. Bull.*, v. 42, pp. 2813-2857.

Schweiker, R. A., and Cowan, D. S., 1975, Early Mesozoic tectonic evolution of the western Sierra Nevada, California: *Geol. Soc. America Bull.*, v. 86, no. 10, pp. 1329-1336.

Silberling, N. J., 1973, Geologic events during Permian-Triassic time along the Pacific margin of the United States, *in* Logan, A. and Hills, L. V., eds., *The Permian and Triassic systems and their mutual boundary*: Canadian Soc. Petrol. Geol., pp. 345-362.

Silberling, N. J., and Roberts, R. J., 1962, *Pre-Tertiary stratigraphy and structure of northwestern Nevada*: Geol. Soc. America Spec. Paper 72.

CHAPTER IX

CENOZOIC ROCKS AND STRUCTURES OF THE MAIN PART OF THE CORDILLERA; LATER MODIFICATIONS OF THE FUNDAMENTAL STRUCTURE

1. YOUTHFUL STRUCTURES AND TOPOGRAPHY

The remainder of this book will be devoted primarily to those Tertiary and Quaternary modifications that have so greatly changed the aspect of the western part of the Cordillera after the great deformations of Mesozoic and Paleozoic time, creating the modern landscape and the topographic mountains we see today.

We have already discussed such modifications in the Eastern Ranges and Plateaus (Chapter VII, section 7), where the low-standing ranges and basins that existed at the close of the Laramide orogeny were transformed into the present lofty mountains, plateaus, and plains. This was accomplished in part by folding and faulting later than the main deformation, but to a much larger extent by a great regional upwarp, shared not only by the Rocky Mountains but by the Great Plains on the east and the Colorado Plateau on the west. Differentiation of mountains, plateaus, and plains was thus primarily a result of etching out of the upwarped rocks by erosion.

In that part of the Cordillera west of the Eastern Ranges and Plateaus, the later modifications of the fundamental structure were more varied, and crustal activity manifested itself not only regionally but locally—by folding and faulting of the rocks and by construction of volcanic plateaus and mountains. Here a great number of modern topographic features are the direct result of crustal forces and only to a lesser degree the result of erosion and sedimentation.

2. BASIN AND RANGE PROVINCE

Drainage, topography, and structure. The first of the younger features we will discuss will be those of the Basin and Range province, some of which were given passing mention in earlier chapters. Before going further, however, we should clarify our terminology and keep in mind the distinctions between:

(a) The *Great Basin* or region of interior drainage, from which no streams flow to the sea, and which occupies much of Nevada and adjacent parts of Utah, Oregon, and California.

(b) The *Basin and Range province*, which includes not only the Great Basin, but also extensive regions of exterior drainage on the south and southeast in southern Arizona, much of New Mexico, and parts of western Texas.

(c) *Basin and Range topography*, or the characteristic landscape of the Basin and Range province—the peculiar, sub-parallel ranges and intervening desert basins whose appearance on the map suggested to Major Dutton "an army of caterpillars crawling northward out of Mexico."

(d) *Basin and Range structure*, or later deformations of the crust that influenced or produced the Basin and Range topography (Fig. 96). To some extent the topography is a product of the erosion of a deformed terrane, but to a greater extent than in most regions it appears to be a direct product of the deformation itself.

In some areas all four of these terms are applicable; in others, only one or two. Much of Nevada possesses an interior drainage of Great Basin type as well as topography and structure of Basin and Range type; its interior drainage is due to some extent to its topography and structure, but quite as much to its scanty rainfall and remoteness from the sea. Wide areas to the south and southeast with Basin and Range topography are not part of the Great Basin and are drained to the sea by tributaries of the Colorado River and Rio Grande. Fi-

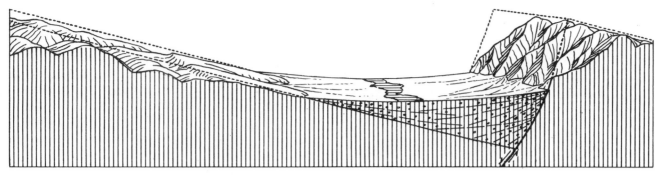

FIG. 96. Block diagram showing typical topography of the Basin and Range province and the block-faulting believed to have shaped it. After W. M. Davis (1927).

nally, many areas of Basin and Range topography have been so greatly eroded that there is no means of determining the original Basin and Range structure, whatever it may have been.

It is well to bear in mind also that the characteristic topography (and probably the structure, too) of the Basin and Range province has been superposed on a variety of earlier rocks and structures. In the Great Basin it was superposed on eugeosynclinal and miogeosynclinal rocks that were strongly deformed by the Cordilleran orogenies; in New Mexico it was superposed on rocks that were laid down on the continental platform and only lightly deformed later (compare the complex internal structures of the ranges in Fig. 94 with the simple internal structures of the ranges in Fig. 80). In southeastern Oregon it involves at the surface only Tertiary and later volcanic rocks, and the nature of the rocks and structures beneath them is unknown. Basin and Range topography and structure were thus not a necessary sequel of any particular sort of fundamental Cordilleran structure; the structures on which they were superposed are diverse.

INTERPRETATION OF BASIN AND RANGE TOPOGRAPHY AND STRUCTURE. Origin of Basin and Range topography and its structural implications have long been debated among geologists; the question has sometimes been dignified as the "Basin Range problem."

Many geologists, including Clarence King's men of the Fortieth Parallel Survey, remarked on the strong deformation of the rocks in the ranges—especially in the Great Basin and to a lesser extent elsewhere—and concluded that the topography is merely an effect of erosion working on deformed rocks in an arid climate. It was thus assumed that, if folded and faulted rocks such as those in the Valley and Ridge province of the Appalachians were placed in such a climate, erosion would wear down parts of them into desert basins and leave other parts projecting as discontinuous mountain ranges.

To some extent this is so, but not wholly, for in many places folds and faults within the ranges strike out to their edges, where they are cut off; their extensions must lie beneath the basins. Yet where the basins have been entrenched by rivers such as the Colorado and Rio

Grande, it may be seen that these are thickly filled by Tertiary and Quaternary sediments laid down in troughs much like the present ones. It would appear, therefore, that some other structure has been interposed between the Cordilleran structures exposed in the mountains and the modern topography of ranges and basins.

G. K. Gilbert, whose work for the Powell Survey we have already noted (Chapter VI, section 3), early suggested a probable explanation: that the ranges were bordered on one or both sides by faults that have raised or rotated them in relatively recent geologic time and depressed the intervening basins. Basin and range topography would thus have been caused directly by late Tertiary and Quaternary faulting, whose effects are still manifest in the modern landscape.

Somewhat later William Morris Davis, the great geomorphologist, followed the ideas suggested by Gilbert and systematized these heterogeneous observations into a sequence (Fig. 97):

(A) The King formations (named for Clarence King of the Fortieth Parallel Survey), or the sequences of stratified rocks of the region, primarily of Paleozoic and Mesozoic ages.

(B) The King folds (also named for King), or the deformed structures produced by the Cordilleran orogenies.

(C) The Powell surface (named for J. W. Powell, whose survey demonstrated the far-reaching effects of denudation in the Cordillera), or the erosion surface developed on the deformed terrane after the orogeny.

(D) The Louderbacks (named for G. D. Louderback of the University of California, who made significant observations in the Great Basin), or the Tertiary and Quaternary lavas which were spread as thin to thick sheets over the eroded surfaces of the earlier rocks.

(E) The Gilbert fault blocks (named for G. K. Gilbert), into which all these prior features were broken later in geologic time.

This outline is useful as a statement of the general manner in which successive features of the Basin and Range province were superposed on each other, but one should keep in mind that it is an extreme simplification

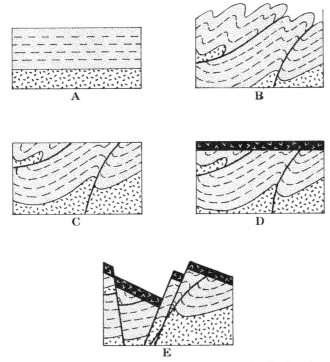

FIG. 97. Diagrams showing the sequence of features that developed in the Basin and Range province, as postulated by W. M. Davis: (A) The King formations. (B) The King folds. (C) The Powell surface. (D) The Louderbacks. (E) The Gilbert fault blocks.

of diverse features that developed through a long period of time over a very wide area. The Davis sequence may very well apply in its entirety in a few areas and be only partly represented in others. In most of the ranges the neatly pigeon-holed categories are overlapped and blended.

A similar comment applies to the criticisms of the theories of Gilbert and Davis, of which there have been many. Neither the theory itself nor the alternative explanations can be wholly right or wholly wrong, for many sorts of structures and land forms are found from one part of the Basin and Range province to another. We can accept these as facts, yet we may find it necessary to reject at least some of the large generalizations that have been built upon them.

FAULTS ALONG EDGES OF RANGES. Gilbert conceived of his explanation when engaged in his early exploration of the West for the Wheeler Survey, when he did not have an opportunity to study closely the bedrock structure of the ranges. He therefore inferred the structure that produced the ranges very largely from the topographic forms—a procedure that was novel at the time.

The novelty of the method aroused much skepticism among geologists; the skeptics pointed out that numerous faults could be observed within the ranges that had no direct relation to the topography, and that if great faults actually bordered the ranges they were concealed by alluvial deposits along their bases. Some of the skep-

tics challenged anyone to find actual exposures of a fault that blocked out a range or that had aided in producing the present topography.

We now know, however, that faulting has gone on for a very long period in the Basin and Range province—in fact, from the time of the Cordilleran orogenies during the Mesozoic down to the present. Sequences of faulting vary from one area to another, in places ending well back in the Tertiary, in others continuing until the present time; some of this faulting accords with the classic concept of Basin and Range structure, some does not. Obviously, direct topographic effects of the older faults would have been obliterated long since by erosion, and the effects would become progressively greater the younger the fault (Fig. 98).

In parts of the region, as in southern Arizona and the Mojave Desert of California, blocking out of the ranges must have been an ancient event that was little renewed recently. Here most of the ranges are zigzag spiny ridges that have been deeply frayed and embayed by erosion (Fig. 98C, D, and E). The plains around many of them are erosional surfaces (or pediments) produced by the wearing down of the same rocks as those which form the mountains. The plains in some other areas are covered by Quaternary or later Tertiary sediments that overlap the edges of the ranges without an intervening fault at the surface. If any block-faulting shaped ranges such as these, it must have been at a time so remote that the original block form has been destroyed by erosion. As the original form of the range has been destroyed, it may well have been something quite different from a set of fault blocks.

Nevertheless, many other ranges throughout the Basin and Range province are actually block-like, do possess straight, steep edges on one or both sides that do cut across structures produced by earlier deformations where such ranges consist of deformed rocks (Fig. 98A and B).

Despite the skeptics, faults have been proved along the edges of many of the ranges. In places, little hills of bedrock project from the desert basins and consist of the same rocks as those that occur high up in the adjacent ranges; they demonstrate that the bedrock beneath has been so depressed that only the highest parts are still visible as "islands" nearly submerged by the basin deposits. Some of these hills lie close to, or even against the lower part of the bedrock of the range scarp, with a contact so abrupt that it can only be the result of faulting rather than of folding or warping.

If a geologist is fortunate enough to discover such a locality, he may also be able to observe the actual fault contact between the bedrock of the range and the hill in the basin. Moreover, at some other places where no bedrock hills are present, renewal of range uplift has brought the bordering fault into view, with bedrock

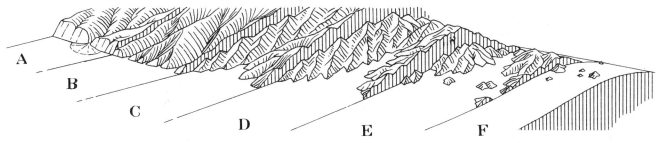

FIG. 98. Block diagram showing stages of erosion of a mountain in the Basin and Range province. An initial fault-block form is assumed in stage A, but succeeding stages might have developed from any initial tectonic form. (A) Fan-free and fan-based. (B) Fan-dented. (C) Fan-bayed. (D) Fan-frayed. (E) Fan-wrapped. (F) Pan-fan. After Davis (1925).

moved up against the Quaternary and Tertiary deposits that had been shed off the range after the earlier and greater period of block-faulting. In many places, too, the basin deposits themselves are faulted close to the range fronts and are stepped up toward them in little fault scarps; some of these scarps can be related directly to recorded earthquakes.

The faults that have been observed along the edges of the ranges dip toward the basins or downthrown blocks and are therefore normal faults. Their dip is generally much steeper than the slope of the range escarpment behind; this is to be expected, as an exposed fault scarp will be worn back by erosion until it reaches the angle of repose for the material in transit across it. The highest part of the scarp, being first to emerge, will have been eroded longest and worn back farthest; the lower part, which emerged later, will be less eroded; if it has been uplifted recently and rapidly enough, its slope may not yet have attained erosional equilibrium.

FAULT SCARPS VERSUS FAULT-LINE SCARPS. Modern critics of the theories of Gilbert and Davis have generally conceded the existence of great faults along the margins of the ranges. They have objected, however, that the range fronts were not direct products of deformation or fault scarps, but were produced by removal of weak beds from the downthrown sides by erosion, hence are fault-line scarps.

The critics point out that many of the features that have been interpreted as evidence for direct tectonic control of the scarps could have been produced as well by erosional processes. Also, many of the plains that slope away from the bases of the scarps, which have been considered depositional surfaces, are actually erosional surfaces or pediments cut on the edges of more or less deformed Tertiary deposits. It is even conceivable that the basins were once filled by poorly resistant Tertiary deposits to the levels of the intervening mountain tops and that they have since been excavated by erosion.

Where rivers such as the Colorado and Rio Grande cross the Basin and Range province, the basin deposits have been planed off by erosion so that their original depositional surfaces have been destroyed. But in nearby basins with interior drainage the surfaces of the deposits have remained depositional; in these, where no streams have flowed out for a long period, it seems unlikely that any extensive excavation and removal of material could have been accomplished. It is true that the earlier deposits of most of the basins have been deformed, especially near the edges of the mountains, but the basins did not become stable afterward as many are broken by fresh scarplets near or along their edges.

Thus, the fault-line scarp hypothesis of Basin and Range topography and structure does not alter their essential nature; if valid, the hypothesis moves the time of formation of the gross features farther back into the past. The chief virtue of the explanation is to emphasize that understanding of the Basin Range problem cannot be attained from the present aspect of the region alone, but requires knowledge of how its features evolved through time.

EVOLUTION OF GREAT BASIN AREA. Let us, therefore, examine the evolution of Basin and Range topography and structure since the time of the Cordilleran orogenies. To illustrate this it will be profitable to sample the history of one area where many data are available—the Great Basin area between the Colorado Plateau and the Sierra Nevada.

In doing so we will find that deposits were laid down on the lower parts of the surface during a considerable span of Tertiary time, during which the geography evolved as a result of continued crustal movements. Earlier deposits were derived from uplands different from those of the present ranges in form and even in position; as these deposits appear now only in fragments, it is not easy to decipher the geography under which they were formed. With further movements the earlier deposits were faulted, uplifted, and eroded, and those in which resistant lavas were embedded were raised in places to mountainous heights. Later Tertiary and Quaternary deposits bear a closer relation to modern geography, yet even these are more or less deformed and eroded.

The fragmentary record of earlier Tertiary (Paleocene and Eocene) time suggests that the eastern half of the Great Basin received deposits in lakes, swamps, and floodplains that were probably westward extensions of those in the Rocky Mountain region, and like them, they stood at altitudes of only 300 meters or so above sea level. The western half of the Great Basin and the Sierra Nevada beyond was a low upland. The marine Ione Formation deposited along the western edge of the highland in California contains clays of remarkable purity, evidently carried westward by sluggish streams from a worn down and deeply decayed surface of unroofed Nevadan plutonic rocks. By early Tertiary time the topography that had developed on the site of the Great Basin from orogenically deformed miogeosynclinal and eugeosynclinal rocks had thus become decadent, but the basins and ranges of later time had not yet developed; much of the region apparently possessed an exterior drainage.

Volcanic activity began in the Great Basin during the Oligocene. The older, mainly andesitic lavas are much disturbed and mineralized, and are the hosts of the fabulously rich *Comstock Lode* of the Virginia City district. Later, during the Miocene and Pliocene, the central part of the Great Basin was the scene of gigantic silicic eruptions from a succession of calderas that spread out extensive sheets of ignimbrite. These highly mobile ash flows spread like water far over the landscape, which must have had a nearly level surface, and they now form successions of well-bedded, resistant units that can be matched from one range to another. Their present occurrence at diverse structural levels, including mountain tops, indicate that most of the present Basin and Range topography and structure was produced after the late Miocene (about 17 million years ago).

Fossil plants occur in many places in the late Miocene and early Pliocene volcaniclastic sediments; these provide a good index of the geography, as they are enough like modern forms to have lived in environments of similar altitude and rainfall. In places on the crest of the Sierra Nevada, at present at altitudes of 2,700 meters, are late Miocene deciduous plants that could not have lived higher than 750 meters; in the Great Basin at about the same time were coniferous forests like those that now grow at the margins of woodland and chaparral country. The environments indicated by the different plant assemblages suggest that the crest of the Sierra Nevada stood at altitudes less than 900 meters, with the Great Basin about 300 meters lower. The ridge of the Sierra Nevada created no more than an ineffective rain shadow over the country to the east, and was evidently crossed in many places by streams draining to the Pacific from headwaters well back in the Great Basin.

Later in the Pliocene the floras of the Great Basin changed to a savanna and grassland assemblage, adapted to less than 38 centimeters of rainfall. The Sierra Nevada block was now being uplifted and exerted a climatic influence over the region to the east. Uplift continued into Pleistocene time until the block had been raised 1,500 to 1,800 meters in the north and 2,300 to 2,700 meters in

the south. At the same time the Great Basin was being disrupted by block-faulting, which disturbed not only the Paleozoic and Mesozoic bedrock, but the Tertiary deposits as well. From Pliocene into Pleistocene time the basin floors were raised from altitudes of less than 600 meters to their modern altitudes of 900 to 1,600 meters.

This record indicates that the western part of the Cordillera—in contrast to the Rocky Mountains, where much of the regional uplift had been accomplished by mid-Tertiary time—remained low until late in the Tertiary, after which, in Pliocene and Pleistocene time, it likewise underwent regional uplift as well as major block-faulting.

ABSOLUTE UPLIFT VERSUS ABSOLUTE DEPRESSION. The odd structures that have developed in the Basin and Range region in the near past arouse our curiosity and stimulate our speculation. Before speculating, however, let us explore a question that bears considerably on their origin: What were the actual movements of the basins and ranges?

Obvious movements in the region were, of course, the uplift of the ranges and depression of the basins, but these movements were relative. Actual movements may have been the same, or they may have been something quite different in relation to a sea-level datum—for example, subsidence of the whole region with the basins going down the most, or uplift of the whole region with the ranges raised the farthest.

There is, nevertheless, much evidence for an absolute depression of some of the basins and an absolute uplift of some of the ranges. The floor of Death Valley now lies 86 meters below sea level, and recent geophysical work indicates that it is underlain by about 2,100 meters of basin deposits; its floor must have been lowered far below its original level—so far that subsequent filling never caught up with its subsidence. On the other hand, mountains at the edge of the Basin and Range province—the Sierra Nevada, the Wasatch Mountains, and the eastern of the New Mexico ranges—are hinged on more stable crustal blocks and were absolutely uplifted above the remainder of these blocks. Even well within the Basin and Range province some of the mountains project higher than they ever could at an earlier period; the Ruby Range in the Great Basin near Elko, Nevada, rises to heights of 3,459 meters, with landscapes as alpine as those in the Sierra Nevada, and the Snake Range to the southeast projects to 3,980 meters; even if the surroundings of these ranges had risen as a unit the ranges themselves were forced still higher.

Clues as to the regional behavior of at least the Great Basin part of the Basin and Range province are afforded by its Tertiary history, which we have already outlined. Evidently the Great Basin has not subsided as a whole since the Cordilleran orogenies, but has been raised—

160

the basins from a position 300 meters or so above sea level in early Tertiary time to more than 1,500 meters today, and the ranges still higher.

In the Great Basin part of the province regional uplift must have been accompanied by broad arching. The explorer Frémont remarked on the fact that the modern lakes of the Great Basin are at its eastern and western edges in Utah and western Nevada—an effect heightened during Pleistocene time when the now-vanished *Lake Bonneville* and *Lake Lahontan* were spread even more widely over the same areas. In the central Great Basin of eastern Nevada, even the basin floors stand nearly 600 meters higher than those along the edges, and the crests of the Ruby and Snake Ranges attain the greatest heights in the Great Basin.

These relations are underscored by the distribution of earthquake epicenters (Fig. 99). Numerous earthquakes, some of large magnitude, have occurred in western Nevada, from the front of the Sierra Nevada to about the center of the state. Another belt of earthquake epicenters extends along the western edge of the Colorado Plateau from southern Utah north past the Wasatch Mountains, and thence into the Northern Rocky Mountains nearly to the International Boundary. By contrast, eastern Nevada and western Utah are nearly without epicenters. The earthquake record indicates that modern crustal activity is concentrated at the eastern and western edges of the Great Basin, and that the central part has nearly attained stability today.

CRUSTAL STRUCTURE. What of the substructure of the Basin and Range province? The deep crustal layers of the Great Basin have been probed recently by seismic-refraction surveys and indicate some anomalous relations. The Sierra Nevada to the west has a deep root, 40 to 50 kilometers thick, and the crust beneath the Colorado Plateau to the east is 40 kilometers thick, but in the intervening Great Basin it is 30 kilometers thick or less—unusually thin for a continental area. However, a considerable thickness of the upper mantle beneath the Great Basin has a lower velocity and lower density than normal, with seismic velocities of less than 8 kilometers per second. How far these peculiar crustal properties extend into other parts of the Basin and Range province has not been determined from seismic surveys so far available.

ORIGIN OF BASIN AND RANGE STRUCTURE. Let us now speculate on possible mechanisms of the formation of Basin and Range structure.

The normal faults that border the ranges, and that are an essential item of their structure, are a product of tension rather than of compression, or of extension rather than shortening of the crust. It has been estimated that this extension has widened the Great Basin by 100 kilometers or more. How does this regional tension relate to the other deformational forces that were active at the same time in other parts of the western Cordillera?

We have learned that during the Cordilleran orogenies the Basin and Range province was being deformed by compressional forces. With the close of these orogenies compression relaxed, and it was long believed that extensional faulting such as that in the province was a necessary sequel to the orogenic cycle. Some of the earlier geologists even proposed that the Cordilleran orogenies produced a great arch in the Great Basin, and that during relaxation the arch collapsed, its parts subsiding into a mosaic of fault blocks. But an arch of the implied breadth and height seems so incredible that no geologist today believes that it ever existed. Besides, as we have seen, the Tertiary record implies that the region as a whole has risen steadily, rather than subsided. Also, the supposed collapse, if it occurred, took place nearly 50 million years after the compressional climax. The compressional deformation is so far separated in time from the extensional faulting that they can hardly have been part of the same process, but the latter must have originated from a new set of forces that came into existence late in the history of the western Cordillera.

Later on, it was proposed that the Basin and Range structure was a continental expression of the East Pacific Rise, or belt of sea-floor spreading in the eastern Pacific Ocean basin, which was known to approach the North American continent, and seemingly enter it at the lower end of the Gulf of California. However, it is now believed that the East Pacific Rise is cut off in the Gulf of California by a system of transform faults, of which the San Andreas fault is a major component, and does not reappear in the Pacific Ocean basin until north of Cape Mendocino in northern California.

Instead, the extensional Basin and Range faulting appears to be a manifestation of a regional right-lateral shift of all the western part of the Cordillera by interaction with the Pacific Ocean plate to the west. A major expression of this is the right-lateral shift along the San Andreas and related faults, which amounts to hundreds of kilometers (see section 4 of this chapter), but the effects are felt to a somewhat lesser degree eastward as far as the edge of the Colorado Plateau.

One result of this is the occurrence in the Great Basin, along with the extensional block-faults, of strike-slip faults of moderate displacement. The map relations of the block-faulted ranges in the Great Basin and elsewhere in the Basin and Range province reveal intriguing variations in pattern, not all of which are readily explainable. Over wide tracts of country successive ranges are parallel in one direction, but in adjacent tracts the parallel ranges trend in some other direction (Fig. 100). In some of the zones where the changes occur, strike-slip faults can be proved.

Thus, in eastern California between the Sierra Nevada and Death Valley, the ranges trend north-northwest,

161

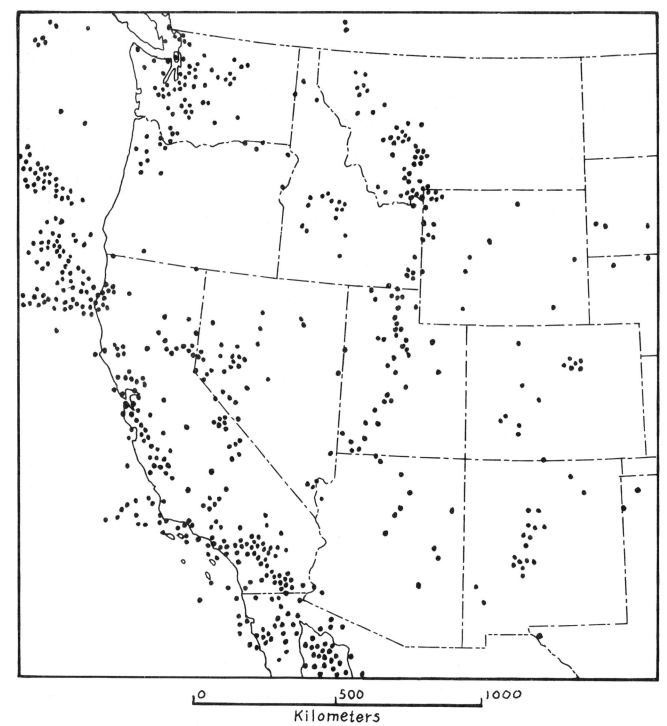

FIG. 99. Map of western United States, showing distribution of earthquake epicenters. The map shows all major earthquakes recorded between 1865 and 1965. The strong seismicity of the west coastal area is obvious, but note also the significant concentration of epicenters in the eastern and western parts of the Great Basin, and their near absence in its central part. After National Atlas (1970), sheet 66-67; data for north-western Mexico and the offshore areas from other sources.

whereas in western Nevada all the ranges trend consistently north-northeast. The intervening zone contains the Death Valley fault zone, and a set of structures about 50 kilometers farther east termed the Walker Lane that extends southeastward into the Las Vegas shear zone. Cumulative right-lateral offsets of geologic features on these structures amounts to more than 150 kilometers, partly by strike-slip faulting, partly by oroflexural bending. Another change in trend of the ranges occurs farther east, so that in eastern Nevada and western Utah all of them extend north-south. The nature of the boundary between this tract and that to the west is obscure, but

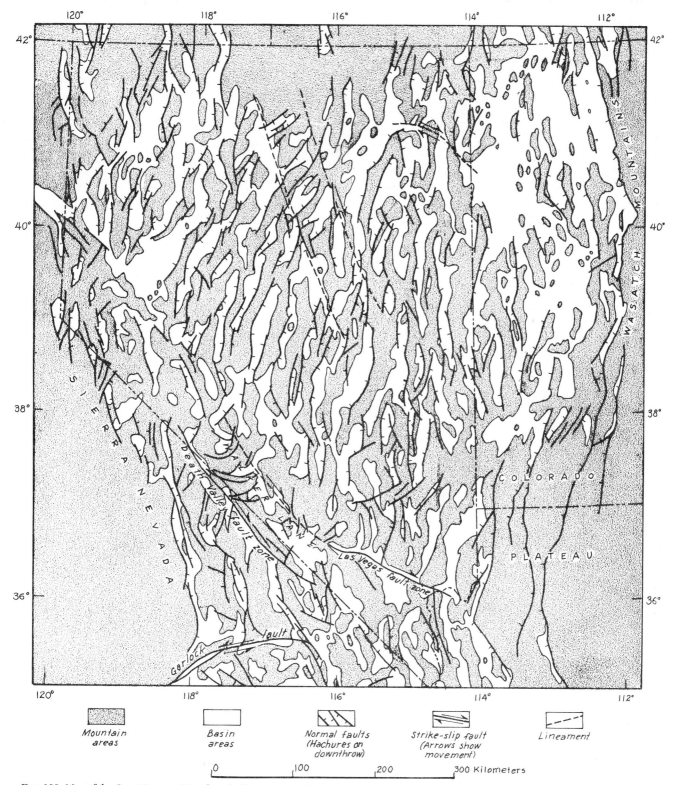

Fig. 100. Map of the Great Basin in Nevada and adjacent states, showing the extent and trends of ranges and basins, the positions of faults
that separate them, and the position of proved or possible zones of
strike-slip movement. Compiled from Geologic Map of United
States (1974).

163

may be a zone of oroflexural bending rather than observable strike-slip faulting. A further change occurs in southeastern California, where the north-northwest-trending ranges are terminated southward along the east-trending Garlock fault with left-lateral displacement, beyond which in the Mojave Desert the ranges trend in diverse directions without consistent pattern. These features are mentioned merely as examples; others undoubtedly exist, both here and elsewhere in the Basin and Range province.

Tensional block-faulting and right-lateral strike-slip faulting both appear to be components of the regional right-lateral shift of the western part of the Cordillera in relation to the North American continental block during the latter part of Cenozoic time.

3. NORTHWESTERN VOLCANIC PROVINCE

VOLCANIC MODIFICATIONS OF FUNDAMENTAL STRUCTURE. We will now consider another sort of modification of fundamental Cordilleran structure—one produced by volcanism, and specifically the volcanism of Tertiary and Quaternary time—which has formed a mighty body of rocks and structures in the northwestern states of Oregon and Washington and contiguous parts of Idaho and California.

We have already discussed the modifications resulting from volcanism in the Eastern Ranges and Plateaus—local volcanic fields of long or short duration in various stages of destruction by erosion and their associated stocks, dikes, and laccoliths. But these are intermingled with other features of various kinds and ages and are merely an incidental part of the total structure.

In Oregon and Washington, by contrast, volcanic rocks and structures dominate the scene—lava plateaus, volcanic cones, and eruptive ranges produced by upbuilding, and folded or block-faulted ranges produced by deformation of the volcanic materials. In these states no rocks older than the Cenozoic volcanics and sediments are exposed in an area extending 500 kilometers parallel with the coast and 650 kilometers inland; volcanic rocks also cover an even greater area to the south and southeast where older rocks emerge in places (Fig. 101). The volcanic regime was prolonged and extended through most of Tertiary and Quaternary time from one place to another. Nothing comparable to this great volcanic area occurs elsewhere in North America, except far to the south in Mexico and Central America (Plate I).

SUBDIVISIONS OF VOLCANIC PROVINCE. Broader topographic features of the northwestern province are not unlike those of the southwestern province, in California and Nevada. Backbone of the province, with its highest peaks, is the Cascade Range, which is set well back from the coast like the Sierra Nevada. Along the coast is a lower Coast Range, and between this and the Cascade Range is a belt of depressions that remind us of the Great

Valley of California. East of the Cascade Range is lower country, broadly termed the Columbia Plateaus, in the same position as the Great Basin.

Geologically, however, differences between the topographically analogous features are so great as to lead one to suspect that the resemblances are no more than coincidence. If the features in the two regions were produced by the same forces, these have worked on materials so unlike that they have expressed themselves in a very different manner.

The *Coast Ranges* of Oregon and Washington begin on the south at the edge of the Klamath Mountains and terminate on the north at the latitude of Seattle in the Olympic Peninsula. Most of the Coast Ranges are low; their highest peaks in the *Olympic Mountains* attain only 2,428 meters, although the latter support snow fields and local glaciers because of their northern position. The Coast Ranges consist primarily of broadly folded early to middle Tertiary sediments with interbedded basaltic lavas; in Oregon they form a single anticlinorium, but in Washington their trend is crossed by southeast-trending warps creating a succession of mountain knots and intervening sags.

Between the Coast and Cascade Ranges is a partly discontinuous belt of topographic depressions, forming the *Puget Trough* in Washington and the *Willamette Valley* in Oregon, which have a general synclinal structure.

The *Cascade Range* is a belt of lofty peaks and rugged mountain ridges that originates on the south between the Sierra Nevada and Klamath Mountains in California and extends northward beyond the International Boundary. Its highest summits are great volcanic cones built up late in geologic time on a foundation of earlier rocks and structures. One of these cones, Lassen Peak, erupted in 1914; another, Mount St. Helens, erupted only 2,500 years ago; the others are probably merely dormant. The highest cone, Mount Rainier, attains an altitude of 4,392 meters, or only a little short of the highest summits of the Sierra Nevada and Rocky Mountains.

From central Washington northward, the Cascade Range is formed of an emerged basement that was metamorphosed and plutonized during Nevadan and subsequent Mesozoic orogenies, but southward this is buried beneath an increasing thickness of Eocene to Pliocene rocks, mainly andesitic volcanics (Fig. 102). The volcanic part of the range owes its height partly to upwarping, partly to excessive upbuilding.

East of the Cascade Range are the broad, diversified *Columbia Plateaus*. The *Columbia Plateau proper* is that part in southeastern Washington and northeastern Oregon which is overspread by middle Tertiary basaltic lava, parts of which have been so little deformed as to produce a plateau topography. At the southeast edge of this area in northeastern Oregon the basalts and associated Tertiary strata have been raised in a chain of folds and uplifts

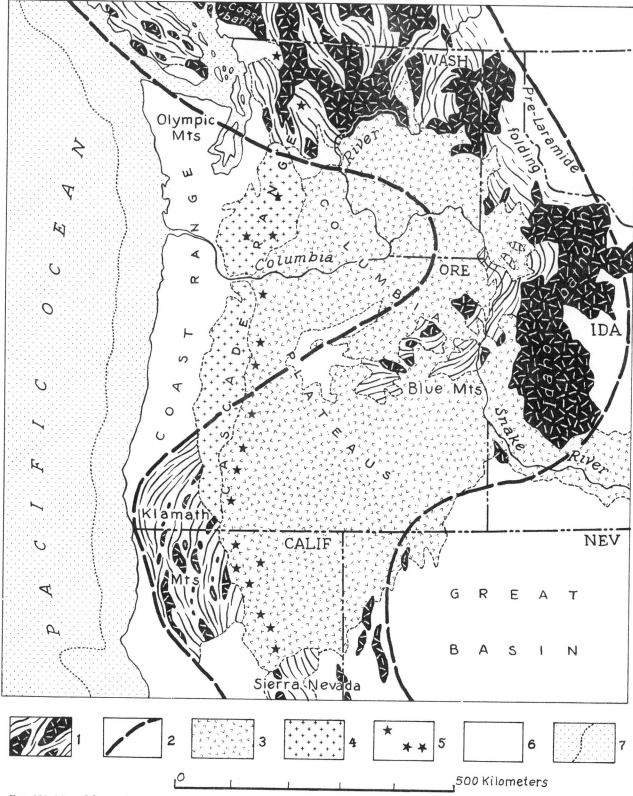

Fɪɢ. 101. Map of the northwestern volcanic province of Washington, Oregon, and adjacent states, showing its relation to the Columbia arc. Data from Geologic Map of United States (1974).

Explanation of symbols: 1–Basement rocks deformed by Nevadan orogeny; metamorphic rocks lined, plutonic rocks solid. 2–Inferred margins of Nevadan orogenic belt. 3–Plateau basalts of Miocene and later age. 4–Andesitic volcanics of Cascade Range. 5–Volcanic cones of Cascade Range, mostly of Quaternary age. 6–Other rocks; mainly sedimentary rocks of Mesozoic and Tertiary ages, but including some older Tertiary volcanics. 7–Edge of continental area.

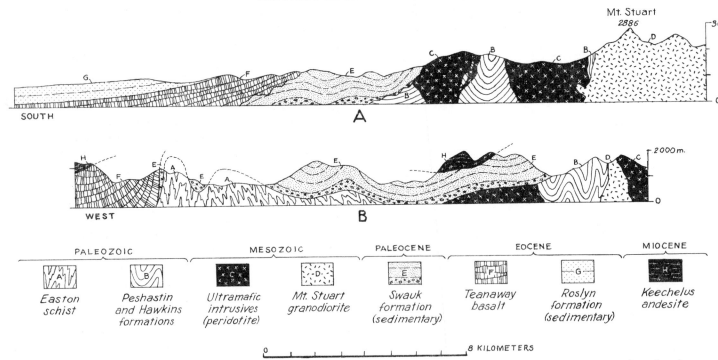

FIG. 102. Sections showing relations between the Tertiary sedimentary and volcanic rocks of the northern Cascade Range and their Mesozoic and Paleozoic basement. Sections are on southeast side of the range in central Washington. After Smith (1904) and Smith and Calkins (1906).

trending west-southwest, in which basement rocks have been revealed by erosion in the *Blue Mountains* and nearby highlands (Fig. 101). The basement rocks, as we have seen (Chapter VIII, section 4), are an emerged segment on the southeast side of the Columbia arc between the Klamath Mountains on the southwest and the highlands in Idaho on the northeast. Upwarp of the Tertiary rocks represents a renewal of movement along the same trend.

Volcanic rocks continue beyond these uplifts into southeastern Oregon and adjacent states, forming a region that has sometimes been called the *Malheur Plateaus*, composed of more varied rocks and structures than the Columbia Plateau proper. The volcanics here are mainly younger than those farther northwest; to the south they are involved in the block-faulting of the Basin and Range province.

Eastward these younger volcanics fill the great transverse downwarp of the *Snake River Plain*, extending as a transverse rift nearly across the Cordillera, which we mentioned briefly earlier (Chapter VIII, section 3).

FOUNDATION OF THE VOLCANIC PROVINCE. What was the cause of this remarkable localization of volcanic rocks and structures in the northwestern states? No doubt the answers are to be found in the basement rocks on which the volcanics lie, but little information on these is available except in "islands" of the older rocks that emerge in uplifts like the Blue Mountains.

The volcanic activity may be related to the great *Columbia arc* of the Nevadan orogenic belt, which we have

inferred extends from northern Washington through central Idaho and the Blue Mountains into the Klamath Mountains (Fig. 101). This arc is reflected in the Tertiary cover—by west-northwest-trending folds that cross the Cascade and Olympic Mountains of northwestern Washington, and by west-southwest-trending folds near the Blue Mountains of northeastern Oregon.

An intriguing question arises: Could the western edge of the Columbia arc have formed the continental border until late in Mesozoic time, before which the recess was floored by oceanic rather than continental crust? If so, the recess was later made continental by filling with sediments and volcanics, and the coast was straightened by growth of a new set of volcanic structures along the Cascade Range. Some geologists have even suggested that the Nevadan orogenic belt was originally formed in a nearly north-south course along the western side of the continent, and that it was oroclinally bent early in the Tertiary into the Columbia arc with its recess of oceanic crust. But this would have produced such incredible distortions of the adjacent western part of the continent that I find it difficult to accept until confirmatory evidence is obtained.

THE BORDERLAND OF "CASCADIA." The possible occurrence of oceanic crust in the recess of the Columbia arc is at variance with the theory that now-vanished borderlands once existed off the edges of the present continent. We have already set forth objections to the existence of an "Appalachia" off the southeastern coast of North America (Chapter IV, section 5); the same objections apply to the supposed borderland of "Cascadia," whose type area was offshore from the present Cascade Range.

Existence of a "Cascadia" is perhaps most strongly indicated along the California coast farther south where strips of crystalline basement strike out to sea; even here other explanations are more likely, as we will find later (section 4 of this chapter).

But in the type area farther north, available information affords little basis for the notion of a "Cascadia." All the earlier rocks are deeply covered by Tertiary sediments and volcanics, and no record of them is available; the Tertiary rocks themselves were laid down on a continental margin with only open ocean to the west. Moreover, the continental shelf is very narrow along the Pacific Coast in Washington, Oregon, and California, so that there would have been little room for any earlier offshore lands—unless one accepted some unlikely process of foundering of the lands to oceanic depths, and their subsequent conversion from sialic to simatic crust.

EARLY TERTIARY COASTAL PLAIN OR GEOSYNCLINE. We have allowed ourselves to wander into the fields of speculation. Let us put our feet on the ground once more and consider the known Tertiary and Quaternary history of the volcanic province.

Earlier Tertiary history of the province is revealed mainly in the Coast Ranges, where rocks of these ages are extensively exposed; in the Cascade Range and Columbia Plateaus to the east, early Tertiary rocks emerge only in scattered inliers.

The Coast Ranges are principally built of early Tertiary sediments and volcanics, mainly Eocene but extending upward into the Oligocene; they are 3,000 to 4,500 meters thick in most places but are many times thicker in the Olympic Mountains. The sediments are fine to coarse clastics containing volcanic detritus in part, but including components derived from plutonic and other basement rocks farther inland. In the Coast Ranges they are all marine and include thick units with graded bedding, probably deposited by turbidity currents in waters of considerable depth. On the east side of the ranges these pass into littoral and brackish water deposits, and farther inland, into continental, coal-bearing sediments.

Interbedded and interfingered with the sediments are masses of basaltic lava, mostly in the Eocene, partly in the Oligocene. They are generally subordinate to the sediments but in places exceed them in thickness, forming a series of giant lenses whose total volume has been estimated to be about 250,000 cubic kilometers. A large part of the basalt was erupted beneath the sea, as shown by its pillow structure, but it was locally built up above the water, for some of the flows are amygdaloidal, and weathered zones lie between them. The basalts are of remarkably uniform composition and must have been derived from a simatic layer beneath, without contamination from any sialic crust.

The environment of these early Tertiary sediments and volcanics has been termed variously a coastal plain or a geosyncline. The nature of the sedimentary rocks suggest a comparison with those of about the same age along the Gulf Coast, which we discussed in Chapter V, section 2—with continental deposits inland and marine deposits offshore, some probably laid down in deep water along or at the foot of the continental slope. The deposits of both regions seemingly were built forward from the continental into the oceanic area. Significant differences are the much larger volume of volcanic material in the northwestern province, and the greater deformation to which its rocks were subjected later; although the early Tertiary deposits of the Gulf Coast and the northwestern province are analogous, the latter have formed on a more mobile part of the crust.

COLUMBIA RIVER BASALT. To continue our story of the volcanic history of the province let us pass to rocks and events in the Columbia Plateaus, leaving those of the Cascade Range for consideration later.

After Eocene and Oligocene time, centers of volcanism apparently shifted eastward, or farther into the recess of the Columbia arc. Here in the Columbia Plateau proper the *Columbia River Basalt* was spread out during Miocene time. The lava flood did not, perhaps, exceed in volume that of the earlier Tertiary basalts farther west, but the latter are only fragmentarily exposed because of subsequent deformation and erosion. Much more of the Columbia River Basalt is preserved intact, making it one of the most impressive lava bodies in North America.

The Columbia River Basalt covers an area of 260,000 square kilometers, and has a volume of 180,000 cubic kilometers. Where the lava sequence has been tilted, more than 1,500 meters are exposed in single sections, and the total thickness may reach 5,000 meters. Individual flows are 30 to 150 meters thick, and must have been very fluid when erupted, as some have been traced 200 kilometers or more without reaching their edges; a recognizable stratigraphy can now be discerned over wide areas. The lava is of strikingly uniform composition; it is all basalt without interbedded flows of other sorts, and all the basalt is tholeiitic, a variety free of olivine.

The Columbia River Basalt was not erupted from volcanoes, but welled up through fissures. Such fissures, or feeder dikes, are common in northeastern Oregon and southeastern Washington in an area that may have been the center from which the flows originated. Eruption of the lavas must have required both a subsidence of their floor and an upbuilding sufficient to maintain an outward flow. Subsidence tilted the Nevadan basement and earlier Tertiary deposits toward the eruptive center from the north, east, and south; outward flow of the lava blocked the valleys on the tilted Nevadan surface at their lower ends so that lakes were formed in which sediments accumulated. Toward the west near the lower course of the Columbia River, the lavas spread seaward across the site of the Cascade Range, and their feather edges interfinger with marine deposits.

In general, the basin form of the Columbia River Basalt is still preserved; the basalt lies nearly flat over wide areas or is tilted gently toward the center of the basin. In some places, however, it has been warped or folded, mainly by reactivation of earlier structures.

The Columbia River Basalt is of the class termed plateau or flood basalts, which implies certain structural and compositional features. Like plateau basalts everywhere in the world it is of very uniform composition; it welled up from fissures and was not erupted from central volcanoes; from the fissures it spread over a wide area. Plateau basalts are supposed to have ascended in areas of crustal tension and fracturing from one of the more mafic lower layers of the crust without contamination from any more silicic upper layers through which they might have passed. Petrologists have debated the nature of the mafic source layer—whether it was a basaltic or simatic substratum underlying continents and oceanic areas alike, a tholeiitic subdivision of the substratum lying only beneath the continents, or a still deeper peridotitic stratum. Be that as it may, interpretation of the source of the Columbia River Basalt would seem to require consideration of its peculiar structural relations—within the recess of the Columbia arc where truly continental crust may not have developed until after Mesozoic time, and where such crust may have been thinner than normal at the time of the eruptions.

YOUNGER TERTIARY LAVAS TO THE SOUTHEAST AND EAST. Most of the surface of the Malheur Plateaus and the Snake River Plain southeast of the Blue Mountain axis is formed of lavas younger than the Columbia River Basalt, of Pliocene and even Pleistocene age. This suggests a southeastward spread of volcanism with time, but in places, earlier volcanic rocks are exposed beneath them, as though volcanism had begun earlier.

In contrast to the more uniform composition of the Columbia River Basalt, the lavas to the southeast are diversified; some basalts are tholeiitic like the Columbia River, others are olivine-bearing; many lavas are andesitic, dacitic, or rhyolitic. Some lavas of this southeastern area ascended through fissures, but others were spread from central vents or shield volcanoes.

Contrast between the composition and habit of the lavas northwest and southeast of the Blue Mountains axis suggests that the latter, lying beyond the recess of the Columbia arc, are in a region where sialic crust was thicker, hence that it could interact to a greater degree with the lavas during their ascent.

EVOLUTION OF THE CASCADE RANGE. In our examination of the volcanic province we have so far by-passed the most prominent part, the Cascade Range, leaving its complex story until the last.

The Cascade Range, like the Coast Ranges and Columbia Plateau, is built largely of volcanic rocks; their volume amounts to about 150,000 cubic kilometers. These volcanics contrast with the adjacent basaltic ones, for about 75 percent are pyroxene andesite or basaltic andesite. Also, instead of being largely erupted as flows, they include an equal or greater volume of breccias, tuffs, and mudflows formed by explosive volcanism; they contain numerous inclusions of earlier Tertiary sediments, and they were subjected to extensive hydrothermal alteration. The andesites of the Cascade Range were erupted during a long span of Tertiary time, the oldest being Eocene and the youngest Pliocene or later, but most are probably of Oligocene and Miocene age—of about the same age as parts of the basaltic outpourings in the Coast Ranges and the Columbia Plateau.

These features indicate that a special volcanic condition existed along the axis of the Cascade Range during Tertiary time unlike that on either side. The Cascade Range is a typical volcanic arc, like those in the island arc-trench systems in the western Pacific, and like them formed above a subduction zone and inland from a submarine trench that still exists, partly filled, off the west coasts of Oregon and Washington. During the later Mesozoic and the early Tertiary, the submarine trench and subduction zone existed along the whole west coast of the United States. During that time andesitic volcanics were erupted along the axis of the Sierra Nevada, as well as farther north. By mid-Tertiary time a new tectonic regime began south of Cape Mendocino and the Fortieth Parallel, for reasons that will become apparent later (section 4). Trench formation ceased off the coast in this southern area, and the andesites of the Sierra Nevada region were succeeded by a different and more varied suite of volcanic eruptives. To the north in the Cascade Range, the andesitic volcanic arc continued to grow during later Tertiary time, and its growth continues in diminished form today.

The Cascade Range, partly a belt of uplift, partly a belt of excessive volcanic accumulation, developed in Tertiary time directly across the recess of the Columbia arc in an area where there is little evidence of prior deformation. Growth of the range is shown by comparing the Eocene and modern vegetation east and west of it; Eocene floras on both sides both grew in tropical lowland forests and were closely related; modern floras on the east side are adapted to much drier climate than those on the west because of the interposition of the Cascade barrier.

In Oregon the Tertiary rocks of the western part of the Cascades are complexly fractured and tilted eastward. In Washington the Cascade axis crosses a succession of west-northwest-trending folds expressed in part by alignments of the drainage. These parallel the grain of the basement rocks on the northwestern side of the Columbia arc, but run well out into the Columbia Plateau on the east, where they deform the Columbia River Basalt, and extend westward across the Puget Trough into the Olympic Mountains. The west-northwest folds evidently antedate the north-south Cascade axis, yet their later growth involves rocks formed after the axis began to rise.

At some time during the Tertiary the andesites and other rocks of the Cascade Range were invaded by numerous masses of granodiorite and quartz diorite, which form some of the youngest plutonic bodies in the Cordillera. The largest is the *Snoqualmie batholith* in central Washington, 32 kilometers in diameter, which invades continental sediments and andesites of Eocene and later age. After these plutonic masses had been un-roofed by erosion in mid-Tertiary time they were again partly covered by other andesitic volcanics during a final and mainly Quaternary period of volcanism.

QUATERNARY EVENTS IN THE CASCADE RANGE. Growth of the Cascade Range during Tertiary time was followed by a period of quiesence and deep erosion. Volcanic activity was renewed again later, mainly in Quaternary time, when there were again andesitic eruptions.

During this later period of activity, a great chain of volcanic cones was built on the foundation of older rocks and structures; these now stand as a line of sentinels along the crest of the range (Fig. 101)—in Washington: Glacier Peak, Mount Baker, Mount Rainier, Mount St. Helens, and Mount Adams; in Oregon: Mount Hood, Mount Jefferson, Mount Washington, Three Sisters, "Mount Mazama," and Mount McLoughlin; in California: Mount Shasta and Lassen Peak. One of these, "Mount Mazama," no longer exists; it "blew its top" in a great eruption 6,600 years ago, depositing a layer of ash over most of the northwestern states, and the gaping hole that remained was filled by the waters of Crater Lake. Another, Mount St. Helens, was mostly built only a few thousand years ago, and still another, Lassen Peak, erupted vigorously in 1914 and 1915, and is the only recently active volcano in the forty-eight states.

THE "CASCADIAN REVOLUTION." The Cascade Range is of incidental interest as the type area of the alleged "Cascadian Revolution," which, according to some textbooks of historical geology, neatly ended Tertiary time and ushered in the Quaternary Period. But in the story of the Cascade Range as we have outlined it, what was so revolutionary? As we have seen, the range was long in growth and the end of Tertiary time seems to have been a time of quiesence rather than of tectonic and volcanic activity. Even if the concept of a Cascadian Revolution were apt for its type area, the combination of volcanic upbuilding and deformation by which the range was created seems too special to deserve application to a general milestone in geologic history.

HISTORY OF THE COLUMBIA RIVER. The Columbia River, whose sources are in the Northern Rocky Mountains on the east, enters the Pacific in the midst of the volcanic province. Much of its drainage basin is blessed with greater rainfall than the country farther south, and its volume far exceeds that of any other stream on the western slope of the Cordillera. Similar greater rainfall probably prevailed through much of the post-Mesozoic history of the Cordillera, so that an ancestor of the Columbia no doubt existed well back in Tertiary time.

With the onset of the eruptions of Columbia River Basalt the course of the river downstream from the highlands of the Nevadan orogenic belt was obliterated by the flood of lava. The lower ends of the valleys of the river and the valleys of its tributaries in the highlands to the north and northeast were dammed by the basalt and formed a series of lakes. Each lake drained around a spur end to the next lower one on the west, and thus established an exit for the water along the edge of the volcanic field; with downcutting, this became the new course of the Columbia, part of which the river still follows. Farther downstream in southern Washington, however, the river is deflected well eastward into the lava country, probably because of outbuilding of andesitic debris from the Cascade Range on the west.

In southern Washington the river crosses several anticlinal folds in the basalt that plunge southeast from the Cascade Range. Each fold is expressed topographically by a ridge, and in each ridge the river and several of its tributaries have cut deep gorges. The Columbia and its tributaries were probably antecedent to the anticlines—they had much their present courses before the folding and maintained them by downcutting as the anticlines were raised. Farther downstream the river cuts a much larger gorge through the complexly upbuilt and upwarped Cascade Range; many geologists believe that the river is antecedent to the growth of the Cascade Range also, but some would ascribe its course through the range to a complex process of superposition.

The history thus outlined was variously interrupted during the Pleistocene ice age. The course of the river around the northern side of the Columbia Plateau was covered by the edge of the Cordilleran ice cap, so that it was temporarily diverted across the northwestern part of the plateau, where it excavated the now-empty gorge of Grand Coulee. There was also a catastrophic punctuation about 30,000 years ago when the morainic dam of Lake Missoula suddenly collapsed, sending into the Columbia River drainage the 2,000 cubic kilometers of water that were impounded in northwestern Montana. The resulting *Spokane flood* spread across the northwestern part of the Columbia Plateau, stripping off the mantle of loess and eroding the basaltic bedrock beneath into the fantastic forms of the channeled scabland. When the flood reached the gorge of the river through the Cascade Range, the waters rose 230 meters above normal level before finding their way to the sea.

4. COAST RANGES OF CALIFORNIA

In this final section of the book we will discuss the Coast Ranges of California. These make a large subject, to whose varied facets many geologists have devoted years of labor. Within the scope of this book we can scarcely hope to exhaust the subject, yet perhaps we can set forth the fundamental features of the region and suggest some possible answers to its many problems.

TOPOGRAPHIC AND GEOLOGIC PROVINCES. Let us review the topographic and geologic provinces of California (Fig. 103), keeping in mind that they are products of relatively late earth movements that modified the fundamental Cordilleran structures of Mesozoic time.

(a) The *Great Basin* part of the Basin and Range province, with its discontinuous ranges and intervening desert basins, formed by late deformation, mainly block-faulting, that was superposed on the deformed eugeosynclinal and miogeosynclinal rocks of the Cordillera. The Great Basin lies mainly in Nevada, but its western edge extends over the border into California.

(b) The *Mojave Desert* part of the Basin and Range province, lying southwest of the Great Basin and projecting far westward as a peculiar wedge between other provinces of southern California.

(c) The *Sierra Nevada* lying west of the Great Basin in central California—a great block of eugeosynclinal and plutonic rocks that was upfaulted on its eastern side and tilted westward toward the Great Valley.

(d) The *Klamath Mountains* of northern California, which, like the Sierra Nevada, are made up of eugeosynclinal and plutonic rocks. Here, however, the present mountains were not raised by block-faulting but by broad warping.

Let us now continue with the remaining provinces, about which we have said little hitherto:

(e) The *Great Valley*, consisting of the San Joaquin and Sacramento Valleys west of the Sierra Nevada in central California. This is a great alluvial-floored depression with the structure of a complex synclinorium, yet it was formed while sedimentation was still in progress. Its eastern side is underlain by the down-tilted western edge of the Sierra Nevada block.

(f) The *Salton Trough* east of the Peninsular Ranges in the southeastern part of the state, which is also an alluvial-floored depression that is actually the upper end of the Gulf of California, now cut off by the deltaic deposits of the Colorado River. Here, sedimentation is not as complete as in the Great Valley so that its lowest point, in the Salton Sea, is still 71 meters below sea level.

(g) The *Coast Ranges proper* between the Great Valley and the Pacific coast—a series of sub-parallel ridges much lower than the Sierra Nevada. The Coast Ranges are broken through at mid-length by San Francisco Bay, formed by local subsidence, so that it is convenient to speak of Northern and Southern Coast Ranges. The Coast Ranges include deformed Tertiary rocks lying on a basement of Mesozoic and older rocks; unlike the Sierra Nevada they are not a single tilted block but a series of fault slices trending generally north-westward at a slight angle to the coast.

(h) The *Transverse Ranges*, trending east and west, against which the southeast-trending Coast Ranges terminate on the south. That part to the west—the Santa Ynez Mountains, the Santa Monica Mountains, and the Channel Islands—are largely covered by Tertiary rocks like the Coast Ranges farther north; that part to the east, north of the Los Angeles lowland—the San Gabriel and San Bernardino Mountains—are much more uplifted and expose mainly metamorphic and plutonic rocks.

(i) The *Peninsular Ranges*, south of the Transverse Ranges and the Los Angeles lowland and extending into Baja California. Like the Coast Ranges proper they trend north-northwest, but like the San Gabriel and San Bernardino Mountains and the Sierra Nevada they consist mainly of metamorphic and plutonic rocks, and their sedimentary cover is patchy.

FAULTS OF CALIFORNIA. On these morphologic and geologic provinces are imposed the great faults of California (Fig. 103).

Throughout its 650-kilometer length the *Sierra Nevada* faces the Great Basin on the east in a series of lofty scarps that have been outlined mainly by faults, although the faults are not continuous and are offset en echelon in many places. So far as we know these faults have mainly relatively simple dip-slip displacements, the side on the east being dropped, and the side on the west in the Sierra Nevada being raised and rotated. Movements have occurred on some of these faults within historic time, and have produced scarps in the alluvial deposits of Owens Valley.

More complex and less well understood is the *San Andreas fault*, which extends diagonally southeastward through the Coast Ranges of California, running out into the Pacific near Cape Mendocino north of San Francisco and probably passing under the Gulf of California to the southeast. The true nature of the San Andreas fault was not fully appreciated until the great San Francisco earthquake of April 18, 1906, which made clear that it was a major throughgoing fracture, still in process of movement. Unlike the faults of the Sierra Nevada, movement on the San Andreas fault is dominantly strike-slip, or sidewise, in a *right-lateral direction*; this is

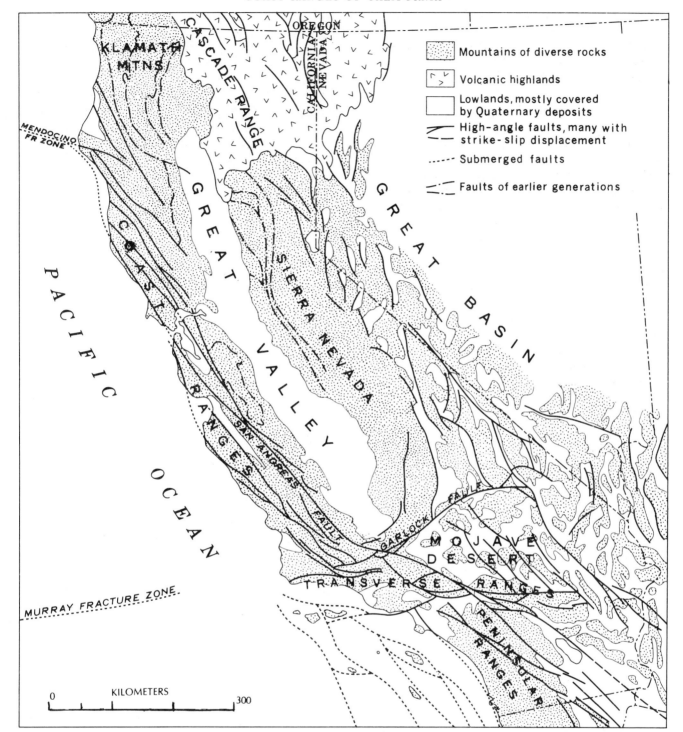

FIG. 103. Map of California, showing the topographic provinces and the principal faults. Compiled from Geologic Map of United States (1974) and other sources.

illustrated by the saying "San Francisco and Los Angeles are coming closer together," the two cities lying respectively northeast and southwest of the fault. The nature of the latest strike-slip movements on the fault can be demonstrated, among other ways, by offset of stream valleys that cross it; streams flowing northeastward turn southeast along the fault for half a kilometer or so before resuming their northeastward course. In places great vertical movements are suggested by contrasting rocks and topography on opposite sides of the fault, but this may be an illusion resulting from sideward shift of high-standing areas against low-standing areas. Total amount of this sideward movement is much debated; we will explore the possibilities later.

171

The San Andreas fault is only the largest and most spectacular of a host of kindred faults in the Coast, Transverse, and Peninsular Ranges, many of great magnitude in their own right, which branch from it at low angles, or run nearly parallel with it for long distances. Of the many we might mention specifically the *Hayward fault* east of San Francisco Bay and of the San Andreas fault, which was responsible for a major earthquake in 1868, and the *San Jacinto fault* in the Peninsular Ranges west of the San Andreas fault.

Besides these faults, another set, mainly in the Transverse Ranges, trends more to the eastward, some with dip-slip, some with strike-slip displacement. The most conspicuous of these are the *Garlock fault*, which extends northeastward from the San Andreas and forms the northern edge of the peculiar wedge of the Mojave Desert, and the *Big Pine fault*, which extends southwestward from the San Andreas fault into the Transverse Ranges. Offset of features along these faults indicates a *left-lateral strike-slip displacement* (or the opposite of that on the San Andreas). The San Andreas fault shows its only notable deflection near the Big Pine and Garlock faults in the Transverse Ranges, where it bends from its usual southeastward course into a more easterly course for 150 kilometers or so.

SCARPS ON PACIFIC OCEAN FLOOR. No discussion of the faults of California, either of the San Andreas system or the Transverse Range system, would be complete without considering the remarkable system of scarps produced by faulting on the floor of the Pacific Ocean to the west (Plate I).

The *Mendocino Escarpment* extends westward from Cape Mendocino in northern California, and has been traced for at least 1,600 kilometers into the Pacific Ocean basin. Near the shore off Cape Mendocino the scarp faces north, but farther out to sea it is reversed and faces south, in places rising to heights of 3,000 meters. This scarp is notable in that it offsets the edge of the continental shelf by more than eighty kilometers in a right-lateral direction (Fig. 104). Moreover, at Shelter Cove a little south of Cape Mendocino the ground was disturbed at the time of the San Francisco earthquake, indicating that movements related to those on the San Andreas fault extended into this area.

The *Murray Escarpment* trends westward from southern California, and has been traced at least 3,000 kilometers across the Pacific Ocean basin near to or past the Hawaiian Islands. The escarpment faces north and its relief is less than that of the Mendocino Escarpment, seldom being more than 1,500 meters, but it is paralleled closely by other scarps and ridges that are probably parts of the same fracture system. The Murray Escarpment lies on the same trend as the Transverse Ranges; the connection between them is lost on the continental

slope, yet the two sets of features may be parts of the same system of deformation.

BASEMENT OF THE COAST RANGES. Let us now deal specifically with the Coast Ranges and examine details of their geology.

We have said that the Coast Ranges are characterized particularly by their Tertiary rocks, but although these attain great thickness in parts of the ranges, they do not cover its whole surface. The Tertiary rocks lie on older rocks of various sorts and ages that emerge in places. In some areas the Tertiary lies in part on Cretaceous strata and the Cretaceous in part on Jurassic strata. Elsewhere the Tertiary or the Cretaceous lies on a true basement of crystalline rocks. The areas in which these crystalline rocks occur have a significant distribution (Fig. 104).

One long strip where crystalline rocks lie at the surface extends from Bodega Head and Point Reyes north of San Francisco past the Farallon Islands, and southeastward nearly to the Transverse Ranges; it has been called *Salinia* for its characteristic development near the Salinas Valley. The crystalline basement of Salinia consists of highly metamorphosed sedimentary rocks of probable Paleozoic age, the *Sur Series*, invaded by plutonic rocks such as the Santa Lucia Granodiorite. The crystalline rocks have traditionally been considered to be of pre-Franciscan age, as the Franciscan, where present nearby, shows no sign of plutonic alteration (see below for discussion of the Franciscan and its problems). Although once suspected to be very old, radiometric determinations on the plutonic rocks have yielded ages of 77 to 117 million years, indicating that they are of Cretaceous age like those in the eastern part of the Sierra Nevada.

Another strip of crystalline rocks follows the Transverse Ranges from the Channel Islands on the west eastward into the San Bernardino Mountains; from one of the islands it has been called *Anacapia*. This basement is more heterogeneous than that of Salinia and more is known about its ages. In the San Gabriel Mountains it includes Middle Proterozoic gneisses and anorthosite with ages of 1,650 to 1,220 million years, the late Paleozoic Mount Lowe Granodiorite with an age of 220 million years, and various Cretaceous granitic plutons. Paleozoic fossils have been found in meta-sedimentary rocks in the San Bernardino Mountains; and the Pelona Schist of the San Gabriel Mountains, once assigned to the Precambrian, is probably of upper Mesozoic age. Lower Jurassic slate occurs in the Santa Monica Mountains.

Besides the strips of crystalline rocks in Salinia and Anacapia, there are broader areas of crystalline rocks in the Peninsular Ranges farther south that closely resemble those in the Sierra Nevada. They consist of metamorphosed early Mesozoic eugeosynclinal rocks that were invaded by granitic plutons of later Mesozoic

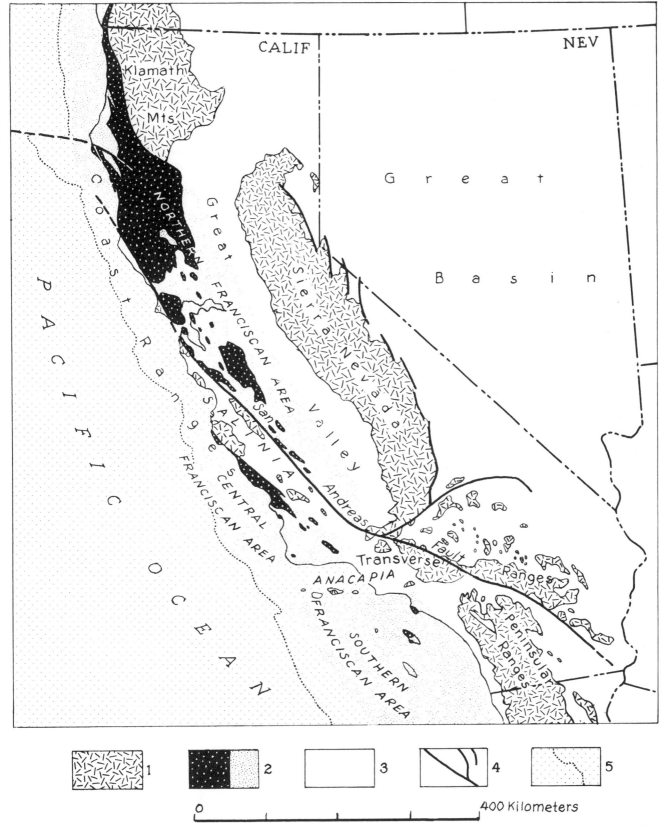

FIG. 104. Map of California, showing areas of crystalline basement and the three areas of Franciscan basement. Adapted from Reed (1933) and Reed and Hollister (1936).

Explanation of symbols: 1–Outcrops of crystalline basement (metamorphic and plutonic rocks that were part of the Nevadan orogenic belt). 2–Areas of Franciscan basement (outcrop areas solid, areas where Franciscan is overlain by younger rocks shaded). 3–Areas where basement is covered by Cretaceous, Tertiary, and Quaternary rocks (also areas of undifferentiated rocks and structures east of Sierra Nevada). 4–Major faults. 5–Ocean, with edge of continental crust shown by dotted line.

age. In southern California and adjacent Baja California, plutons have been dated as between 100 and 120 million years, or middle Cretaceous. In Baja California they invade middle Cretaceous eugeosynclinal rocks and are overlain unconformably by undeformed latest Cretaceous deposits of shallow-water origin.

FRANCISCAN GROUP. Between the areas of crystalline rocks the younger sedimentary rocks of the Coast Ranges lie on a quite different basement, the Franciscan Group. Although these rocks can also be called "basement" and are much deformed and indurated, they are less metamorphosed than the crystalline basement rocks.

The Franciscan Group occurs in three separate areas (Fig. 104). The *northern Franciscan area* makes up most of the Coast Ranges north of San Francisco Bay, extending northward into southwestern Oregon, and southward for a long distance northeast of the San Andreas fault and Salinia. The *central Franciscan area* forms that part of the southern Coast Ranges southwest of Salinia (from which it is separated by the Sur-Nacimiento fault) and north of the Transverse Ranges; its Franciscan rocks are exposed along the Pacific Coast for many kilometers southward from Point Sur. The *southern Franciscan area* lies mostly at sea off southern California, south of the Transverse Ranges and west of the Peninsular Ranges. Its rocks (known as the Catalina Schist) emerge in the Palos Verdes Hills, Santa Catalina Island, and various islands and promontories along the coast of Baja California; otherwise its extent is suggested mainly by occurrence of its characteristic debris in younger sedimentary rocks along the coast, especially in the Miocene San Onofre Breccia.

Rocks of the Franciscan Group are an old-looking much deformed, thoroughly indurated mass of graywackes, shales, bedded cherts, limestone lenses, and interbedded pillow basalts, with embedded bodies of serpentinite and other ultramafic rocks. Parts of it form reasonably ordered sequences but other parts are a mélange of tectonically disordered blocks and slices, formed of rocks of heterogeneous lithologies and origins. Its thickness is indeterminable, but must be much greater than 10,000 meters. (The term *group* which I use here for the Franciscan is to some extent misleading, as this implies a regular sequence of formations; it is more aptly an *assemblage* of characteristic lithologies).

A curious feature of the Franciscan is that its base is nowhere visible. Geologists once assumed that it lay unconformably on the crystalline basement rocks of Salinia, yet wherever these are juxtaposed the contact is a fault; moreover, the plutonic rocks of Salinia are of Cretaceous age, or contemporaneous or younger than the Franciscan. There is thus no evidence of the sort of crustal material on which the Franciscan rocks were laid; probably it was something quite different from the adjacent crystalline basement, and may well have been oceanic rather than continental crust.

Before proceeding farther with the Franciscan, we must say something of the other body of upper Mesozoic rocks in western California—the *Great Valley sequence*. We have mentioned (Chapter VIII, section 4) the Upper Cretaceous Chico Formation, a near-shore deposit that overlaps the western edge of the deformed older rocks of the Sierra Nevada. Westward, the Chico passes into a thicker, deeper-water deposit that is underlain by similar rocks of the Horsetown, Paskenta, and Knoxville Formations of Lower Cretaceous and Upper Jurassic ages, which attain a thickness of 15,000 meters where they are turned up on the western side of the Sacramento Valley. This sequence is largely younger than any of the rocks in the Sierra Nevada, but the lower part of the Knoxville contains fossils of Kimmeridgian age, or equivalent to part of the Mariposa Formation. The sequence was long assumed to be wholly younger than the Nevadan orogeny, but it now appears to have been a continental shelf and continental slope deposit built westward as a great embankment while the Nevadan orogeny was in progress. In contrast to the Franciscan on the west, it is a well-ordered sequence of regularly layered flysch or turbidite. Its base, where exposed along the western side of the Great Valley, lies on an oceanic crust or ophiolite—a thick layer of serpentinite and other ultramafic rocks followed by pillow basalts and radiolarian cherts.

The age of the Franciscan has long been a puzzle, as fossils are scanty and the next formations that overlie it are generally Tertiary. It was once thought to underlie the Upper Jurassic Knoxville Formation, and likewise to be of Jurassic age and younger than the Nevadan orogeny. It is now known, however, that the Knoxville and the rest of the Great Valley sequence with their basal ophiolites lie over it tectonically along the *Coast Range thrust*, which has carried them westward across the Franciscan (Fig. 105). Moreover, sufficient fossils have now been recovered from the Franciscan itself to demonstrate that it includes rocks not only of Jurassic but of various Cretaceous ages; in a coastal belt between San Francisco and Cape Mendocino it also includes fossiliferous rocks of Eocene age. The Franciscan was therefore accumulating at the same time and even later than the Great Valley sequence rather than earlier, and was a western facies, laid down west of the great embankment of Great Valley rocks, probably on the Pacific Ocean floor in a submarine trench along the edge of the continent.

The Franciscan has been rather pervasively metamorphosed in the blueschist facies, formed under low-temperature high-pressure conditions during rapid and deep tectonic burial. For the most part the metamorphism is of low grade; many of the rocks have

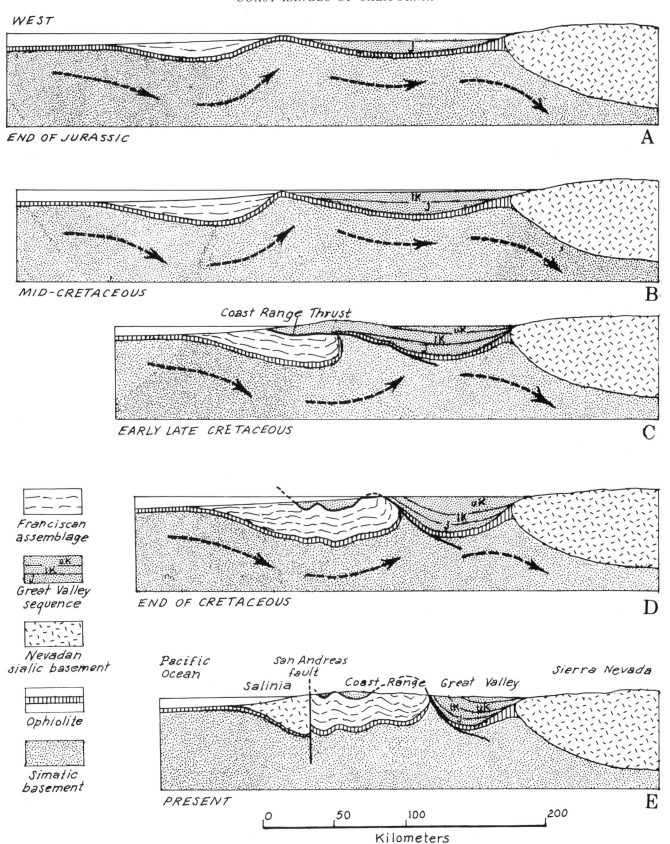

WEST

END OF JURASSIC
A

MID-CRETACEOUS
B

Coast Range Thrust

EARLY LATE CRETACEOUS
C

Franciscan
assemblage

Great Valley
sequence

Nevadan
sialic basement

Ophiolite

Simatic
basement

END OF CRETACEOUS
D

Pacific
Ocean

Salinia

San Andreas
fault

Coast Range   Great Valley

Sierra Nevada

PRESENT
E

0   50   100   200

Kilometers

FIG. 105. Sequential sections showing evolution of the Northern Coast Ranges in Mesozoic and Cenozoic time: (A) End of Jurassic. (B) Mid-Cretaceous. (C) Early Late Cretaceous (Turonian). (D) Late Cretaceous. (E) Present conditions. After Bailey and others (1970).

175

been jadetized, preserving the original sedimentary structures, but in places, especially to the east beneath the Coast Range thrust, they have been converted to blueschists containing glaucophane and lawsonite. After their deep burial and metamorphism, the Franciscan rocks were uplifted and accreted to the continent during the continuing evolution of the Coast Ranges.

THEORIES ON ORIGIN OF THE COAST RANGES. To one like myself who has followed from afar for many years the development of ideas on Coast Range geology, one of its intriguing features has been the diversity of interpretations offered to explain it. Truly the difficulties of the area have been a challenge to every geologist who has worked there, and each has responded to the best of his ability—yet not always with harmonious results.

The pattern was set by the giants of the past, Andrew C. Lawson of the University of California at Berkeley and Bailey Willis of Stanford University. Although both men lived into their nineties and nearly to our own day, most of their work and conflicts on the Coast Ranges occurred many years before. (In 1927 Willis published an article, "Folding or shearing, which?" that was much derided by his contemporaries, but which anticipated many of the ideas that are commonly accepted today). Of greater interest now are the interpretations of their successors of thirty or forty years ago, and especially of three geologists.

Bruce L. Clark, who was professor of paleontology at the University of California at Berkeley, did outstanding work on the Tertiary stratigraphy of the Coast Ranges, during which he also evolved a theory of Coast Range evolution and structure. He supposed that the ranges were a mosaic of fault blocks, each with a more or less independent history during Cenozoic and earlier times, rising or sinking erratically so that at one time a block might be uplifted and eroded, at another submerged and covered by sediments. Folds that occur within the fault blocks were believed to be an incidental result of their slicing and compression.

Ralph D. Reed, who was chief geologist in California for The Texas Company, opposed the notions of Clark and had another picture of Coast Range structure. He believed folding to be the normal, dominant feature; faulting, incidental and in places merely an effect of the folding. He emphasized the contrasting nature of the basement in different parts of the ranges, and suggested that the three areas of Franciscan rocks were formed in independent geosynclinal basins separated by axes of crystalline basement in Salinia and Anacapia; this framework of the basement much influenced the nature of the folding and faulting in the overlying Cretaceous and Tertiary sediments.

Nicholas L. Taliaferro was professor of geology at the University of California for many years, but most of the results of his work on the Coast Ranges were published somewhat later than those of Clark and Reed. Of interest is his conclusion that Salinia, Anacapia, and the Franciscan areas were not ancient positive and negative elements, but originated no farther back than Late Cretaceous time. Franciscan deposits were supposed to have been laid on the crystalline Salinian basement entirely across the Coast Ranges, but during a Late Cretaceous orogeny the basement was raised along certain belts from which the Franciscan was removed by erosion.

Viewing Clark's and Reed's theories in retrospect one can find many virtues in both, and the answers lay somewhere between the two extremes. To some extent Taliaferro's interpretation reconciled these opposing views, but we now know that it likewise had many defects, so that a much revised synthesis has become necessary, as explained below.

DISPLACEMENT ON SAN ANDREAS FAULT. Strangely, all three geologists placed little emphasis on the San Andreas fault and the proved strike-slip movements that have taken place on it and its kindred. The great lateral shifts that Willis and others suspected along them were thought to be incredible and without proof, the really important displacements being better explained by vertical uplift or depression of the adjacent blocks. Taliaferro, for example, estimated that the lateral shift on the San Andreas fault could have been no more than a mile.

In the meantime a number of geologists worked on the San Andreas fault and the rocks adjoining it. Among the first was Levi F. Noble, who studied for the U.S. Geological Survey the segment between Soledad Pass and Cajon Pass on the north side of the San Gabriel Mountains in southern California (Fig. 106). Here scars were still visible that were produced during the Fort Tejon earthquake of 1857, a disturbance that was probably greater in magnitude than the one of 1906 farther north. Stream valleys that cross the fault are shifted as much as a kilometer in a right-lateral direction, and Pleistocene deposits are shifted in the same direction by eight or nine kilometers (Fig. 107A and B). Late Tertiary formations are still more discordant; one must go 30 or 50 kilometers eastward on the north side of the fault to find a counterpart of the rocks on the south side (Fig. 107C). The older Tertiary formations show even greater anomalies but are too fragmentarily exposed to yield decisive evidence. In the segment studied by Noble, the older Cenozoic rocks have been displaced progressively greater distances the older the age, suggesting that the fault has been moving steadily, or perhaps spasmodically, at least since early Tertiary time.

Total displacement on the San Andreas fault should be indicated by offset of the basement rocks, which have shared all its later movements. Matching of basement rocks on the two sides is as yet inconclusive, but geologists working in southern California have found remarkable resemblances between the basement of the San Gabriel Mountains southwest of it and those of the Orocopia and Chocolate Mountains northeast of it, which lie near the Salton Sea 250 to 300 kilometers to the southeast (Fig. 107E). The anorthosites and the Pelona Schist of the San Gabriel Mountains have their counterparts in units in the Orocopia and Chocolate Mountains.

Earlier syntheses of Coast Range history will thus require extensive modification, as the fault blocks into which the area is divided have been shifted laterally with respect to each other through time, by amounts that have produced major geographic changes.

PROPOSED HISTORY OF THE COAST RANGES. During the last few decades a new synthesis of Coast Range geology and history has evolved, quite different from the earlier proposals, on whose larger aspects there is now general agreement. This is not the product of a single individual, but of many geologists working on various aspects of the problem on the land, and of oceanographers at sea. We will now discuss these newer concepts.

We recall that the Nevadan orogeny of mid-Mesozoic time deformed, metamorphosed, and plutonized the Cordilleran eugeosynclinal rocks of earlier Mesozoic and Paleozoic ages along a belt extending from the Klamath Mountains, through the Sierra Nevada, to the Peninsular Ranges. There is little evidence that Nevadan orogeny affected the site of the Coast Ranges to the west, although this has often been assumed in the past. It is more likely that the zone of greatest deformation lay to the east and that the site of the Coast Ranges was an oceanic area. The Nevadan deformed belt was probably the western edge of the continent at the time, and was bordered on the west by a continental shelf and slope on which the late Jurassic and Cretaceous deposits of the Great Valley sequence accumulated. Beyond this was a deep-sea trench which received the deposits of the Franciscan Group—like the trenches which still exist offshore along Central America and Mexico, and the Aleutian Trench off Alaska, but which are lacking today off the coast of California.

Existence of a trench implies plate convergence—eastward movement of a plate of Pacific Ocean floor from a spreading center farther out, and subduction of the plate by underthrusting beneath the continent. One manifestation of the underthrusting is the Coast Range thrust, along which the Franciscan has been carried eastward beneath the Great Valley sequence; also, more obscure east-dipping thrusts have been observed within the Franciscan itself in the Northern Coast Ranges. Another manifestation of the underthrusting is the bodies of mélange in the Franciscan, that were derived from diverse places on the surface of the subducting plate, and which are composed of rock masses that were

crowded together and broken. Still another is the blueschist metamorphism, which implies deep, rapid burial of the subducted plate.

Oceanographic studies and reconstructions add many complications to the story. The Pacific Ocean floor next to North America consisted not of one plate, but three: a Pacific plate west of a spreading center and a Farallon plate east of it, and north of a triple junction a Kula plate. The Pacific Ocean plates were moving not only toward the continent but northward. In late Mesozoic time the Kula plate lay off the California coast and was moving northward past the continent along a transform fault. By early Tertiary time the south edge of the Kula plate had moved to the latitude of northern California. The Farallon plate was now off the coast and was being carried eastward from the spreading center into a submarine trench and was being subducted beneath the North American plate. In later Tertiary time the whole Farallon plate had been consumed by subduction in the trench, leaving only a small triangular remnant north of the Mendocino fracture zone (the Gorda plate). The spreading center then passed into the subduction zone and disappeared, bringing the Pacific plate west of the spreading center against the California coast. This change in tectonic regime occurred about 30 million years ago, or during the Oligocene.

One effect of this situation is the curious asymmetry of the magnetic anomaly striping on the ocean floor in the segment off California and Baja California. Magnetic stripes extend parallel to the spreading centers, and in most oceanic areas stripes on one side can be matched with those on the other, both sets increasing in age away from the spreading center. In the California segment, by contrast, the youngest stripes lie close to the edge of the continent and become progressively older westward. It is only south of the mouth of the Gulf of California and north of the Mendocino fracture zone that a few of the corresponding stripes to the east are preserved.

These events correspond well with the land geology. In the Southern Coast Ranges, both the Franciscan and the rocks of the Salinian block are overlain unconformably by the Vaqueros Formation of late Oligocene and early Miocene age. The Vaqueros truncates the mélange and other confused structures in the Franciscan, proving that they formed earlier, but both the Vaqueros and its basement are displaced by high-angle strike-slip faults, indicating that these formed later.

With the disappearance of the subduction zone and trench, the Pacific plate became locked to the edge of the North American continent, and northward movement of the Pacific plate carried slices of the continent along with it, creating the modern San Andreas fault system. Hitherto, the continental edge had consisted of continuous parallel belts of Nevadan basement, of continental shelf and slope (Great Valley sequence), and of

submarine trench deposits (the Franciscan). Parts of these were now detached and carried northward. The Salinian block was detached from the edge of the Nevadan belt at some point well to the south of its present position, and moved northward hundreds of kilometers so that it now lies west of the Sierra Nevada belt, the Great Valley sequence, and the Franciscan of the northern area.

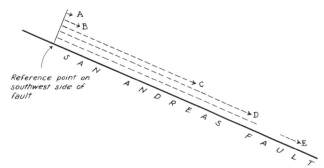

FIG. 107. Diagram illustrating progressive movements through time on the San Andreas fault, as observed between Soledad Pass and Cajon Pass, southern California. (A) Offset of modern streams, 1 kilometer. (B) Of Pleistocene deposits, 8 to 10 kilometers. (C) Of Miocene and Pliocene formations, 30 to 50 kilometers. (D) Of early Tertiary formations, amount undetermined but greater than C. (E) Of basement rocks, amount undetermined, but may be as great as 250 kilometers. Data from Noble (1954).

Another effect of the northward movement was the detachment of the peninsula of Baja California from the Mexican mainland. This long sliver of continental rocks is now separated from the mainland by the Gulf of California and the Salton Trough, which geophysical surveys indicate are floored by oceanic crust.

The San Andreas fault and its kindred, with right-lateral strike-slip displacement, are thus transform faults in the sense that they form the boundary between two crustal plates that moved past each other, with neither rifting apart nor crowding together in subduction zones. However, as they involve continental rocks, the effects are somewhat different from those along the more typical transform faults on the ocean floor.

This oversimplified outline of Coast Range history leaves a number of problems unresolved, so that the crustal movements and their chronology must have been considerably more complex than indicated. It leaves out of account, for example, the role of the Transverse Ranges of southern California, in which the narrow belt of basement rocks of Anacapia has been shifted westward to the edge of the continent, including some rocks of Precambrian age. It also does not account for indications in many places of a northward movement of Salinia before the Oligocene, nor of indications of an early exist-

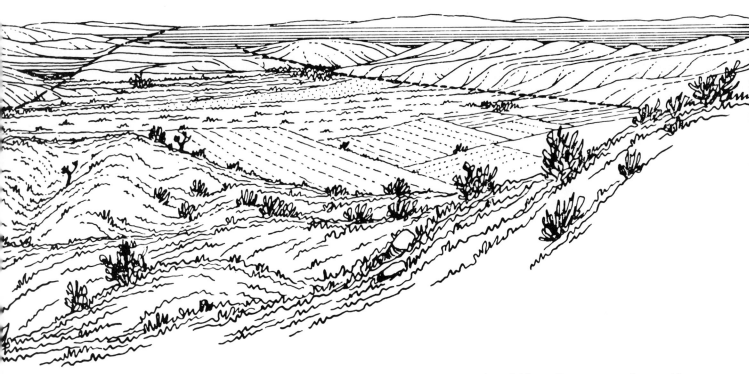

FIG. 106. View of San Andreas fault zone at Valyermo on the north side of San Gabriel Mountains, southern California. View is west-northwest, with San Gabriel Mountains on left and Mojave Desert on right. Long dashes indicate the trace of the main San Andreas fault. Short dashes indicate the traces of lesser faults at north and south edges of the fault zone, which are about 5 kilometers apart. Drawn by P. B. King.

ence in some form of the Gulf of California. Present data indicate that movement along the San Andreas fault has not been continuous since Mesozoic time; a great surge of movement, amounting to about 300 kilometers of slip, began about 20 million years ago, before which there was a period of little or no faulting. Some aspects of the geology suggest that an earlier period of right-lateral movement occurred during late Cretaceous and Paleocene time, probably related to the northward shift of the Kula plate. This took place along a proto-San Andreas fault located west of the present fault and amounted to more than 200 kilometers of right-slip displacement, resulting in an early northward movement of Salinia. There has been speculation that the chronology of movements south of the Transverse Ranges has been somewhat different from that farther north, and that the whole system was not integrated until after the Oligocene.

We are thus faced with a complex jig-saw puzzle, on which much progress has been made, and in which geologists are still engaged in filling in the details. But like Humpty-Dumpty, all the King's horses and all the King's men cannot put the Coast Ranges back together again.

TERTIARY SEDIMENTATION AND DEFORMATION. The

framework of the Coast Ranges was thus established by Nevadan orogeny; by deposition of the continental shelf and slope deposits of the Great Valley sequence west of the orogenic belt and the Franciscan trench deposits west of it; and by progressive lateral shift of the crustal blocks, beginning as early as the Late Cretaceous. These primarily Mesozoic events leave much room for doubt and speculation. The record becomes clearer during the Tertiary, although no less complex.

During Tertiary and Quaternary time, not only were crustal blocks shifted right-laterally but compression of the rocks of the Coast Ranges was exerted at frequent intervals. The results differ significantly from those in the orogenic belts that we have considered so far, such as the Appalachians and the Cordillera; there was no foreland, no miogeosyncline and eugeosyncline, nor metamorphic and plutonic belt. Instead, there was more or less continuous deformation from Cretaceous time to the present, with different things happening at different times and different places, depending on the geometry of the faults and the types of juxtaposed rocks. The difference between the Coast Range deformation and that of the usual orogenic belts was apprehended early by some geologists, notably by Bailey Willis (although derided by others at the time); Walter H. Bucher characterized the Coast Ranges as a heterogeneous mobile belt.

During the Coast Range deformations, extensive thrust faults and normal faults were formed as accessories to the strike-slip faults, resulting in many small basins of subsidence juxtaposed against small areas of uplift. As the basins and uplifts were shifted about, the pattern of sedimentation and paleogeography changed repeatedly. Some areas show a record of nearly continuous deformation for long periods, and contain so many unconformities that it is difficult to generalize them into any orogenic climaxes. One receives a blurred impression, however, of two principal climaxes—one near the middle of the Miocene, the other late in the Pliocene and early in the Pleistocene, the latter especially in the basins of southern California (Fig. 108). The mid-Pleistocene deformation has so impressed geologists working there that they believed it to be "the greatest orogeny since the Nevadan," and the German geologist Hans Stille called it the *Pasadenan orogeny*. However, its extreme effects are very local, and it is merely a late manifestation of deformation that was as great or greater in other places at earlier times.

Tertiary sedimentation and deformation were strongly influenced by the nature of the basement on which the deposits were laid; deposits laid over the relatively rigid crystalline rocks were much less deformed than those laid over the weaker rocks of the Franciscan Group. In places Tertiary and Quaternary sedimentation took place in more or less separate basins between higher-standing crystalline blocks. Two of them, the *Los Angeles* and *Ventura basins* of southern California were rapidly deepened in late Tertiary time, then filled by enormous thicknesses of Pliocene and early Pleistocene deposits laid down in progressively shallower water; later on these were deformed by the mid-Pleistocene orogeny.

The mid-Miocene deformation shaped the ridges and

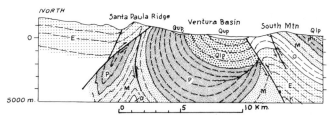

FIG. 108. Section showing strong deformation of Pliocene and lower Pleistocene strata in Ventura basin of southern California, as a result of the so-called Pasadenan orogeny. The lower Pleistocene is folded with the Pliocene and the whole is overlain unconformably by upper Pleistocene terrace deposits. After Bailey and Jahna (1954).

Explanation of symbols: K–Cretaceous. E–Eocene. O–Oligocene. M–Miocene. P–Pliocene (Pico Formation and lower part of Santa Barbara Formation). Qlp–lower Pleistocene (upper part of Santa Barbara Formation and San Pedro Formation). Qup–upper Pleistocene (terrace deposits).

troughs of the Coast Ranges into their general present configuration but left wide tracts still submerged; the Pliocene and early Pleistocene deformation brought about a widespread emergence. During times of greatest submergence the Coast Range area probably resembled the present offshore borderland region of southern California—with shallow shelves and banks interspersed with deeper troughs, and with linear islands like the present Channel Islands. During times of greatest emergence the Coast Range area probably resembled the present topography around San Francisco Bay—with mountain ridges and intervening troughs and valleys, in which continental sediments were being deposited and whose lowest parts, like the present bay, were covered by shallow ramifying seas. Tectonic instability continues to the present, with rapid uplift, sedimentation, and changing paleogeography, as major strike-slip faults remain active and, by some indications, are more active now than earlier in the Tertiary. The overall effect is the modern instability of coastal California, with its earthquakes, landsliding, subsidence, flooding, and other environmental hazards.

REFERENCES

2. *Basin and Range Province*

Albers, J. P., 1967, Belt of sigmoidal bending and right-lateral faulting in the western Great Basin: *Geol. Soc. America Bull.*, v. 78, no. 2, pp. 143-156.

Axelrod, D. L., 1957, Late Tertiary floras and the Sierra Nevada uplift: *Geol. Soc. America Bull.*, v. 68, no. 1, pp. 19-45.

Davis, W. M., 1925, The Basin Range problem: *Natl. Acad. Sci. Proc.*, v. 11, pp. 387-392.

Longwell, C. R., 1960, Possible explanation of diverse structural patterns in southern Nevada: *Am. Jour. Sci.*, v. 258A (Bradley volume), pp. 192-203.

Stewart, J. H., 1971, Basin and Range structure; a system of horsts and grabens produced by deep-seated extension: *Geol. Soc. America Bull.*, v. 82, no. 3, pp. 1019-1044.

Thompson, G. A., 1964, The rift system of the western United States, *in* Irvine, T. N. **ed.**, *The world rift system*: Canada Geol. Survey Paper 66-14, pp. 280-289.

3. *Northwestern Volcanic Province*

Christiansen, R. L., and Lipman, P. W., 1972, Cenozoic volcanism and plate-tectonic evolution of the western United States. II Late Cenozoic: *Royal Soc. London Phil. Trans.*, v. 271, pp. 249-284.

Hodge, E. T., 1938, Geology of the lower Columbia River: *Geol. Soc. America Bull.*, v. 49, pp. 831-930.

Lipman, P. W., Prostka, H. J., and Christiansen, R. L., 1972, Cenozoic volcanism and plate-tectonic evolution of the western United States. I. Early and middle Cenozoic: *Royal Soc. London Phil. Trans.*, v. 271, pp. 217-248.

Macdonald, G. A., 1966, Geology of the Cascade Range and Modoc Plateau, *in* Bailey, E. H., ed., *Geology of northern California*: California Div. Mines and Geol. Bull. 190, pp. 65-96.

Snavely, P. D., Jr., and Wagner, H. C., 1963, *Tertiary geologic history of western Oregon and Washington*: Washington Div. Mines and Geol. Rept. Inves. 22.

Waters, A. C., 1955, Volcanic rocks and the tectonic cycle, *in* Poldervaart, Arie, ed., *The crust of the earth*: Geol. Soc. America Spec. Paper 62, pp. 663-684.

Williams, Howel, 1940, *The geology of Crater Lake National Park, Oregon, with a reconnaissance of the Cascade Range southward to Mount Shasta*: Carnegie Inst. Washington Publ. 540.

4. *Coast Ranges of California*

Atwater, Tanya, 1970, Implications of plate tectonics for the Cenozoic evolution of western North America: *Geol. Soc. America Bull.*, v. 81, no. 12, pp. 3513-3536.

Bailey, E. H., Irwin, W. P., and Jones, D. L., 1964, *Franciscan and related rocks, and their significance in the geology of western California*: California Div. Mines and Geol. Bull. 183.

Clark, B. L., 1930, Tectonics of the Coast Ranges of middle California: *Geol. Soc. America Bull.*, v. 41, pp. 747-828.

Hill, M. L., and Dibblee, T. W., Jr., 1953, San Andreas, Garlock, and Big Pine faults, California: *Geol. Soc. America Bull.*, v. 64, pp. 443-458.

Nilsen, T. H., and Clarke, S. H., Jr., 1975, *Sedimentation and tec-tonics in the early Tertiary continental borderland of central California*: U.S. Geol. Survey Prof. Paper 925.

Noble, L. F., 1954, The San Andreas fault zone from Soledad Pass to Cajon Pass, California, *in* Jahns, R. H., ed., *Geology of southern California*: California Div. Mines Bull. 170, chap. 4, pp. 37-48.

Page, B. M., 1966, Geology of the Coast Ranges of California, *in* Bailey, E. H., ed., *Geology of northern California*: California Div. Mines and Geol. Bull. 160, pp. 255-276.

Reed, R. D., and Hollister, J. S., 1936, Structural evolution of southern California: *Am. Assoc. Petrol. Geol. Bull.*, v. 20, pp. 1533-1704.

Taliaferro, N. L., 1943, *Geologic history and structure of the central Coast Ranges of California*: California Div. Mines Bull. 118, pp. 119-163.

Willis, Bailey, 1927, Folding or shearing, which?: *Am. Assoc. Petrol. Geol. Bull.*, v. 11, no. 1, pp. 31-47.

181

EPILOGUE

With our examination of the Coast Ranges of California we have completed our arm-chair journey across North America. Our journey has been more circuitous than an actual traveler would care for—we commenced in the far north in the Canadian Shield, passed into the Interior Lowlands and across the Appalachian Mountains to the Atlantic Ocean, then proceeded southward across the Gulf Coastal Plain to the West Indies; finally we arrived at the front of the Cordillera and crossed this westward from the Great Plains to the Pacific Coast.

Our journey has also taken us through vast reaches of geologic time—from the earliest beginnings that can be discovered in the Precambrian rocks of the nucleus of the continent, through the mountains that were built up later in successive belts around the original nucleus. In the end, we arrived amidst the Cenozoic rocks and structures that formed, and are still forming, along the Pacific Coast.

During our journey we enlisted the aid of many skills—the strictly geological, by which the little deformed and strongly deformed rocks have been analyzed; the geophysical, by which the deeper layers of the crust have been probed; the geochemical, by which the plutonic and volcanic activity of the earth have been explained, and which has furnished us, as well, with a new means of dating the rocks and measuring geologic time.

We have finally, like the Forty-niners, made it through to the Golden Gate and have come out on the farther side of the continent. In our dash to the coast we have, like the pioneers, had to discard many things that might seem precious—in our case, areas or geologic features of much interest in themselves that did not seem to illustrate fully our general theme. Despite this loss, it is to be hoped that the essentials have been saved—an exposition of the evolution of North America, both in its grand design and in some of its infinite details.

FIG. 109. The Pacific Coast of California. Steeply tilted early Tertiary flysch at San Pedro Point, San Mateo County, south of San Francisco. Redrawn from Lawson (1915).

183

SOURCES OF ILLUSTRATIONS

Plate I. King, P. B., and Edmonston, G. J., 1972, Generalized tectonic map of North America: U.S. Geological Survey Miscellaneous Geological Investigations Map I-688; with modifications from other sources.

End papers inside front cover. Original drawing, published in King, P. B., 1964, Geology of the central Great Smoky Mountains: U.S. Geol. Survey Prof. Paper 349-C, fig. 4, p. 11.

End papers inside back cover. Redrawn from photograph by National Park Service.

Figure 1. Based on Wilson, J. T., 1954, The development and structure of the crust, in The Earth as a Planet: Univ. Chicago Press, fig. 2, p. 148. Ewing, Maurice, and Press, Frank, 1955, Geophysical contrasts between continents and ocean basins, in Poldervaart, Arie, ed., The Crust of the Earth: Geol. Soc. America Spec. Paper 62, fig. 1, p. 5.

Figure 2. Original drawing.

Figure 3. Generalized from: Hamilton, Warren, and Krinsley, David, 1967, Upper Paleozoic glacial deposits of South Africa and southern Australia: Geol. Soc. America Bull., v. 78, fig. 1, p. 795. Published by permission of Geological Society of America.

Figure 4. Original drawing.

Figure 5. Original drawing.

Figure 6. Original drawing.

Figure 7. Original drawing.

Figure 8. Compiled from Stockwell, C. H., and others, 1969, Tectonic Map of Canada: Canada Geol. Survey Map 1251 A. Douglas, R.J.W., compiler, 1969, Geologic Map of Canada: Canada Geol. Survey Map 1250 A.

Figure 9. Leith, C. K., Lund, R. J., and Leith, Andrew, 1935, Precambrian Rocks of the Lake Superior Region: U.S. Geol. Survey Prof. Paper 184, pl. 1.

Figure 10A. Based on Lee, Wallace, 1956, Stratigraphy and structural development of the Salina basin area: Kansas Geol. Survey Bull. 121, pl. 4B. B—Bridge, Josiah, 1930, Geology of the Eminence and Cardareva quadrangles: Missouri Bur. Geol. and Mines, v. 24, 2nd ser., geologic map, section B-B'.

Figure 11. Kay, Marshall, 1951, North American geosynclines: Geol. Soc. America Mem. 48, pl. 12, p. 32. Published by permission of Geological Society of America.

Figure 12A. Based on Richardson, G. B., 1909, Description of the El Paso district [Texas]: U.S. Geol. Survey Geol. Atlas, folio 166, fig. 8, p. 8. B—Darton, N. H., 1928, "Red beds" and associated formations of New Mexico: U.S. Geol. Survey Bull. 794, fig. 23, p. 99.

Figure 13. Original drawing.

Figure 14A. Based on Cumings, E. R., and Shrock, R. R., 1928, Niagaran coral reefs of Indiana and adjoining states and their stratigraphic relations: Geol. Soc. America Bull., v. 39, pp. 579-619. B—King, P. B., 1948, Geology of Southern Guadalupe Mountains, Texas: U.S. Geol. Survey Prof. Paper 215, pl. 7.

Figure 15A. Centennial Geologic Map of Michigan: Michigan Geol. Survey Pub. 39, Geol. Ser. 33, 1936. B and C—Willman, H. B., and others, 1967, Geologic Map of Illinois: Illinois Geol. Survey, sections A-A' and B-B'.

Figure 16. Compiled from: Willman, H. B., and others, 1967, Geologic Map of Illinois: Illinois Geol. Survey. Jillson, W. R., and others, 1929, Geologic Map of Kentucky: Kentucky Geol. Survey Ser. 6.

Figure 17. Original drawing.

Figure 18. Compiled from: Wasson, Theron, and Wasson, I. B., 1927, Cabin Creek field, West Virginia: Am. Assoc. Petrol. Geol. Bull., v. 11, fig. 2, p. 710. Lafferty, R. C., 1941, Central basin of Appalachian geosyncline: Am. Assoc. Petrol. Geol. Bull., v. 25, figs. 4 and 5, pp. 786-789.

Figure 19A. Cohee, G. V., 1948, Cambrian and Ordovician rocks in Michigan basin and adjacent areas: Am. Assoc. Petrol. Geol. Bull., v. 32, fig. 8, p. 1440. B—Ibid., fig. 9, p. 1444. C—Cohee, G. V., 1948, Thickness and lithology of Upper Ordovician and Lower and Middle Silurian rocks in the Michigan basin: U.S. Geol. Survey Oil and Gas Inves. Chart 33, sheet 2, fig. 10. D—Landes, K. K., 1945, The Salina and Bass Island rocks of the Michigan basin: U.S. Geol. Survey Oil and Gas Inves. Map 49, fig. 1. E—Cohee, G. V., 1947, Lithology and thickness of the Traverse Group in the Michigan basin: U.S. Geol. Survey Oil and Gas Inves. Chart 28, fig. 1. F—King, P. B., and Beikman, H. M., 1974, Geologic Map of the United States, Exclusive of Alaska and Hawaii, U.S. Geol. Survey.

Figure 20A—Cohee, G. V., 1948, Cambrian and Ordovician rocks in Michigan basin and adjacent areas: Am. Assoc. Petrol. Geol. Bull., v. 32, fig. 2, pp. 1428-1429. B—Ibid., fig. 6, pp. 1434-1435. C—Cohee, G. V., 1948, Thickness and lithology of Upper Ordovician and Lower and Middle Silurian rocks in the Michigan basin: U.S. Geol. Survey Oil and Gas Inves. Chart 33, sheet 2, fig. 7. D—Ibid., fig. 9 E. E—Landes, K. K., 1945, The Salina and Bass Island rocks of the Michigan basin: U.S. Geol. Survey Oil and Gas Inves. Map 40, fig. 3. F—Cohee, G. V., 1947, Lithology and thickness of the Traverse Group in the Michigan basin: U.S. Geol. Survey Oil and Gas Inves. Chart 28, fig. 2.

Figure 21. Based on Hershey, H. G., 1969, Geologic Map of Iowa: Iowa Geol. Survey.

Figure 22. Original drawing.

Figure 23. King, P. B., 1942, Permian of west Texas and southeastern New Mexico: Am. Assoc. Petrol. Geol. Bull., v. 26, fig. 18, p. 665. King, P. B., 1948, Geology of the Southern Guadalupe Mountains, West Texas: U.S. Geol. Survey Prof. Paper 215, fig. 3, p. 25.

Figure 24. West Texas Geological Society, 1942, Résumé of geology of the south Permian basin, west Texas: Geol. Soc. America Bull., v. 53, pl. 2, p. 560. Published with permission of Geological Society of America.

Figure 25. King, P. B., 1948, Geology of Southern Guadalupe Mountains, Texas: U.S. Geol. Survey Prof. Paper 215, pl. 17, sections E-E' and K-K'.

Figure 26A—Keith, Arthur, 1901, Description of the Maynardville quadrangle [Tennessee]: U.S. Geol. Survey Geol. Atlas, folio 74. B—Darton, N. H., 1899, Description of the Monterey quadrangle [Virginia-West Virginia]: U.S. Geol. Survey Geol. Atlas, folio 61.

Figure 27. Based on Butts, Charles, 1927, Fensters in the Cumberland Mountain overthrust block in southwestern Virginia: Virginia Geol. Survey Bull, 28, pl. 2, pp. 4-5. Rich, J. L., 1934, Mechanics of low-angle overthrust faulting as illustrated by Cumberland thrust block, Virginia, Kentucky, and Tennessee: Am. Assoc. Petrol. Geol. Bull., v. 18, figs. 4-5, p. 1589. Miller, R. L., and Fuller, J. O., 1947, Geologic and structure contour maps of Rose Hill oil field, Lee County, Virginia: U.S. Geol. Survey Oil and Gas Inves. Map 78.

Figure 28. Gwinn, V. E., 1970, Kinematic patterns and estimates of lateral shortening, Valley and Ridge and Great Valley provinces, Central Appalachians, south-central Pennsylvania, in Fisher, G. W., Pettijohn, F. J., Reed, J. C., and Weaver, K. N., Studies of Appalachian Geology; Central and Southern: Interscience Publishers, New York, fig. 4, p. 131. Published by permission of John Wiley & Sons.

Figure 29A—Gray, Carlisle, and others, 1960, Geologic map of Pennsylvania: Pennsylvania Topog. and Geol. Survey, section D-E. B—Rodgers, John, 1953, The Folds and Faults of the Appalachian Valley and Ridge Province: Kentucky Geol. Survey Spec. Publ. 1, fig. 3, pp. 164-165; and other sources.

Figure 30. Billings, M. P., 1955, Geologic Map of New Hampshire: New Hampshire Planning and Development Commission; with modifications from later data.

Figure 31A—Barrell, Joseph, 1915, Central Connecticut in geologic past: Connecticut Geol. Survey Bull. 23, fig. 2, p. 15. B—Longwell, C. R., 1933, The Triassic belt of Massachusetts and Connecticut, in Eastern New York and southern New England: 16th Int. Geol. Cong. Guidebook 1, fig. 23, p. 102.

Figure 32. Stose, A. J., and Stose, G. W., 1944, Geology of the Hanover-York District, Pennsylvania: U.S. Geol. Survey Prof. Paper 204, pl. 16, p. 57.

Figure 33. Compiled from many sources, including: A—Doll, C. G., and others, 1961, Centennial Geologic Map of Vermont: Vermont Geol. Survey. Billings, M. P., 1955, Geologic Map of New Hamp-

shire: New Hampshire Planning and Development Commission. B—Hadley, J. B., and Nelson, A. E., 1971, Geologic map of the Knoxville quadrangle, North Carolina, Tennessee, and South Carolina; *U.S. Geol. Survey Misc. Geol. Inves. Map I-654.* Griffin, V. S., 1974, Analysis of the Piedmont in northwest South Carolina: *Geol. Soc. America Bull.,* v. 85, fig. 3, p. 1126.

Figure 34. Based on: Emery, K. O., and Uchupi, Elazar, 1972, Western North Atlantic Ocean; topography, rocks, structure, water, life, and sediments: *Am. Assoc. Petrol. Geol. Mem. 17,* figs. 135-136, pp. 172-173. Sheridan, R. E., 1974, Atlantic continental margin of North America, *in* Burke, C. A., and Drake, C. L., *The Geology of Continental Margins*: Springer-Verlag, New York, figs. 8-9, pp. 398-399. Published by permission of American Association of Petroleum Geologists and Springer-Verlag.

Figure 35. Prepared from data in Broughton, J. G., and others, 1962, *Geologic Map of New York*: New York State Mus. and Sci. Serv., Geol. Survey Map and Chart Ser. 5. Zen, E-an, 1967, *Time and Space Relationships of the Taconic Allochthon and Autochthon*: Geol. Soc. America Spec. Paper 97.

Figure 37. Moore, R. C., 1941, Stratigraphy, *in Fiftieth Anniversary Volume: Geol. Soc. America,* fig. 7, p. 200; based on work by G. H. Chadwick and G. A. Cooper.

Figure 38. Original drawing.

Figure 39. Original drawing.

Figure 40. Williams, Harold, and Stevens, R. K., 1974, The ancient continental margin of eastern North America, *in* Burke, C. A., and Drake, C. L., eds., *The Geology of Continental Margins*: Springer-Verlag, New York, fig. 6, p. 793. Published by permission of Springer-Verlag.

Figure 41. Original drawing.

Figure 42. King, P. B., 1937, *Geology of the Marathon Region, Texas*: U.S. Geol. Survey Prof. Paper 187, pl. 15, p. 118.

Figure 43. Ibid., pl. 1 B, p. 6; redrawn from photograph.

Figure 44. Original drawing.

Figure 45. Compiled from many sources, including: Miser, H. D., 1954, *Geologic Map of Oklahoma*: U.S. Geol. Survey. Haley, B. R., Stone, C. G., and Glick, E. R., 1977, *Geologic Map of Arkansas*: Arkansas Geol. and Conservation Div. Flawn, P. T., and others, 1961, *The Ouachita System*: Texas Univ. (Bur. Econ. Geol.) Publ. 6120, pl. 2. Harlton, B. H., 1966, Relation of buried Tishomingo uplift to Ardmore basin and Ouachita Mountains, southeastern Oklahoma: *Am. Assoc. Petrol. Geol. Bull.,* v. 50, fig. 1, p. 1367. Vernon, R. C., 1971, Possible future petroleum potential of pre-Jurassic, western Gulf basin, *in* Cram, I. C., ed., Future petroleum provinces of the United States; their geology and potential: *Am. Assoc. Petroleum Geol. Mem. 15,* fig. 1, p. 971.

Figure 46A—Compiled from many sources, including: Berry, R. M., and Trumbly, W. H., 1968, Wilburton Gas field, Arkoma basin, Oklahoma, *in* Cline, L. M., ed., *A Guidebook to the Geology of the Western Arkoma Basin and Ouachita Mountains, Southeastern Oklahoma*: Oklahoma City Geol. Soc. Guidebook. Hendricks, T. A., and others, 1947, Geology of western part of Ouachita Mountains of Oklahoma: *U.S. Geol. Survey Oil and Gas Inves. Map 66,* sheet 3, section A-A′. Miser, H. D., Structure of the Ouachita Mountains of Oklahoma and Arkansas: *Oklahoma Geol. Survey Bull. 50,* section A, pl. 3. B—Viele, G. W., 1973, Structure and tectonic history of the Ouachita Mountains, Arkansas, *in* De Jong, K. A., and Sholten, Robert, eds., *Gravity and Tectonics*: Wiley-Interscience, New York, fig. 8, p. 372. Published by permission of John Wiley & Sons.

Figure 47. Compiled from: Tomlinson, C. W., 1929, The Pennsylvanian system of the Ardmore basin: *Oklahoma Geol. Survey Bull. 46,* section A-A′, pl. 17. Ham, W. E., and McKinley, Myron, 1955, Geologic map and sections of the Arbuckle Mountains, Oklahoma, *in Field Conference on Geology of the Arbuckle Mountains Region*: Oklahoma Geol. Survey Guidebook 3, section B-B′. Ham, W. E., Denison, R. E., and Merritt, C. A., 1964, Basement rocks and structural evolution of southern Oklahoma: *Oklahoma Geol. Survey Bull. 95,* section B-B′, pl. 1.

Figure 48A—Swesnik, R. M., and Green, T. A., 1950, Geology of the Eola area, Garvin County, Oklahoma: *Am. Assoc. Petrol. Geol. Bull.,* v. 34, fig. 7, p. 2188. B—Selk, E. L., 1951, Types of oil and gas traps in southern Oklahoma: *Am. Assoc. Petrol. Geol. Bull.,* v. 36, fig. 602. Published by permission of American Association of Petroleum Geologists.

Figure 49. Compiled from many sources, including: Hiestand, T. C., 1935, Regional investigations, Oklahoma and Kansas: *Am. Assoc. Petrol. Geol. Bull.,* v. 19, fig. 9, p. 963. Tulsa Geological Society, 1941, Possible future oil provinces of northern mid-continent region: *Am. Assoc. Petrol. Geol. Bull.,* v. 25, fig. 8, p. 151. Mallory, W. W., 1948, Pennsylvanian stratigraphy and structure, Velma pool, Stephens County, Oklahoma: *Am. Assoc. Petrol. Geol. Bull.,* v. 32, fig. 2, pp. 1954-1955.

Figure 50. Fisk, H. N., and McFarlan, E., Jr., 1955, Late Quaternary deltaic deposits of the Mississippi River, *in* Poldervaart, Arie, ed., *The Crust of the Earth*: Geol. Soc. America Spec. Paper 62, fig. 7, p. 288. Published by permission of Geological Society of America.

Figure 51. Original drawing.

Figure 52. Imlay, R. E., 1940, *Lower Cretaceous and Jurassic Formations of Southern Arkansas and Their Oil and Gas Possibilities*: Arkansas Geol. Survey Inf. Circular 12, section E-E′, p. 3; extensively revised from later data.

Figure 53. Carsey, J. B., 1950, Geology of Gulf Coastal area and continental shelf: *Am. Assoc. Petrol. Geol. Bull.,* v. 34, p. 367. Published by permission of American Association of Petroleum Geologists.

Figure 54. Lowman, S. W., 1949, Sedimentary facies in Gulf Coast: *Am. Assoc. Petrol. Geol. Bull.,* v. 33, fig. 23, p. 1972. Published by permission of American Association of Petroleum Geologists.

Figure 55. Compiled from: Lehner, Peter, 1969, Salt tectonics and Pleistocene stratigraphy on continental slope of northern Gulf of Mexico: *Am. Assoc. Petrol. Geol. Bull.,* v. 43, fig. 43, p. 2473. Emery, K. O., and Uchupi, Elezar, 1972, Western North Atlantic Ocean; topography, rocks, structure, water, life, and sediments: *Am. Assoc. Petrol. Geol. Mem. 17,* fig. 186, p. 218. Martin, R. G., and Case, J. E., 1976, Geophysical studies in the Gulf of Mexico, *in* Nairn, A.E.M. and Stehli, F. G., *The Ocean Basins and Margins*, vol. 3. *The Gulf of Mexico and the Caribbean*: Plenum Press, New York, fig. 9, p. 81. Published by permission of American Association of Petroleum Geologists and Plenum Press.

Figure 56. Original drawing.

Figure 57. Raitt, R. W., Fisher, R. I., and Mason, R. G., 1955, Tonga Trench, *in* Poldervaart, Arie, ed., *The Crust of the Earth*: Geol. Soc. America Special Paper 62, fig. 9, p. 253. Published by permission of Geological Society of America.

Figure 58A—Senn, Alfred, 1940, Paleogene of Barbados and its bearing on history and structure of the Antillean-Caribbean region: *Am. Assoc. Petrol. Geol. Bull.,* v. 24, fig. 3, p. 1596. Published by permission of American Association of Petroleum Geologists. B—Daviess, S. N., 1971, Barbados, a major submarine gravity slide: *Geol. Soc. America Bull.,* v. 82, fig. 2, p. 2598. Published by permission of Geological Society of America.

Figure 59. Original drawing.

Figure 60. Compiled from: King, P. B., and Edmonston, G. J., 1972, Generalized tectonic map of North America: *U.S. Geol. Survey Misc. Geol. Inves. Map I-688.* Molnar, Peter, and Sykes, L. R., 1969, Tectonics of the Caribbean and Middle America regions from focal mechanisms and seismicity: *Geol. Soc. America Bull.,* v. 80, fig. 1, p. 1641. Malfait, B. T., and Dinkelman, M. G., 1971, Circum-Caribbean tectonic and igneous activity and the evolution of the Caribbean plate: *Geol. Soc. America Bull.,* v. 83, fig. 5, p. 257.

Figure 61. Original drawing.

Figure 62. King, P. B., and Beikman, H. M., 1974, *Geologic Map of the United States, Exclusive of Alaska and Hawaii*: U.S. Geol. Survey.

Figure 63. McKee, E. D., 1931, *Ancient Landscapes of the Grand Canyon Region*: privately printed, fig. on p. 8.

Figure 64. Darton, N. H., 1925, A résumé of Arizona geology: *Arizona Bur. Mines Bull.* 119, fig. 13, p. 182.

Figure 65. Mallory, W. W., 1972, Regional synthesis of Pennsylvanian System, *in* Mallory, W. W., ed., *Geologic Atlas of the Rocky Mountain Region*: Rocky Mountain Assoc. Geologists, Denver, fig. 4, p. 115.

Figure 66. Original drawing.

Figure 67. Based in part on Hintze, L. F., 1963, *Geologic Map of Utah*: Utah State Land Board and Univ. of Utah, southwestern sheet. Wilson, E. D., Moore, R. T., and Cooper, J. R., 1969, *Geologic Map of Arizona*: U.S. Geol. Survey.

Figure 68. Original drawing.

Figure 69. Original drawing.

Figure 70. Based on King, P. B., 1955, Orogeny and epeirogeny through time, *in* Poldervaart, Arie, ed., *The Crust of the Earth*: Geol. Soc. America Spec. Paper 62, fig. 4, p. 732; incorporating unpublished data by Erling Dorf. Cobban, W. A., and Reeside, J. B., Jr., 1952, Correlation of the Cretaceous formations of the western interior of the United States: *Geol. Soc. America Bull.*, v. 63, pp. 1011-1044.

Figure 71. Original drawing.

Figure 72. Powell, J. W., 1876, Report on the geology of the eastern portion of the Uinta Mountains and a region of country adjacent thereto *U.S. Geol. Geograph. Survey of the Territories, 2nd Div.*, pl. 4 of atlas.

Figure 73. Original drawing.

Figure 74. Original drawing, based on areal geologic maps, such as *Geologic Map of the United States* (1974).

Figure 75. Weed, W. H., 1899, Description of the Little Belt Mountains quadrangle: *U.S. Geol. Survey Geol. Atlas*, Folio 56, structure section sheet. Ross, C. P., Andrews, D. A., and Witkind, I. J., 1955, *Geologic Map of Montana*: U.S. Geol. Survey.

Figure 76. Cohee, G. V., 1962, *Tectonic Map of the United States, Exclusive of Alaska and Hawaii*: U.S. Geol. Survey. King, P. B., and Beikman, H. M., 1974, *Geologic Map of the United States, Exclusive of Alaska and Hawaii*: U.S. Geol. Survey.

Figure 77. Original drawing.

Figure 78A—Lovering, T. S., 1935, *Geology and Ore Deposits of the Montezuma Quadrangle, Colorado*: U.S. Geol. Survey Prof. Paper 178, pl. 4, section B-B'. Van Tuyl, F. M., and McLaren, R. L., 1933, Geologic map of Golden area, in Colorado: *16th Int. Geol. Cong. Guidebook 19*, pl. 15, p. 138. B—Burbank, W. S., and Goddard, E. N., 1937, Thrusting in Huerfano Park, Colorado, and related problems of orogeny in the Sangre de Cristo Mountains: *Geol. Soc. America Bull.*, v. 48, fig. 4, p. 968.

Figure 79. Cohee, G. V., 1962, *Tectonic Map of the United States, Exclusive of Alaska and Hawaii*: U.S. Geol. Survey. King, P. B., and Beikman, H. M., 1974, *Geologic Map of the United States, Exclusive of Alaska and Hawaii*: U.S. Geol. Survey.

Figure 80. Generalized from: A—Wood, G. H., and Northrop, S. A., 1946, Geology of the Nacimiento Mountains, San Pedro Mountains, and adjacent plateaus of Sandoval and Rio Arriba Counties, New Mexico: *U.S. Geol. Survey Oil and Gas Inves. Map 57*, section E-E'. B—Read, C. B., and others, 1944, Geologic map and stratigraphic sections of Permian and Pennsylvanian rocks of parts of San Miguel, Santa Fe, Sandoval, Bernalillo, and Valencia Counties, north-central New Mexico: *U.S. Geol. Survey Oil and Gas Inves. Map 21*, section A-A'. C—Kelley, V. C., and Wood, G. H., 1946, Lucero uplift, Valencia, Socorro, and Bernalillo Counties, New Mexico: *U.S. Geol. Survey Oil and Gas Inves. Map 47*, section D-D'. D—Denny, C. S., 1940, Tertiary geology of the San Acadia area, New Mexico: *Jour. Geology*, v. 48, fig. 3, section A-A', p. 82. E—Wilpolt, R. H., and Wanek, A. A., 1951, Geology of the region from Socorro and San Antonio east to Chupadera Mesa, Socorro County, New Mexico: *J.S. Geol. Survey Oil and Gas Inves. Map 121*, sheet 2, section F-F'. F—King, P. B., 1948, *Geology of the Southern Guadalupe Mountains, Texas*: U.S. Geol. Survey Prof. Paper 215, pl. 3, section B-B' and fig. 18, p. 122.

Figure 81. Original drawing.

Figure 82. Powell, J. W., 1876, Report on the geology of the eastern portion of the Uinta Mountains and a region of country adjacent thereto: *U.S. Geol. Geograph. Survey of the Territories, 2nd Div.*, fig. 3, p. 15.

Figure 83. Compiled from many sources, including: Okulitch, V. L., 1956, The Lower Cambrian of western Canada and Alaska, *in* Rodgers, John, ed., *El sistemo Cambrico, su paleogeographia y el problema de su base*: 20th Int. Geol. Cong. (Mexico), fig. 4, p. 270. Price, R. A., 1964, The Precambrian Purcell System in the Rocky Mountains of southern Alberta and British Columbia: *Canadian Petrol. Geol. Bull.*, v. 12, fig. 4, p. 415. Harrison, J. E., 1972, Precambrian Belt basin of northwestern United States; its geometry, sedimentation, and copper occurrences: *Geol. Soc. America Bull.*, v. 83, fig. 7, p. 1226.

Figure 84. Warren, P. S., 1927, Banff area, Alberta: *Canada Geol. Survey Mem. 153*, fig. 1, p. 4.

Figure 85. Based on: Stewart, J. H., and Poole, F. G., 1974, Lower Paleozoic and uppermost Precambrian Miogeosyncline, Great Basin, western United States, *in* Dickinson, W. R., ed., *Tectonics and Sedimentation*: Soc. Econ. Paleon. Mineralog. Spec. Publ. 22, fig. 6, p. 37; and other sources.

Figure 86A—Price, W. A., and Mountjoy, E. W., 1970, Geologic structure of the Canadian Rocky Mountains between Bow and Athabaska Rivers; a progress report, *in* Wheeler, R. O., *Structure of the Canadian Cordillera*: Geol. Assoc. Canada Spec. Paper 6, fig. 2-1, structure section. B—Bally, A. W., Gordy, P. L., and Stewart, G. A., 1966, Structure, seismic data, and orogenic evolution of the southern Canadian Rocky Mountains: *Canadian Petrol. Geol. Bull.*, v. 14, pl. 5, section E-E'.

Figure 87. Gallup, W. B., 1951, Geology of the Turner Valley oil and gas field, Alberta, Canada: *Am. Assoc. Petrol. Geol. Bull.*, v. 35, fig. 5, p. 806. Hume, G. S., 1957, Fault structures in the foothills and eastern Rocky Mountains of southern Alberta: *Geol. Soc. America Bull.*, v. 68, fig. 2, p. 398. Published by permission of American Association of Petroleum Geologists and Geological Society of America.

Figure 88. Willis, Bailey, 1902, Stratigraphy and structure, Lewis and Livingston Ranges, Montana: *Geol. Soc. America Bull.*, v. 13, fig. 5, p. 334; redrawn from original photograph.

Figure 89. King, P. B., and Beikman, H. M., 1974, *Explanatory Text to Accompany the Geologic Map of the United States*: U.S. Geol. Survey Prof. Paper 901, fig. 9, p. 29.

Figure 90. Original drawing.

Figure 91. Modified from Bateman, P. C., and Wahrhaftig, Clyde, 1966, Geology of the Sierra Nevada, *in* Bailey, E. H., ed., *Geology of Northern California*: California Div. Mines and Geol. Bull. 190, fig. 2, p. 124.

Figure 92. Original drawing.

Figure 93. King, P. B., 1969, *The Tectonics of North America*; a discussion to accompany the Tectonic Map of North America, scale 1:5,000,000: U.S. Geol. Survey Prof. Paper 628, fig. 6, p. 14; compiled from county geologic maps of Nevada and from publications of U.S. Geological Survey.

Figure 94A—Ferguson, H. G., Roberts, R. J., and Muller, S. W., 1952, *Geology of the Golconda Quadrangle, Nevada*: U.S. Geol. Survey Geol. Quadrangle Map GQ-15, section A-A'. B—Ferguson, H. G., Muller, S. W., and Roberts, R. J., 1951, *Geology of the Winnemucca Quadrangle, Nevada*: U.S. Geol. Survey Geol. Quadrangle Map GQ-11, section D-D'. C—Roberts, R. J., 1951, *Geology of the Antler Peak Quadrangle, Nevada*: U.S. Geol. Survey Geol. Quadrangle Map GQ-10, section C-C'. Sections extensively modified from later data.

Figure 95. King, P. B., 1976, *Precambrian Geology of the United States; An Explanatory Text to Accompany the Geologic Map of the United States*: U.S. Geol. Survey Prof. Paper 902, fig. 30, p. 78.

Figure 96. Davis, W. M., 1927, lecture sketch.

Figure 97.Original drawing.

Figure 98. Davis, W. M., 1925, The Basin Range problem: *Natl. Acad. Sci. Proc.*, v. 11, fig. 2, p. 292.

Figure 99. U.S. Geological Survey, 1970, *National Atlas*: sheet 66-67.

Figure 100. Compiled from: King, P. B., and Beikman, H. M., 1974, *Geologic Map of the United States, Exclusive of Alaska and Hawaii*: U.S. Geol. Survey.

Figure 101. Original drawing; geologic patterns from King, P. B., and Beikman, H. M., ibid.

Figure 102A—Smith, G. O., 1904, Description of the Mount Stuart quadrangle [Washington]: *U.S. Geol. Survey Geol. Atlas*, Folio 106, section A-A'. B—Smith, G. O., and Calkins, F. C., 1906, Description of the Snoqualmie quadrangle [Washington]: *U.S. Geol. Survey Geol. Atlas*, Folio 134, section B-B'.

Figure 103. Based on King, P. B., and Beikman, H. M., 1974, *Geologic Map of the United States, Exclusive of Alaska and Hawaii*: U.S. Geol. Survey; and other sources.

Figure 104. Based on Reed, R. D., 1933, *Geology of California*: Am. Assoc. Petrol. Geol., fig. 16, p. 73. Reed, R. D., and Hollister, J. S., 1936, Structural evolution of southern California: *Am. Assoc. Petrol. Geol. Bull.*, v. 20, fig. 2, p. 1549.

Figure 105. Modified from: Bailey, E. H., Blake, M. C. Jr., and Jones, D. L., 1970, *On-land Oceanic Crust in California Coast Ranges*: U.S. Geol. Survey Prof. Paper 700-C, fig. 6, p. 79.

Figure 106. Original drawing by P. B. King; published in Noble, L. F., 1954, The San Andreas fault zone from Soledad Pass to Cajon Pass, California, *in* Jahns, R. H., ed., *The geology of Southern California*: California Div. Mines Bull. 170, chap. 4, fig. 5, p. 42.

Figure 107. Original drawing; data from Noble, L. F., ibid., pp. 37-38.

Figure 108. Bailey, T. H., and Jahns, R. H., 1954, Geology of the Transverse Range province, southern California, *in* Jahns, R. H., ed., *Geology of Southern California*: California Div. Mines Bull. 170, chap. 2, fig. 8, p. 96.

Figure 109. Lawson, A. C., 1915, Description of the San Francisco district [California]: *U.S. Geol. Survey Geol. Atlas*, Folio 194, pl. 1; redrawn from original photograph.

GENERAL INDEX

INDEX OF AUTHORS CITED

Library of Congress Cataloging in Publication Data

King, Philip Burke, 1903-
   The evolution of North America.

   Includes bibliographical references and index.
    1.   Geology—North America.   I.   Title.
QE71.K54   1977   557   77-71987
ISBN 0-691-08195-6
ISBN 0-691-02359-X pbk.